THE
CAT Orchestra
& THE
ELEPHANT Butler

The Strange History of Amazing Animals

THE CAT Orchestra & THE ELEPHANT Butler

The Strange History of Amazing Animals

Jan Bondeson

TEMPUS

This revised edition first published 2006.

First published 1999 as *The Feejee Mermaid and other Essays on Natural and Unnatural History.*
Published by arrangement with Cornell University Press.

Tempus Publishing Limited
The Mill, Brimscombe Port,
Stroud, Gloucestershire, GL5 2QG
www.tempus-publishing.com

British Library Cataloguing in Publication Data.
A catalogue record for this book is available from the British Library.

ISBN 0 7524 3934 0

Typesetting and origination by Tempus Publishing Limited
Printed in Great Britain

CONTENTS

I

The Cat Orchestra;

AND A

PREFACE

The first person to exhibit performing cats with any degree of success was the Scotsman Samuel Bisset. Born in Perth around 1721, he served as a shoemaker's apprentice for some time, before settling in London. After marrying a woman who had inherited some property, he left his shoemaker's shop and set up business as a broker, with considerable success. But one day, having read about a 'thinking horse' exhibited at a fair in St Germains, he became curious if he could repeat this trick himself. Having plentiful leisure time due to his success as a broker, he bought a horse and a dog and patiently started training them. Having succeeded beyond all expectation, he also bought two monkeys and took up animal training in earnest. Some months later, the animals were ready for their first appearance in public, held in Bisset's own house. The monkeys vaulted on the rope, played the barrel organ, rode upon the horse's back, and went through several regular dances with the dog.

Mr Bisset's next project was much more ambitious. He purchased three young cats, which he taught with the greatest of patience, aiming to produce an act that was entirely unique in the world. First, he trained them to strike the dulcimer with their paws, to produce several tunes. Next, it was time for them to sing, or rather mew, in different keys or tones; first, second and third, until the result was a proper concert. This amazing Cat's Orchestra became the talk of London, although the modest animal trainer still held the performances in his own house. In the word of Bisset's biographer in the *Eccentric Magazine*, 'In such a city as London, these feats could not fail of making some noise; his house was every day crouded, and great interruption given to his business'.

In 1758, the showman Mr Pinchbeck came to Bisset's house to see his performing animals. He was amazed when the orchestra of cats, sitting demurely with their music books in front of them, began playing their dulcimers and singing their arias with perfect composure. He suggested to Bisset that they should rent a large exhibition room in the Haymarket and make their fortune. The modest cat trainer reluctantly agreed, and a grand opening night was prepared. The day before the performance, Pinchbeck withdrew and Bisset was left to fend for himself. But the Cat's Opera, as they were now called, and Bisset's other performing animals, rose to the occasion. The cats strummed at their instruments and mewed in their high-pitched voices, the monkeys danced a minuet with the dog, and a hare walked on its rear legs, beating a drum. The shows attracted crowded houses, and in just a few weeks, they brought in nearly a thousand pounds to their owner, a sum illustrating the Londoners' great delight in animal amusements.

It would take many years until London saw performing cats that could rival Mr Bisset's Cat Orchestra. But in January 1829, a handbill announced that Signor Cappelli's troupe of learned cats, the greatest wonder in England, had taken up lodgings at No. 248 Regent Street. Cappelli was an itinerant Tuscan conjurer who had taken up cat training as a means to make his performances more interesting. The exhibition room was open every day, with shows every half-hour from twelve until five in the afternoon. The entertainment began with Signor Cappelli performing some conjuring tricks as the audience gathered; then there was a hush as the cats were introduced. The troupe of cats consisted of four red and white cats: a six-year-old mother, her daughter and two sons. There was also a large black cat, which a fanciful reviewer likened to 'a jet-black and maternal looking Negress'.

In turn, the feline actors went through their various routines. One of them beat a drum, another turned a spit or worked a rice grinder, a third rang a bell, and a fourth roasted coffee. The star performer drew water out of a well at her master's command, which she understood equally well in French and in Italian. In the evening, after the final show of the day, Signor Cappelli was always willing to attend private families in their own residences, to have his cats perform as a unique evening amusement.

To begin with, Signor Cappelli's cats made good headway in London show business, which was as competitive then as it is now. A reviewer in the *Literary Gazette* declared himself quite heartened by the cats and their antics, finding the restoration of these recalcitrant animals to rational functions ample proof of the progress of education. They went through their routines of bell-ringing, rice-grinding and water-pulling in a capital manner. Ending his article with an unpleasant racist jibe, the reviewer stated that it gave food for zoological speculation, and even for parallel reasoning concerning the human species, that the black cat lacked both the intellect and the industriousness so clearly shown by her red and white associates.

Although the shows cost as much as two shillings for front seats and one shilling for back seats, they were reasonably well attended. But in late May, Cappelli had to halve the entrance fee 'to render his entertainment more popular', a sign that all was not well. Indeed, a week or so later he left London with his cats, for a tour of England, Scotland and Ireland.

In 1832, Signor Cappelli gave the London entertainment world a second try, performing with his cats at No. 19 Giltspur Street during Bartholomew Fair. According to his new handbill, he now had a cat with musical ambitions, although the ability of this 'great harmonical genius' did not go beyond turning the barrel-organ, in the same manner her colleagues worked the rice grinder or turned the spit.

After Signor Cappelli had made his final bow before the Londoners, it again took several decades before the appearance of any cat trainer of repute. A Danish conjurer named Pedersen was active in London in 1870 with two particularly docile cats, who allowed white pigeons to sit on their heads. But this rather primitive act was not particularly successful. The reason may be deduced from a newspaper interview, in which the simple-minded Dane divulged that the most important part of his act was to have a plentiful supply of pigeons handy, since the cats were *not always* in a docile frame of mind. Somewhat more successful were the Clever Cats, performing various acrobatic tricks at the London Pavilion in 1888.

By the turn of the century, several American circuses employed performing cats. One of them had a clown travel across the stage in a chariot pulled by fifty-four cats; another circus fitted their cats with boxing gloves and had them spar against each other. The Russian clown Vladimir Durow had a troupe of jumping Angora cats, one of which could leap from a platform twenty feet off the ground. The German cat trainer Georg Techow's animals could balance on barrels and bottles, turn cartwheels, and unlock and open a door to take out a bowl of milk. An article in the French magazine *La Nature* of 1902 describes the fierce competition between the various feline performers in Paris at that time. Whereas M. Léonidas and his trained cats and dogs were triumphant at the Folies-Bergère, M. Farelly's Cat Orchestra performed to full houses at Barnum's circus.

A star performer in Germany in the years before the Great War was Peter Alupka, the Speaking Cat. Peter toured Europe with some of the leading circuses of the time, always to great acclaim. When the circus historian Alfred Lehmann saw Peter perform in 1908, he was amazed how clearly the cat could pronounce certain words, like 'nein', 'Anna' and 'Helene'. When the name of Kaiser Wilhelm was mentioned, the patriotic cat exclaimed 'Hurrah! Hurrah!' Peter could also sing 'O Tannenbaum' in a high mewing voice, although Lehmann remarked that it needed much imagination to liken this katzenjammer to the tune in question. He also observed that Peter's mistress held his neck in a loving embrace when he performed, clearly to modulate his voice with her fingers.

Today's leading cat trainer must surely be the Russian clown and juggler Yuri Kuklachev. In 1971, he found a stray cat begging for food by walking on her hind legs and doing somersaults for onlookers. Kuklachev took the cat home and named her Strelka; soon they were performing together at the Moscow State Circus. In 1990, he founded his Cat's Theatre, which has been spectacularly successful. He has visited eighty countries and won many awards. Of his 120 cats, he brought the twenty-six most talented performers with him on a tour of the United States in 2005.

In New York and elsewhere, his unique act drew unbounded applause. Three of the cats performed a tightrope routine, one of them hanging upside down and using only two legs. One cat rocked vigorously on a rocking horse, another did headstands, a third balanced on a mirrored ball. Kuklachev's favourite cat Marusa could stand on her front paws on the palm of his hand, her tail waving gracefully. No two shows were exactly the same, due to the temperament of the feline actors. If a cat did not want to do one trick, she did another instead, without annoying her jovial owner, who appears to know just as much about cat psychology as his great forerunners, Mr Bisset and Signor Cappelli.

In my book collection, there is a shelf for old natural history books intended for the general public. Some of these, like Oliver Goldsmith's *History of the Earth and Animated Nature*, and Buffon's *Natural History*, are encyclopaedias intended to present a complete overview of the animal kingdom. Other, like Sir Ray Lankester's *Diversions of a Naturalist* and Philip Henry Gosse's *Romance of Natural History*, are collections of essays about various remarkable occurrences and unsolved mysteries concerning the animal kingdom. Intended to amuse as well as educate, these books were among the best sellers of their time; within their particular genre, they were eclipsed only by Frank Buckland's *Curiosities of Natural History*, a justly famous collection of essays on all kinds of oddities and peculiarities within the natural sciences.

Frank Buckland was a qualified surgeon, but his passion was for practical zoology. As a copious and amusing writer and journalist, he did much to enliven various nineteenth-century periodicals dedicated to hunting, fishing, and animal lore. He was also something of an inventor and devised many curious schemes, like making gloves and shoes from the skins of rats. Another of Frank Buckland's interests was the acclimatisation of foreign animals into Britain: he envisioned herds of eland and antelopes galloping through the Surrey countryside. This was not wholly due to enthusiasm for zoology, nor entirely altruistic, since Frank Buckland had an almost fanatical desire to taste all kinds of animal meat. At his dinner parties, guests were served emu, hippopotamus, elephant's trunk soup and boiled boa constrictor, the gastronomic merits or demerits of which were discussed at length in his periodical *Land and Water*. A roast panther was pronounced 'not very good', but this is not surprising, since it had been dug up by Frank Buckland and his friends after being buried for several days. Through contacts at various zoos and menageries, Frank Buckland could usually procure beef-steaks from various rare animals; when these were in short supply, he had to rely on various household pests, served up as boiled mole, toasted earwigs, ragout of bluebottle flies, or garden slugs masquerading as *escargots*.

As demonstrated by the introductory chapter on the Cat Orchestra, this collection of essays on various odd, uncanny or macabre aspects of the animal kingdom and its relation with mankind is deliberately laid out in a way resembling these old natural history books. Like in Frank Buckland's *Curiosities of Natural History*, the reader will encounter learned pigs, sagacious elephants, and strange monsters like the Basilisk and the Vegetable Lamb. Like in Philip Henry Gosse's *Romance of Natural History*, there will also be little fishes raining down from the sky, and toads living for thousands of years immured in blocks of stone. It is a fitting tribute to this parliament of wonders: porcine performers, strange beasts, odd happenings and impossible events, to quote the description of Bartholomew Fair in William Wordsworth's *The Prelude*:

> All moveables of wonder, from all parts,
> Are here – Albinos, painted Indians, Dwarfs,
> The Horse of Knowledge, and the learned Pig,
> The Stone-eater, the Man that swallows fire,
> Giants, Ventriloquists, the Invisible Girl,
> The Bust that speaks and moves its goggling eyes,
> All out-of-the-way, far-fetch'd, perverted things
> All Freaks of Nature, all Promethean thoughts
> Of Man, his dulness, madness, and their feats
> All jumbled up together to make up
> A Parliament of Monsters…

2

THE Dancing HORSE

> If Banks had lived in olden times, he would have shamed all the enchanters in the world, for whosoever was most famous of them could never master or instruct any beast as he did.
>
> Sir Walter Raleigh, *History of the World*.

The annals of performing animals stretch far back into time. Whereas some noble Romans kept small private zoological gardens, the *profanum vulgum* had to content themselves with watching the dancing dogs and apes shown by itinerant jugglers. In medieval times, brutal animal baitings were a popular pastime, but the art of training animals became almost entirely forgotten. Bears, bulls, horses, wild boars and badgers were baited with dogs; this degraded form of entertainment was relished by both high and low, and in Britain as well as on the European continent. The earliest animal trainer of whom authentic records survive was the Englishman William Banks, active in Elizabethan times. His celebrated dancing horse Marocco was as well known throughout Britain and Europe as any other two- or four-legged performer. Marocco even enjoyed the unparalleled honour, for a member of the equine race, of being mentioned in Sir Walter Raleigh's *History of the World*.

William Banks was born in Staffordshire, probably some time in the 1560s. One source describes him as a 'Staffordshire gentilman', but it is more likely that he spent his youth as one of the retainers of the Earl of Essex. In view of his great familiarity with horses, it would not have been surprising if his duties had included tending the Earl's stables. His career as a horse-trainer seems to have begun in the late 1580s. In the summer of 1591, he visited Shrewsbury with a performing white horse, which could count money, bow and curtsy to the bailiff, and recognise some person from the colour of his coat. Some years earlier, Mr Banks had purchased a young bay foal and trained it with the utmost care. The horse's name – Marocco – was derived from a type of saddle used at the time. Marocco was a small, muscular horse with remarkable litheness and agility; he also proved particularly intelligent and easy to educate. Mr Banks had high hopes for his young charge. In spite of the novelty of their act and the consequent uncertainty of success – there are no previous records of any performing horse having been exhibited with profit – he decided to take up residence in London. Some time in 1592 or 1593, the adventurous Mr Banks sold his belongings in Staffordshire, shod his horse with silver and set out for the Metropolis.

Exactly at what time the dancing horse first made his bow to a London audience has not been recorded; it is certain, however, that the shows were a great success from the start. Marocco could dance on either two or four legs with amazing agility. He could play dead in a particularly realistic manner. If Mr Banks indicated some person in the crowd, wearing a distinguishing garment, the horse ran toward him and pulled him into the arena. Sir Kenelm Digby wrote that Marocco 'would restore a glove to the due owner after the master had whispered the man's name in his ear, and would tell the just number of pence in any silver coin newly showed him by his master'. In an amusing trick, Mr Banks ordered his horse to bow to the Queen of England, Marocco did so with great reverence, ceremoniously scraping his hoof. But when ordered to bow to that arch-enemy of all Britons, the King of Spain, Marocco flatly refused. When Mr Banks insisted, the horse neighed furiously, showing his teeth, and kicked out behind. The conclusion of this caper was that the infuriated horse, whose political opinions had been so grossly insulted, chased his master out from the arena. This popular trick was aped by Marocco's successors among London's performing animals: a 'jackanapes', an elephant, and even Mr Holden's old, unwieldy camel all shared Marocco's dislike of the Spanish monarch. In one of his poems, John Donne described a particularly apathetic and indifferent gentleman, who

...doth move no more
Than the wise politique horse would heretofore
Or thou, O elephant, or ape wilt do,
When any names the King of Spain to you.

Marocco was also famous for his arithmetic ability. In one of the tricks, Mr Banks collected a number of coins from the audience and shook them in a large purse. Marocco then took up each of the coins in turn and returned them to their proper owners, after first stamping his hoof to tell how many shillings and pence each of them was worth. William Shakespeare mentioned the horse's money-counting ability in *Love's Labour's Lost*, where he has Moth declare:

How easy it is to put years to the word three
And to study three years in two words,
The dancing horse will tell you.

In the mid-1590s, William Banks and Marocco were among London's most popular entertainers. Mr Banks was swiftly becoming quite a wealthy man: he took lodgings at Belsavage Inn near Ludgate, where Marocco also had his stables. Their arena was near Gracious-street, where Banks had ordered a gallery to be constructed. A musician was employed to entertain the spectators in between the shows, and to play suitable music for the dancing horse; a merry tune, called 'Bankes' Game', was played to accompany Marocco's calisthenics. Some of the horse's early tricks verged on the burlesque: one of them was that he drank a huge bucket of water and then relieved himself when ordered by the trainer. This amused one of Banks's literary friends, the poet John Bastard, who wrote that:

Bankes has a horse of wondrous qualitie,
For he can fight, and pisse, and daunce, and lie,
And find your purse, and tell what coyne ye have:
But Bankes, who taught your horse to tell a knave?

The ladies of London were unamused by these unprepossessing antics, however, and Mr Banks seems to have excluded this trick from his later repertoire. He also had Marocco's tail cut, making him a cut-tail or 'curtall', as the horse was frequently described. Another of Mr Banks's literary friends, the author Thomas Nashe, wrote that:

> Wiser was our brother Bankes of these latter days, who made his jugling horse a Cut, for feare if at any time he should foyst, the stinke sticking in his thicke bushie taile might be noysome to his Auditors.

The ladies who attended the shows still had some unpleasant surprises in store for them. One of Marocco's foremost accomplishments was 'to discern Maids from Maulkins'. Mr Banks ordered his horse first to fetch him a chaste and honourable virgin and then to bring him a harlot of the streets. It is unknown whether Mr Banks trusted his own ability to determine a lady's virtue from her clothing, or if he let the horse select them at random; in either of these two versions, this trick must have given rise to much coarse laughter from the male spectators.

Another variation of this trick was described in one of the many anecdotes about the famous clown Richard Tarleton, about whom it was written that 'for the part called the Clown's part, he never had his match, never will have'. Its authenticity can be questioned, however, because Tarleton had been dead some years before Marocco came to London, unless the horse was older than earlier presumed, and identical to the (dyed?) white horse that Mr Banks had brought to Shrewsbury in 1591. At any rate, the popular *Tarleton's Jests* related that once, when Tarleton and his actor friends were staging a play at the Crosse-Keyes near Gracious-street, Mr Banks and his 'Horse of strange Qualities' were performing near the sign of the Bell. While the actors were wholly unsuccessful, Marocco had a field-day, attracting much notice from the passers-by. When Tarleton finally himself went up to see the dancing horse, his friend Banks recognised him in the crowd. He asked the horse to seek out 'the veriest foole' among the spectators. Marocco immediately ran to Tarleton and pulled him into the ring by the sleeve. Tarleton was laughed at by the crowd, but said nothing else than 'God a mercy, horse!' He challenged Mr Banks that he himself could make Marocco perform an even more startling feat; Banks replied that he allowed him to try, be it what it might. Tarleton then told Marocco to seek out 'the veriest whore-master' among those present: the horse ran to his own master and seized his coat! As Marocco pulled Banks into the centre of the arena, accompanied by the shouts and laughter of the audience,

Tarleton said 'Then God a mercy, horse, indeed!' It must be suspected, however, that these two cunning performers had planned the whole thing beforehand. Their advertising gimmick was a great success, and 'God a mercy, horse' remained a byword in London for many years.

Late sixteenth-century London was a hotbed of literary activity: Shakespeare's contemporaries were tireless in writing and publishing satirical pamphlets, squibs and poems; their work was eagerly bought by the growing, literate middle class. The satirical poems and pamphlets had strange titles, like *Satiro-Mastix*, *Strappado for the Devill*, *Armin's Nest of Ninnies* and *The Mastive, or a Young Whelpe of the Olde Dogge*. Many of them are difficult to comprehend today, due to their extreme topicality. In November 1595, a laudatory poem dedicated to Marocco was printed. This 'Ballad shewing the Strange Qualities of a Yong Nagg called Morocco' was probably meant to be sold at the horse-shows, but its contents are unknown, since not a single copy has been preserved to posterity. The month after, a thirteen-page pamphlet entitled *Maroccus Extaticus; or, Bankes Bay Horse in a Trance*, was published in London. The alleged authors were Iohn Dando, the wier-drawer of Hadley, and Harrie Runt, head ostler of Bosomes Inne, but the pamphlet is likely to have been written by some Oxford undergraduates, since they were among the main providers of contemporary satirical fiction. It was a frequent jest among the Londoners that Mr Banks and Marocco probably could talk to each other, and the pamphlet has the form of a conversation between Banks and the horse. They talk about certain reprehensible features of daily London life, and unanimously deplore the deceitful merchants and ungenerous publicans of the Metropolis. The innkeepers are divided into two categories: those who also keep brothels and those who employ prostitutes from the street. The pamphlet was illustrated with an amusing woodcut, showing Mr Banks and his horse performing before some interested spectators.

After seeing Marocco in action, many people suspected witchcraft to be involved: surely, no mere horse could perform such wonders. When Mr Banks made an extended tour of the provinces from 1595 to 1597, visiting Oxford and Shrewsbury among other cities, many people in the audience sat pale and trembling during the show; they were certain that Mr Banks was a sorcerer and the horse his familiar spirit. In Edinburgh, Marocco again made a lasting impression, as judged from Patrick Henderson's *History of Scotland*:

> There came an Englishman to Edinburgh with a Chestain coloured naig, which he called Marocco. He made him do many rare and uncouth tricks, such as never horse was observed to do the like before in this land. This man would borrow from twenty or thirty of the spectators a piece of gold or silver, put all in a purse, and shuffle them together: thereafter he [the horse] would give every gent his own piece of money back again... He would say to him, 'I will sell you to a carter,' then he would seem to die. Then he would say, 'Marocco, a gent hath borrowed you, and you must ride with a lady of court:' Then he would most daintily hackney, amble and ride a pace and trot, and play the jade at his command when his master pleased.

Although they were pleased to see the horse bow to the King of Scotland as well as to Queen Elizabeth, but bite and strike at a man who mentioned the King of Spain, the superstitious Scotsmen remained ill at ease. They were certain that the horse was an evil spirit, which would one day devour its master, when his incantations could no longer harness it.

When Mr Banks returned to London in the late 1590s, he found that his act had lost its novelty. The Metropolis was full of performing horses, donkeys, apes, baboons and bears. An elephant, imported to London, was a serious competitor, as was Mr Holden's dancing camel, which had its arena on London Bridge itself. Extraordinary measures were needed in order to maintain Marocco's position as London's leading four-footed entertainer, but the clever horse-trainer rose to the challenge. St Paul's Cathedral was, at this time, London's centre-point. The cathedral had been badly neglected after being struck by lightning in 1561, but remained a thoroughfare and meeting-place: the nobility strolled outside its gates, and the streets and shops nearby teemed with people. Jugglers, street-peddlers and beggars were everywhere. The cathedral did not have its present-day cupola, which was added after the Great Fire of London, but instead a tall, square tower, partially repaired after the lightning-stroke. From the summit of this tower, the entire city and its surrounding boroughs could be seen on a clear day; it cost a penny, paid to the verger, to be allowed to climb the tower.

It is not recorded in the annals of St Paul's if there was a separate fee for animals, however. In February 1601, Mr Banks led his horse up the more than 1,000 steps of the endless spiral staircase out onto the church roof, which was, according to a contemporary writer, 'as rotten as your great-grandfather'. Here, more than 520 feet above ground, the horse danced and performed equilibristic tricks. William Banks had of course spread the word about Marocco's great feat: all around the cathedral, people craned their heads not to lose sight of the horse up in the sky. Churchgoers, deacons and clergymen rushed out not to miss this miracle. In a collection of anecdotes called *Jests to make you Merie*, it was told that a misanthropic old man sat in his chambers when his servant came running in, flustered and panting, to tell him about the horse standing 'on the top of Powles' and the great multitudes of people in the streets staring to behold it. The old man looked through his window, to view the chattering crowd around the cathedral, replying 'Away, thou foole, what need I goe so farre to see a horse on the top, when I can looke upon so many asses at the bottome?'

Some years ago, an American newspaper reported that some drunken university students had brought a young bull up twelve flights of stairs into the flat of one of their friends, who, one might suppose, did not particularly appreciate this unexpected nocturnal visit. When the jokers tried to get the bull downstairs, it refused to move, instead becoming furious. The neighbours called the police and the local TV stations after their doors had been gored and kicked by the enraged animal, and the pranksters were arrested. Some experienced policemen declared that it was completely impossible to get any livestock to go down a flight of stairs, since that was against their nature. Instead, the bull was lassoed and pulled up another twenty-six flights of stairs, where the policemen planned to harness it to a helicopter and lift it off the roof of the building. The bull was frightened by the helicopter, however, and suddenly leapt from the roof, nearly taking one of the policemen with it on its headlong plunge toward the street below. Marocco's descent from St Paul's cannot have been any easier. Defying the predictions of the Texan police officers, however, the horse, led on by his master, nimbly climbed down the endless stairway to receive the ovations of the masses below. Some years later, the poet Thomas Dekker considered this feat, in his *Guls Hornebooke*:

> From hence [the top of St Paul's steeple] you may descend, to talke about the horse that went up; and strive, if you can, to know his keeper; take the day of the moneth, and the number of the steppes, and suffer yourselfe to beleeve verily that it was not a horse, but something else in the likenesse of one.

After the triumphant climb of the cathedral tower, the British Isles had become too small for Mr Banks and his star performer, and he planned an extended tour of the continent. In March 1601, he set up headquarters at the Lion d'Argent Inn at Rue Saint Jacques in Paris. Under his new artist's name Monsieur Moraco, the horse made his debut some weeks later, and was an immediate success. The amazement by which the feats of Marocco were received in the French capital has been graphically described by Monsieur Jean de Montlyard, councillor of the Prince de Condé. His eyewitness account of 'cest incomparable cheval' was published as a long footnote to a French edition of *Les Metamorphoses ou L'Asne d'Or* of Apuleios; it describes Mr Banks and Marocco at the summit of their extraordinary career.

The horse stood on two legs, walked forward and backward, and then knelt, extending the hooves straight out in front of him. He danced and capered with the agility of a monkey. Mr Banks threw up a glove, asking the horse to take it to a man wearing spectacles. The horse immediately did so. He then asked the horse to carry one glove to a lady wearing a green muff and another to a lady wearing a violet muff, to demonstrate that the horse knew colours; although there were more than two hundred people present, Marocco performed this task without a false step. When told to seek out a man with a bundle of papers under his arm, the horse did so although the man tried to hide the papers under his coat; he was seized by the cloak and pulled into the ring by Marocco's strong teeth. William Banks then blindfolded his horse and collected a large number of French coins in a purse. The horse was then asked how many coins were in the purse and how many of them were made of gold, giving correct answers by stamping his hoof. Mr Banks then seized a golden écu from the purse and asked his horse how many francs such a coin was worth. Marocco stamped his hoof thrice to mark that it was worth three francs, but did not seem quite satisfied with this answer. Prompted by Mr Banks, Marocco then struck another four blows with his hoof, to designate that the écu was, due to a recent change in the gold standard, now worth three francs and four sols. Chevalier de Montlyard was amazed by this: his imagination had to be stretched to the limit for him to believe that a horse could count money with its eyes blindfolded; then – 'chose plus estrange!' – it also knew the recent changes in the currency!

After this impressive demonstration of Marocco's power of intellect, some burlesque pranks were played to impress the more simple-minded spectators. Marocco neighed and sneezed when ordered to do so, showing his teeth and pricking up his ears. Whenever any spectator threw an object onto the stage, the horse brought it back like a spaniel. Mr Banks commanded his horse to walk as if carrying a lady, and Marocco ambled very gently round the arena. He then asked the horse to walk as if a riding master was mounted upon him, and the horse leaped, scraped, bowed and made the most intricate steps and passades. The jokes continued when Mr Banks harshly scolded his horse for being lazy, threatening to sell him to some carter who would soon work him to death. Marocco hung his head and made other gestures to show his unhappiness. He fell on the earth as if sick, rolling over with an agonising groan. The horse lay absolutely still, playing dead with such skill that many spectators believed that he had really expired. Some rogues may have demanded their money back, but many kind-hearted people felt sorry for the poor horse who had sacrificed his life for the sake of art. Mr Banks promised that the horse would revive if anyone would ask his pardon. Some spectators cried out 'Pardonnez-luy! Il fera bien son devoir!' and the horse immediately leapt up, to everyone's relief. At Banks's beckoning, Marocco ran up to a gentleman with red hair, who had been one of those interceding on his behalf, thanking his saviour with many caresses. Mr Banks then threatened to sell Marocco to the French postal service, who were not known to treat their horses kindly, but Marocco raised up one leg and cantered about on three only, to show that he was lame and unfit for such arduous service.

Jean de Montlyard wrote that the show had once been visited by one of the city magistrates, who was adamant that such things could not be accomplished without magic. Horse and master were both imprisoned for interrogation, but Mr Banks managed to persuade their captors that the tricks were done only by art and by signs, which the horse had been trained to obey since an early age. Another distinguished visitor to the horse-show was the philologist and philosopher Professor Isaac Casaubon. This famous scholar had visited several performances, becoming increasingly puzzled how such tricks could be achieved, if not by magic and sorcery. Mr Banks politely received Isaac Casaubon, and managed to convince him that Marocco's feats were due only to his own careful training. He bragged that, given a year of preparations, he could train any other horse to perform similar tricks.

In 1602, Mr Banks and Marocco arrived in Orléans, having probably visited several other French cities on the way. Their show was, once more, a great success. Orléans had several large Capuchin monasteries and churches, and the monks and priests were keen visitors to the dancing horse's performances. When treated to a similar show to that performed in Paris, they were frightened out of their minds, calling out that Banks must be a sorcerer and the horse a demon from Hell. Banks and Marocco were once more arrested, and threatened with being burnt alive, as witches or conjurers. In order to save himself and the horse, Mr Banks demanded to be allowed to give a farewell performance before the priests and monks, which he was granted. William Banks ordered Marocco to seek out one of the priests who had a large crucifix stuck in his hat; the horse did so, knelt down before the crucifix, and kissed it with the utmost piety. The monks and priests had to confess that they had made a mistake, since the devil did not have power to come near the cross. Instead, they had said that the beast must have been inspired by the Holy Ghost, giving Mr Banks 'money and great commendations' when they left Orléans.

After this fortunate escape, Mr Banks and Marocco continued their European tour for several years. It is likely that they performed in Lisbon, Rome and Frankfurt. In the latter city, Mr Banks told an English cleric, Bishop Morton, about his adventures in Orléans. The Bishop later reproduced this tale in one of his theological pamphlets, *A Direct Answer to the Scandalous Exceptions of Theophilus Higgons*; it was later added to in *The Booke of Bulls*. The poet Ben Jonson later claimed, in an epigram published in 1616, that Banks and Marocco really had been burned at the stake:

> But amongst these Tiberts, who do you think it was?
> Old Bankes the juggler, our Pythagoras,
> Grave tutor to the learned horse. Both which
> Being, beyond sea, burned for one witch…

It is not known how long this European tour went on. The last certain mention of the dancing horse is that the at least sixteen-year-old Marocco was performing at the court of Duke Henry Julius of Brunswick-Wolfenbüttel, in April 1605. This magnate, who was the brother-in-law of James I, was a considerable patron of British actors; in his account-books, it is recorded that 'Reichardt Banckes' received forty thaler for the horse-show, and the accompanying musician received ten thaler. It is odd that this source, like Chambers' *Every-day Book*, gives Banks's first name as Richard; the evidence that his first name was really William rests solely on his vintner's license, signed William Banks. It is unknown whether Marocco died literally in harness, touring Europe until the last. If the much-travelled horse was finally allowed to enjoy some years of retirement, Marocco would have been able to view the manifold performing animals of London with a condescending horse-laugh, as the great predecessor among their ilk. It is likely that the dancing horse expired at some time in 1606 or 1607.

Mr Banks, who had once bragged that he could train another horse to take Marocco's place within a year, never again performed. It is very likely that he had taken Marocco to court during their earlier residence in London. It may well be that Queen Elizabeth herself had seen one of the shows, since there is a fair bit of evidence that Banks enjoyed the favour of her successor, King James I. In January 1604, King James was amused by a troupe of musicians and actors, one of whom was disguised as a horse. A letter quoted in *The Elizabethan Stage* mentions that 'the King made himself merry with threatening to send this colt to the stable and he could not break loose till he promised to dance as well as Bankes his horse'. It is also recorded that after returning to London, Mr Banks received an appointment to the Royal stables. He was paid a considerable sum from the privy purse of Prince Henry 'for teaching of a little naig to vault, at his highnes comand'. In the early 1620s, he was employed to train a horse for the Duke of Buckingham.

William Banks had probably put away a good deal of money during his career as an international celebrity. He was considered a wealthy and honest gentleman among the Londoners, and it is unlikely that he had any shortage of interesting anecdotes from his travels. His daughter married John Hyde of Urmstone, a Lancashire gentleman. Banks was considered a great humorist by his contemporaries, but his recorded jokes have become rather dated. Once, he made a bet with Moll Cutpurse, a notorious female pickpocket and dealer in stolen merchandise, that she would not dare to ride through London dressed in male apparel. This joke failed miserably, however, since she was attacked by a furious mob, full of moral indignation against such an outrage against nature.

In 1632, when William Banks must have been more than seventy years old, he decided to start a new career. He wanted to open a tavern, which was a difficult venture in these days, since the Lord Mayor and

Court of Aldermen of London had limited the number of licenses to keep ale-houses, in a vain attempt to curb the prevalent drunkenness and hooliganism in the Metropolis. Furthermore, Banks wanted to open his tavern in Cheapside, London's dominant mercantile street. After a year of bickering with the authorities, Banks went to the King and obtained a Royal license to open his tavern. The year after, there was another quarrel, after the Lord Mayor had withdrawn his permission to serve food, but the King again supported the old horse-trainer against the authorities. William Banks's tavern was among the most popular ale-houses of London, and in 1637, some of his friends wrote a satirical squib about the strange foreign delicacies one might consume there. In *Shirley's Ball*, published in 1639, a final mention is made of 'mine hoste Bankes'. This is the last record left by the old horse-trainer, but it cannot be excluded that he was alive for several more years, to enjoy the success of his tavern. In 1662, Moll Cutpurse's biographer wrote that 'I shall never forget my fellow Humourist Banks the Vintner in Cheapside who taught his Horse to dance, and shooed him with Silver'.

When Marocco was touring Britain and France, many people were curious to know how the horse could be induced to perform such wonders, but Mr Banks never divulged the secrets of his trade. When Banks had realised that he could never teach another horse to become Marocco's worthy successor, he told a certain Mr Gervase Markham how Marocco had been trained. Markham, a country squire and an early hippologist, considered Banks's information to be of great interest, and 'an explanation of the excellence of a horses understanding, and how to teach them to doe trickes like Bankes his Curtall' became a separate chapter in the 1607 edition of his book *Cavelarice*.

Ever since Marocco had been a young foal, Banks had spent most of each day together with his horse; in order to strengthen the bond between them, no other person was allowed to feed or caress Marocco. The horse followed Banks like a dog when he went about his daily business. Banks always used kindness and patience during Marocco's lessons: when the horse performed well, he was rewarded with loaves of bread, but if Marocco showed obstinacy, he was given no food that day, to become more attentive during the following morning lesson. To teach Marocco how to count money, Banks first made the horse lift his leg on the command *Up*!, then indicating, by means of raising and lowering a rod in front of it, how many times he should stamp his hoof, 'giving him a bit of bread til he be so perfit that, as you lift up your rod, so he will lift up his foot, and as you move your rod downeward, so he will move his foot to the ground'. Soon, Marocco learnt how to perform this trick without the use of a rod: as soon as the command *Up*! made him alert, Marocco could, by means of watching Banks's face, deduce how many times he should stamp his foot. Banks said that 'it is a rule in the nature of horsses, that they have an especiall regard to the eye, face and countenaunce of their keepers'. As soon as this trick had been perfected, it was easy for Banks to ask Marocco to tell him how many knaves, how many harlots and how many rich men were in the audience.

To teach Marocco to bring a glove to any person in the audience, Banks first rewarded the horse when he was bringing back a thrown glove to his master. Then Banks pointed his rod to an assistant and taught the horse to go to him instead. Finally, several assistants were paraded in front of the horse, and the rod pointed toward one of them. If it looked as if Marocco would choose the wrong one, Banks called out *Be wise*!, and the horse at once chose a bystander instead; when the right person was selected, Banks called out *So, boy*! to indicate this. Finally, the horse had become accomplished enough for Banks to direct him merely with his eyes. Marocco's ear for the different commands was soon sure enough for Banks to make them a part of his introduction for each trick, to prepare the horse of what was expected of it. Gervase Markham commented that Marocco's feats proved beyond doubt that a horse was as intelligent and teachable as a dog or jackanapes; it could perform the same tricks as these animals 'except it be leaping upon your shoulders, climbing up houses, or untying knots, all which are contrary to the shape and strength of his great body'. He had himself seen one of the shows, and could well remember that Marocco never removed his eyes from his master's face.

A certain Samuel Rid, author of the curious *Art of Jugling or Legerdemaine*, published in 1612, had also seen Marocco perform. He was clever enough to recognise that when the horse was asked to tell the points on a pair of dice, he stamped his foot until Banks signed him to stop by shrugging his shoulder slightly. Similar hidden signs were used to direct the horse to return a glove or a handkerchief to its rightful owner.

During the reign of Queen Elizabeth, the British Isles enjoyed a time of rapid economic development, with flourishing commerce and freedom from political tyranny and religious fanaticism. During the decades around 1600, there was also a rapid intellectual development, particularly in London. Large classes of society, recently liberated from poverty, had a gluttonous appetite for literature, drama and other forms of entertainment. Seen from this perspective, Mr Banks and Marocco were a phenomenon of their time, like William Shakespeare and other contemporary writers, artists and dramatists. William Banks lacked any predecessor of importance: he was the great innovator within his particular field, and a man of genuine talent.

Marocco's performances occurred in a time still redolent with witchcraft and barbarism. London had, at this time, a large bear-garden, where the most disgusting and cruel 'sport' was advertised several times a week. Not only bears were baited, but also lions, bulls and wild boar. A huge, three-story building contained more than 120 boxes for large mastiff dogs; new recruits to this company of fierce curs were needed, at regular intervals, since the baited animals frequently wrought havoc among their ranks. *The Elizabethan Stage* tells us that when a horse was chased round the arena by four 'mastives', with a screaming ape tied to its back, a visiting Spaniard found this dismal sight 'most laughable'. It is to be hoped that William Banks and Marocco were able to impress the Londoners with some of the respect for animal rights they were so obviously lacking. It was certainly a more edifying spectacle to watch the dancing horse perform, than to see an idiot devour a living cat, a blind bear being whipped, or a badger with its tail nailed to the floor desperately trying to defend itself against four fierce fox-terriers.

Marocco has had many successors. Perhaps the best known of them was the little horse Billy, one of the stars of Astley's circus in London in the late eighteenth century. Billy could dance, count, boil tea and serve it like a waiter. After the circus had gone bankrupt, Billy was sold to a tradesman and had to pull a cart for several years until, one day, he was spotted by one of Astley's circus riders, who thought the dusty and rundown horse resembled the famous Billy he once had known. When the circus man clicked his fingernails as a sign for the horse to start tapping his foreleg, Billy at once did so; he was repurchased by the circus, which was once more solvent, and performed there for many years. After his death, at the venerable age of forty-two, Billy's skin was made into a huge thunderdrum, used for special effects in the circus. In the late nineteenth century, the acrobatic tricks of these circus horses became increasingly dramatic. In 1885, the Italian Signor Corradini showed a horse walking the tightrope at the Theatre Royal, Covent Garden. His competitor Mr Cottrell trained a mule to balance on a row of large bottles, which were, in their turn, situated on a tightrope. Doc Carver, Buffalo Bill's former henchman, had a horse that could dive from a thirty-six-foot platform into a huge basin full of water, whereas Freyer's Pony Circus boasted a team of horses walking on stilts.

Marocco's intellectual achievements have also been challenged by his modern competitors. The best-known of them was Clever Hans, a robust German working horse who could answer questions and perform calculations by means of handling blocks adorned with letters or numerals. But although the German horse-trainer Karl Krall believed that both Clever Hans and his predecessors, the Arab stallions Zarif and Muhammed, possessed a superior intelligence, the animal psychologist Dr Oskar Pfungst dismissed his claims. It is likely that Krall directed his horses with hidden signs just like Banks had done, although this was never conclusively proven at the time. In the 1920s, the American parapsychologist Dr J.B. Rhine was greatly impressed by Clever Hans's American counterpart, the mare Lady Wonder. He alleged, in several scholarly publications, that this horse possessed supernatural gifts, but since Lady was only mind-reading when her owner was present, it is likely that hidden cues again played a part.

Although these learned and acrobatic horses possessed considerable talents, none of them commanded even an inkling of the universal fame enjoyed by Marocco. It is doubtful if even the great modern circuses possess a horse capable of reproducing all the tricks of its great sixteenth-century predecessor. At any rate, Marocco will forever remain the only horse to have climbed the tower of St Paul's Cathedral, since the steeple was reconstructed after the Great Fire of London: no hoofed animal will ever succeed in climbing the present-day cupola.

Mr Banks and Marocco were mentioned more than sixty times in contemporary literature: already during his lifetime, this miraculous horse had become a character of legend. The most exaggerated tales were current about Marocco's acrobatic tricks 'on top of Powles'. Through Ben Jonson's garbled account, several pamphleteers and scandal chroniclers repeated the untrue tale that Marocco and his trainer had been burned at the stake by the papists. In a French humorous pamphlet, published in 1626, the English houyhnhnm is one of the main characters: 'Le joly Monsieur Maroc' plays the part of Dante's Virgil, residing in the nether regions of Hell after the conflagration, and entertaining a visiting Frenchman with great eloquence. Another doubtful authority, the apocryphal mock romance of Don Zara del Fago, goes into further details about these matters:

> Banks his beast; if it be lawful to call him a beast, whose perfections were so incomparably rare, that he was worthily term'd the four-legg'd wonder of the world for dancing; some say singing, and discerning maids from maulkins, finally, having of a long time proved himself the ornament of the British clime, travailing to Rome with his master, they were both burned by the commandment of the Pope.

In 1654, when both Banks and Marocco had been dead for several years, the poet Edmund Gayton wrote his *Pleasant Notes to Don Quixot*, a versified introduction to this popular novel. In one of the poems, Marocco makes a long speech to Don Quixote's horse Rosinante, extolling his own virtues, which went far beyond those of the Spanish knight's faithful steed. The famous dancing horse with silver shoes, who could count money by stamping his hoof, and who climbed the tower of St Paul's Cathedral, whereas Rosinante was only hoisted up a windmill, will thus himself provide a suitable conclusion to this tale:

> Though Rosinante famous was in fields
> For swiftnesse, yet no horse like me had heels.
> Goldsmiths did shoe me, not the Ferri-Fabers;
> One nail of mine was worth their whole weeks labours.
> Let us compare our feats; thou top of nowles
> Of hills hast oft been seen, I top of Paules.
> To Smythfields horses I stood there the wonder;
> I only was at top; more have been under.
> Thou like a Spanish jennet, got in the wind,
> Wert hoisted by a windmill; 'twas in kinde.
> But never yet was seen in Spaine or France,
> A horse like Bancks his, that to the pipe would dance:
> Tell mony with his feet; a thing which you,
> Good *Rosinante* nor *Quixot* ever could doe.

3

LAMENT

OF THE

Learned Pig

O Heavy day! Oh day of woe!
To misery a poster,
Why was I ever farrowed – why
Not spitted for a roaster?

Of what avail that I could spell
And read, just like my betters,
If I must come to this at last,
To litters, not to letters?

This miserable lamentation is spoken by Toby, the Learned Pig, the hero of one of Thomas Hood's many humorous poems, originally published in his 1835 *Comic Annual*. In his time, Thomas Hood was a poet of considerable repute. He wrote witty and apposite comments to current scandals and political affairs, and his punning rhymes and clever metrics were highly thought of by his contemporaries. In his *Collected Works,* the poem about the learned pig is accompanied by such popular favourites as *Miss Kilmansegg and her Precious Leg* and *Faithless Nelly Gray*. Although some critics have blamed Thomas Hood for his frivolousness and lack of depth, his poetry remained quite popular throughout the Victorian era, and still has its admirers today. *The Lament of Toby, the Learned Pig* is about a performing pig which, at the end of its distinguished career, suffers the dire fate of being fattened for the table after no longer being able to earn its keep in the daily shows. It is certainly based on fact, since such learned pigs were no rarity in Thomas Hood's time.

O, why are pigs made scholars of?
It baffles my discerning,
What griskins, fry, and chitterlings
Can have to do with learning.

At least since the sixteenth century, performing animals have been exhibited at the old English fairs and markets. The dancing horse Marocco had many successors, but none of them made history in the same way. In the eighteenth century, there was a rising interest in performing animals, and the London spectators had a lot to choose between: vaulting apes, dancing dogs, counting horses, drumming hares, and Chinese starlings playing cards. For the real connoisseur, there was the quack Colonel Katterfelto's regiment of electric black cats, and Mr Breslaw's famous acting canaries. In one of their theatricals, these remarkable birds were all dressed in military uniforms; they shot an alleged deserter with a small cannon and then buried the corpse, whistling mournful funeral tunes.

The first man to train a pig for the stage was the aforementioned Samuel Bisset. As we know, he became an animal trainer in middle age after working as a shoemaker and as a broker. His star performers were of course the Cat's Opera, whose musical ability so delighted the Londoners that they made Bisset's fortune. After their sojourn in London, Bisset went on tour with his troupe of animals: he had two monkeys who were walking the tightrope and playing the barrel-organ, a hare beating the tabor, canaries that could spell, and a tortoise that could fetch and carry like a dog (although more slowly!). In 1775, Bisset toured Ireland with his animals, where they became great favourites in Dublin, before going on to Leeds, Newcastle and various parts of Scotland. After this arduous tour, he bought a public house in Belfast and settled there with his animals.

Although reluctant to go on tour again, Bisset was still showing his animals at the pub. He also kept widening his repertoire and developing new tricks; he taught sparrows, linnets and turtles, and even a goldfish. After having trained many different species, he asked himself 'whether the obstinacy of the pig might be conquered'. Early in 1782, he purchased a young black piglet at the Belfast market for three shillings. After six or seven months, the young boar had made but little progress. Lesser men would have despaired, but Bisset went on for another sixteen months before the pig was sufficiently accomplished to make its first appearance in public.

Although the mentor of the Learned Pig sometimes stooped to using cruel tricks – the Dancing Turkeys were only waltzing when a section of the stage was heated under them! – he seems to have utilised humane methods during his porcine pupil's long education. The poet Robert Southey, who was interested in learned pigs, once interviewed a man living near the pig-trainer's back yard: 'He told me that he never saw the keeper beat him; but that, if he did not perform his lessons well, he used to threaten to take off his red waistcoat, – for the pig was proud of his dress'.

My Hebrew will all retrograde,
Now I'm put up to fatten,
My Greek, it will all go to grease
The dogs will have my Latin!

In August 1783, 'The Wonderful Pig' made his debut at the Ranelagh in Dublin. The pig could kneel, bow, spell out names using cardboard letters, cast up accounts, and point out married and unmarried people in the audience. It became a great novelty among the Dubliners, who were amazed that a pig could perform such wonders. The pig-trainer rented an apartment in the Dame-street, where the daily performances were always well attended. Mr Bisset earned a considerable sum of money. His heart must have swelled when he thought of his pig's great expectations: after a triumphal tour of the Midlands, it would enter London like a conqueror. If the curiosity-seekers of the Metropolis had been fascinated by his musical cats, then what would they think of the grunting Philosopher, a four-legged artist completely unique in the world?

But fate had other plans for him. Since the Dubliners demanded further performances, Bisset moved to another district of the city. But he forgot to ask the permission of the local magistrates, something that would cost him dearly. During the pig's performance, a policeman entered to disrupt the show. When Bisset resisted, he was given a savage beating, and all the stage equipment was destroyed. The brutal constable swore that if the Learned Pig was ever seen again within his jurisdiction, he would slaughter it on stage, before dragging its owner to prison.

The pig-trainer took to his bed, for several days, after this unprovoked assault. Some weeks later, he left Dublin, taking his pig and other animals with him. He planned to tour England en route to London, but in Chester, Mr Bisset fell ill and died; according to his biographer in the *Eccentric Mirror*, the meek old pig-trainer never quite recovered from the brutal treatment meted out to him in Dublin.

Alas! my learning once drew cash,
But public fame's unstable,
So I must turn a pig again,
And fatten for the table.

Mr Bisset's learned pig was taken over by a certain Mr Nicholson, about whose previous career little is known. It is likely that he was some kind of impresario or theatrical manager. At any rate, he knew well that he had come on to a good thing: under his management, 'the grunting Philosopher' was certainly not kept standing idle. They first went on tour to Scarborough, York, and several other towns and cities. As Nicholson's troupe also boasted a hare that beat the drum, a tortoise that brought back objects like a dog, and six turkey cocks performing a country dance, it is likely that he had purchased Bisset's entire menagerie.

Nor was Nicholson unaware of the value of newspaper publicity. On 16 February 1785, the London papers could announce that the porcine prophet was among the celebrities recently arrived in town. Nine days later, they reported that Mr Nicholson had managed to secure a suitable apartment for his pig, at No. 55 Charing Cross opposite the Admiralty. A newspaper advertisement pointed out that 'this sagacious animal reads, writes, and casts accounts, by means of typographical cards; solves questions in the four rules of arithmetic, tells, by looking at any gentleman's watch, what is the hour and minute, &c, and is the admiration of all who have seen him'. Another advertisement described the pig as a prodigy never seen before by the Londoners: 'neither the tongue of the most florid orator, or the pen of the most ingenious writer, can sufficiently describe the wonderful performance of that sagacious animal'.

If the Learned Pig had been a great novelty in Dublin, it caused even more astonishment in London, outclassing every other four-legged performer in the Metropolis. Every day, huge crowds came to see the animal perform. The caricature *The Wonderful Pig* by Thomas Rowlandson is probably a trustworthy representation of what the shows looked like. Under the tuition of the rotund Mr Nicholson, the black, rather thin pig spells out some words using cardboard letters, in front of a numerous audience of men, women and children. The anonymous author of the curious *London Unmask'd; or the New Town Spy*, wrote that he saw the crowd of people standing outside the showroom, and found it 'quite monstrous and ill-bred not to follow the ton, and go and see the wonderful Learned Pig'. He was agreeably surprised by the pig's ability to arrange its cardboard letters to compose any given names. When he spoke to Mr Nicholson, querying why the pig was so very thin, the impresario replied that a plenitude in the belly would diminish his pupil's adherence to discipline.

Mr Nicholson let the porcine prophet work hard. There were four shows a day, at twelve, two, four and six in the afternoon, seven days a week. Some journalists felt pity for the poor pig, particularly since the April weather was uncommonly hot: 'what with the weather, and the concourse of visitors, the poor animal is so *roasted*, that its skin is almost a *crackling*'. All classes of society were united in their admiration for the grunting Philosopher, and all religious persuasions. According to a rather sneering notice in the *Morning Post* of 26 April, even 'some of the *Synagogue Beaux* made a party to see the learned Pig. Tho' they were, on the whole, entertained with his grunting honour, their ideas of his merits were rather lessened, as the *good peoplesh* have always believed that the Devil inherited a herd of Swine'.

In this world, pigs, as well as men,
Must dance to fortune's fiddlings,
But must I give the classics up,
For barley-meal and middlings?

There was much speculation among the Londoners how much money Mr Nicholson was earning. If every show was attended by fifty people, paying a shilling each to enter, that would mean weekly takings of seventy pounds. But Mr Nicholson also held evening performances in the houses of wealthy people who wanted their dinner guests to see something really unique. It was told that once, an elegant lady was very reluctant to let the pig into her house. But Mr Nicholson said 'No fear, Ma'm, for the carpets! I took him out of the sty early!' Again, the house-trained pig was quite a success during these evening performances, earning considerable sums.

A sneering, envious writer in *The Times* was wholly critical of the learned pig craze among the Londoners. In April 1785, he accused Mr Nicholson of being truly piggish himself, by exhibiting the animal in a common public house, although the receipts were such that he could well afford a place of more decent appearance for the shows. When there was a rumour later the same month that the cost to see the grunting Philosopher had been increased to half a crown, Mr Nicholson had to inform the *Morning Post* that 'that sagacious animal still continues for the inspection of the curious, at his apartments opposite the Admiralty, at the usual price of One Shilling each person'. But the *Times* writer was still not appeased:

> Can anything show the depravity if this age in stronger colours than the encouragement given to the man who is proprietor of the Learned Pig, if it is true that he has already bought 3000 pounds into the funds, while honest industry is left to toil through life, too frequently with bare provision for the calls of nature?

Mr Nicholson was prevailed upon to take the Learned Pig to Oxford, Bath and Bristol, but he publicly declined this offer, since the length of the pig's reign in London exceeded even his own wildest expectations. In July, the pig joined the circus performing at Sadler's Wells Theatre. A review in the *Morning Herald* states that 'he went about his business in a capital style, to the admiration of a crowded house, and was honoured with the loudest plaudits from every part of it'. The review in *The Times* was equally positive: the pig answered questions from the pits, boxes and gallery with the greatest confidence, and was rewarded with loud plaudits. The pig's fame angered the troupe of tightrope performers and acrobats, and soon, the theatre manager, Mr Richard Wroughton, received a deputation consisting of Signor Placide, Mr Redigé (otherwise known as the Little Devil), Monsieur Dupuis, Mr Meunier and La Belle Espagnole, all thinking themselves degraded by being forced to perform together with a pig. When the manager tried to persuade them to stay, the furious acrobats asked him to choose between the pig and them. They were all sacked, on the spot, and the pig had the arena to itself. The Learned Pig's reign of the London amusement lasted until early September 1785, when it finally departed for Oxford and Bath, the first stops of its grand tour of Britain.

Day after day my lessons fade,
My intellect gets muddy;
A trough I have and not a desk,
A stye – and not a study!

In December 1785, the Learned Pig performed in Norwich. One of the shows was seen by the Rev. James Woodforde, who described it in his *Diary of a Country Parson*:

> After Dinner the Captain and myself, went and saw the learned Pigg at the rampant Horse in St. Stephens – there was but a small Company there but soon got larger – We stayed there about an Hour – It was wonderful to see the sagacity of the Animal – It was a Boar Pigg, very thin, quite black with a magic Collar on his Neck. He would spell any word or Number from the Letters and Figures that were placed before him; paid for seeing the Pigg 0.1.0.

Parson Woodforde was not the only observer to note that the 'Pigg' was particularly thin; it is likely that the clever Mr Nicholson was purposely keeping it lean to increase its agility during the shows.

In early March 1786, the Learned Pig was back in London for a second sojourn in the Metropolis, performing at the Lyceum, in the Strand. According to a newspaper advertisement, the tour of the provinces had been a great success: 'He has been received with universal applause in every city, town, and village in which he took up his residence, and honoured with the presence and attention of many persons of great distinction'. The Pig's repertoire was unchanged, except that it was now pointed out that 'he never divulges the thoughts of any lady in the company *but by her permission*'; this might have been due to an embarrassing incident during a previous thought-reading session! Again, the pig was a great success, and the poet Robert Southey wrote that the Learned Pig was 'a far greater object of admiration to the English nation than ever was Sir Isaac Newton'.

The next twists and turns in the Learned Pig's career are somewhat obscure. An advertisement in late April 1786 states that the grunting Philosopher would not long remain in London, since he was engaged to go abroad. But *The Times* of 25 September the same year says that the pig's tour of France had been postponed, allegedly because the French Cabinet intended to lay a duty on swine. But in spite of this flippant note, the Learned Pig seems to have made it to France in the end. The *Morning Herald* of 6 January 1787 tells us that 'the Learned Pig of Charing-cross is one of the rarer monsters of France. It has fed its owners fat through Calais, Boulogne, Montreuil, &c., &c'.

> Farewell to 'Town!' farewell to 'Gown!'
> I've quite outgrown the latter, –
> Instead of Trencher cap my head
> Will soon be in a platter!

When Mr Nicholson's pig was away, several rival learned pigs appeared, to usurp some of the fame of their departed colleague. Already in 1785, a certain Mr J. Fawkes toured the provinces at length with his learned pig, making sure that his itinerary would not coincide with that of Nicholson's animal. In March and April 1786, when the original Learned Pig was back in London, Fawkes and his pig were visiting Reading and Oxford. The usurper's repertoire was very similar to that of Nicholson's pig, except that it could perform even when blindfolded. There were several other rival pigs. 'The Amazing Pig of Knowledge' appeared at the Crown Inn, Astley's circus had a French pig that 'articulated *oui, oui* with an uncommon fine accent', and Hughes's circus boasted an automaton pig, imported from Italy.

This profusion of porcine performers renders it even more difficult to find out what happened to Nicholson's animal upon its return from France. Some help is given by the newspaper clippings in Lysons's *Collectana*: one of them states that the original learned pig was back in Britain in late 1787. Mr Nicholson was still its proprietor, and the advertisements pointed out that this was certainly the same pig that had been so very successful in Charing Cross and at Sadler's Wells. The pig visited Edinburgh and probably some other Scottish cities, before making another extended tour of the English countryside, performing in Retford, Newark, Lincoln and Stamford, on its way back to London.

That the Learned Pig had visited Edinburgh makes it probable that it was the same animal seen there by Robert Burns. When Burns was asked to attend a party for the first edition of his poems, he answered that he would, on condition they also had the learned pig present; he apparently did not want to put himself on a show to advertise his work.

During its long and distinguished career, Mr Nicholson's learned pig was stated by the newspapers to have earned more money 'than any actor or actress within the same compass of time'. In November 1788, articles in several newspapers informed the Londoners that their old friend and favourite, the Learned Pig, had departed this life. The same article also mentioned that the pig-trainer was confined in a madhouse at Edinburgh: 'Too much learning we suppose had driven the pig mad, so he bit his master!' These articles were brief and rather flippant, and the newspapers of the time often unreliable. But the fact remains that there is no trustworthy mention of the original learned pig after November 1788, whether in handbills, advertisements, or the newspaper press.

It is true that some newspaper articles from October and November 1789, included in Lysons's *Collectana*, state that a learned pig, allegedly the same one that, four years since, 'afforded such amusement in most parts of England', had recently returned to Hereford after a long and arduous tour of France. The grunting Philosopher had witnessed the French revolution at first hand, and an advertisement bragged that 'from his frequent interviews with the French patriots, he is almost enabled to hold a discourse upon the Feudal System, the Rights of Kings, and the Destruction of the Bastile'. The last heard of this revolutionary learned pig is that it departed for Monmouth and Abergavenny after its ten-day stay in Hereford. This sounds rather like Mr Nicholson's original animal, possibly under new management. But a vital clue is given by a doggerel poem in one of the newspaper articles: it is the same one used by Mr Fawkes, the early competitor of Nicholson, to advertise his learned pig in 1786, and thus it seems that the usurper pig survived the original porcine performer.

Of all my literary kin
A farewell must be taken
Good Bye to the poetic Hogg
The philosophic Bacon!

Although neither Sir Francis Bacon nor the Scottish poet James Hogg would have been disposed to consider a pig their equal, Toby's talk of his 'literary kin' is not entirely without foundation, since many late eighteenth-century writers mention learned pigs. According to Boswell, Samuel Johnson once discussed learned pigs. In conversation, his friend Miss Seward remarked that she had seen a performing pig in Nottingham in 1784; this was probably Mr Nicholson's animal on its way to London. The subject amused Dr Johnson, and he declared that 'pigs are a race unjustly calumniated. Pig has, it seems, not been wanting to man, but man to pig. We do not allow time for his education, we kill him at a year old.' One of those present feared that brutal methods must have been used to subdue the inherently indocile animal, but Samuel Johnson thought that the pig had no reason to complain, since it had survived the slaughter: 'protracted existence is a good recompense for a very considerable degree of torture'. After Dr Johnson's death, an old enemy wrote an ironical epitaph:

Though Johnson, learned Bear, is gone,
Let us no longer mourn our loss,
For lo, a learned Hog is come,
And Wisdom grunts at Charing Cross.

Happy for Johnson – that he died
Before this wonder came to town,
Else it had blasted all his pride
Another brute should gain renoun.

The poet William Cowper was compared to the learned pig by a waggish correspondent, while another likened his fame to that of the actress and courtesan Anne Bellamy. Cowper responded that 'You tell me that I am rivalled by Mrs Bellamy and he that I have a competitor for fame not less formidable in the learned Pig. Alas! what is an author's popularity worth, in a world that can suffer a prostitute on one side, and a pig on the other to eclipse his brightest glories.' In the humorous journals, Prime Minister William Pitt was often referred to as the Wonderful Pig. Several satirical drawings depicted William Pitt as a pig, with or without learned attributes: one drawing, entitled *The Rival Pigs*, showed William Pitt and his main political adversary Charles James Fox, with other learned pigs, some of them with wigs, in the background.

Many contemporary and Victorian authors allude to the Learned Pig and its accomplishments. Sarah Trimmer, a celebrated early writer of children's books, is likely to have seen the original Learned Pig, since she refers to its accomplishments in her 1786 book *The Robins*. The Learned Pig provided evidence that animals also have an intellect, although Mrs Trimmer was fearful that cruelty had formed part of its training. In her early feminist tract *Vindication of the Rights of Woman*, published in 1792, Mary Wollstonecraft deplored Rousseau's misogynist attitude about girls being naturally attentive to their persons, saying that such tomfoolery 'should be selected with the anecdotes of the learned pig'. None less than Samuel Coleridge made an amusing joke about learned pigs in his *Stateman's Manual*, published in 1816. A Dutch traveller, exiting highly gratified from a showman's caravan with the words 'Learned Pig' gilt on the panels, sees another caravan with the words 'Reading Fly' in letters of the same size. Eager for more curiosities, he takes his seat inside, but soon falls asleep. He is awoken by the driver asking if he was booked all the way to Reading! The punch-line is that for Coleridge, the concept of a Reading Public was more marvellous still.

In *Our Mutual Friend*, Charles Dickens described a country fair, with a Peep-show of the Battle of Waterloo, a Fat Lady and her companion the Learned Pig. In his early work *Mudfog and Other Sketches*, he brought his somewhat heavy-handed wit to bear on the same subject. In a fictitious academy, a number of scholars discuss 'the last moments of the learned pig'. The animal's name was not Toby, but Solomon, and its only relation was an uncle that was shortly after himself 'converted into sausages'. The president of the academy inquired whether the notable Pig-faced Lady, who wore a black velvet mask and took her meals from a golden trough, was any relation of the learned pig but after some hesitation, a member answered that the Pig-faced Lady was in fact his mother-in-law.

O why did I at Brazen-Nose
Rout up the roots of knowledge?
A butcher that can't read will kill
A pig that's been to college.

During the career of the original learned pig, some religious people were deeply affected by its performances, suspecting black magic to be involved. They even demanded that the pig should be burnt and its manager banished, since they did not doubt that he was 'corresponding with the Devil'. Others considered the pig as proof for the transmigration of souls, suspecting that 'the Spirit of the grunting Philosopher might once have animated a Man'.

Several contemporary scholars took a more constructive interest in learned pigs and other performing animals, using them as arguments in the age-old philosophical question whether animals possess reason. The extreme Cartesian view that all creatures great and small were nothing more than automata, whose actions were merely directed by instincts, was challenged by many other seventeenth-century philosophers. When the Cambridge scholars Matthew Wren and John Preston disputed, in front of King James I, the question whether dogs could reason, it was one of the earliest attempts to solve this old philosophical conundrum. Whereas John Locke did not consider beasts to be able to compare ideas or to reason abstractly, David Hartley thought that a clever and well-trained dog might well be compared to a deaf-mute or retarded human being, who could only communicate by signs. David Hume also had a surprisingly high opinion of the dumb creation's intellectual abilities, which might well have been influenced by the many performing animals of his time. He made no sharp distinction of human reason and animal instincts: the difference might instead be that the human being had a larger number of inherent instincts, one of which was the capacity of deductive reasoning.

The eccentric Lord Monboddo, an early evolutionist who was much mocked by his contemporaries, had similar ideas, which went a bit too far: he believed that the orang-utan and the human being belonged to the same species, and that humankind's greater intellectual ability merely was a result of their higher social development. Like Jean Jacques Rousseau, he thought that the language was an invention of society, rather than an innate human attribute separating them from animals. When Lord Monboddo approached some experienced animal trainers in London, they all agreed that the brute creation might well approach the human beings with regard to intellect, if they lived long enough and sufficient pains were taken regarding their education. Charles Darwin's grandfather, Dr Erasmus Darwin, had also been influenced by the Learned Pig. In his *Zoonomia*, published in 1796, he wrote that the pigs were a much-maligned race. Had they been allowed to lead an interesting and variable life instead of being locked up in their sties, and left to develop intellectually instead of being slaughtered at an early age, their position within the animal world would have been an exalted one.

In the popular eighteenth-century natural history books, the animals were often anthropomorphised: the lion was noble and lordly, the dog loyal and servile, the cat wanton and deceitful. For many years, the pigs had been reviled in these natural history books: in spite of their considerable value as food animals, they were castigated as being gluttonous, obstinate and sordid. That a filthy pig, a slovenly, pig-headed brute, could not only perform tricks that had previously been mastered only by apes and dogs, but also read thoughts and play cards, was a great astonishment to many people. This would explain much of the Learned Pig's fame before its contemporaries.

One thing I ask – when I am dead,
And past the Stygian ditches –
And that is, let my schoolmaster
Have one of my two flitches.

'Twas he who taught my letters so
I ne'er mistook or missed 'em
Simply by *ringing* at the nose,
According to *Bell's* system.

The pig-trainer Samuel Bisset was, like William Banks, the great forerunner in his particular line of business. Indeed, there had been trained pigs before his time, but their success had been scant. Most people disliked these foul, smelly brutes, and their tricks had not been impressive. The eccentric King Louis XI of France was an exception: he preferred pigs to all other animals, and always kept many pet pigs at his court. Once, as a joke, he ordered the learned Abbot of Baigne to teach these pigs to sing in concert. The Abbot took the challenge seriously, and retired to his country seat. None of the courtiers believed that he would make it, but after a couple of months of inventive thinking and hard labour, the Abbot returned with a large and complicated apparatus. All the pigs were seated on stools, in strict order of age and heaviness. The court sat down in a comfortable gallery in front of the pig orchestra. When the King had been seated on his throne, the Abbot started playing the remarkable organ he had brought with him: each time a key was touched, a sharp spike, arising from the stool's mechanism, pricked the behind of the pig sitting on it, and the pig yelped. Since the squealing of the young piglets was more shrill than that of the old, heavy sows, the Abbot was able to play pieces of music to the King's entire satisfaction.

It is unknown exactly what methods Samuel Bisset used when training his learned pig, but it is unlikely that the Scottish doctor Joseph Bell's educational system, mentioned by Toby in his long lamentation, was in any way involved. Bisset had no pupils, and his untimely death rendered it impossible for him to impart his secret training methods to anyone. From 1797 until 1798, another learned pig was exhibited in the United States by the conjurer W.F. Pinchbeck, who later sold the pig at a public auction. In his book *The Expositor, or Many Mysteries Unravelled*, Pinchbeck described how he had trained a young piglet to move cards with letters on them: he scolded it in a loud voice when it had made a mistake, and rewarded it with pieces of apple when it had done its work well. To get the animal to move the card into its correct position, to form words, he led it on a leash, teaching it to obey certain hand signs, until he could direct it only using these signs. The same technique, albeit with figures instead of letters on the cards, was used to teach the pig to count and read a watch. Pinchbeck considered pigs to be both clever and ready to learn: 'the animal is so sagacious that he will appear to read your thoughts'. Pigs have excellent hearing, which Pinchbeck used to his advantage, by means of directing the animal with snuffling, clearing his throat, and snapping his fingers.

When trained pigs appear at various circuses today, their feats are often acrobatic rather than scholarly. The American pig-trainer Bobby Nelson shares Dr Johnson and Erasmus Darwin's opinion that the pig is an underestimated animal. Its intelligence and excellent eyesight, hearing, balance, and sense of smell, makes it easy to train if it is taken early from its mother. The sole problem is that the pig's propensity to fatten tends to make it too clumsy for acrobatics already when it is a few years old. A notable late nineteenth-century pig trainer was the Russian clown Vladimir Durow, who usually made his entrée seated in a cart drawn by his huge sow Tschuschka. In a spectacular trick, the pig was standing on top of a pedestal: a goat stood on Tschuschka's back, a greyhound on that of the goat and a cat on the dog's back; this pyramid of animals was crowned by a large rat, sitting on the cat's back. The pig's virtues in this trick were its solidity and the strength of its legs rather than any equilibristic ability. The acrobatic English piglet Bill, belonging to Lord George Sanger's circus, was Tschuschka's absolute opposite: he could balance on one trotter, standing on the nose of a sea-lion. In the 1950s, the Danish pig-trainer Carl Hansen had considerable success with his pig Hansi, which was capable of playing the glockenspiel and balancing on huge barrels (although not at the same time!) The Swiss clown Michels Ghazzi was much less fortunate as a pig-trainer. He had taught a pig to hold a pistol in its muzzle and fire it at a target, but the pig turned unexpectedly and shot the clown instead; the unhappy Swiss expired from blood-poisoning a few days later.

For sorrow I could stick myself,
But conscience is a clasher;
A thing that would be rash in man
In me would be a rasher!

It took until 1817 before a learned pig approaching the fame of Bisset's original porcine performer stood on a London stage. In February that year, Toby the Sapient Pig made his debut at the Royal Promenade Rooms, Spring Gardens, as a part of the show of the conjurer Mr Nicholas Hoare. Toby was always dressed in a large lace collar during the shows; this apparently belonged to the dress code among learned pigs, and collars of this kind were known as 'Toby frills'. Like his predecessors, Toby could spell, read and count; he could also read thoughts and tell the spectators' ages. His foremost show-pieces were to play cards, to read a watch, and to guess the number of objects in a closed box held before him. The pig was soon popular enough to have the conjuring show all to itself. There were shows between one and four o'clock in the afternoon, and between eight and ten in the evening. The entrance fee was a shilling, just like it had been for the original learned pig thirty years earlier.

To promote the shows further, the clever Mr Hoare sold Toby's autobiography for one shilling. This slender volume was adorned with the portrait of its alleged writer, reposing in his literary pig-sty, as a frontispiece. It told the story of its author's life from his first step until his present exalted position as an entertainer. Toby wrote that his expectant mother had strayed into a well-stocked library, devouring many of the books: the bookish sow had thus, in accordance with the contemporary embryological ideas, laid the foundations for her son's precocious young mind, always eager for more learning. Toby also described his youth and schooling with Mr Hoare: his name had of course been derived from Hamlet's soliloquy – *to be* or not *to be*! Toby's early experiences of show business had been disappointing, since drunken yokels had heckled and jeered the porcine scholar, but he praised the educated London public who had become his patrons. The Earls of Verulam and Bathurst had honoured him with their presence, as had Lady Brownlow and her party.

Toby was active in London until late in 1817, before embarking on an arduous tour of the provinces: Birmingham, Bath and Gloucester, among other places. In February 1819, he was back in Bath for a second visit; the advertisements urged the townspeople to make haste and see the Sapient Pig, since he would soon be departing for America. Whether Toby really crossed the Atlantic is not known. An advertisement from 1820 hints that if he went abroad at all, it was just across the English Channel, since it announces that Toby, the Sapient Pig, the Philosopher of the Swinish Race, has returned from France. Having just had the honour of performing before the Duke and Duchess of York, he is currently exhibiting before the Londoners at No. 97 Pall Mall.

In 1822, when Toby was still going strong touring the provinces, he obtained a competitor. This learned pig, under the management of the aforementioned Mr Pinchbeck, was alleged to have studied with a famous Chinese philosopher, before touring Latin America through the good offices of the Spanish Inquisition. Pinchbeck, who apparently did not share his charge's penchant for correct spelling, promised 1,000 guineas to anyone who could show the like of 'this Pillar of Pythagorus [sic], and the wonder of the present age'. In London, this pig had been admired by Princess Augusta and by the Duchess of Gloucester, as well as by many of the nobility. The usurper pig toured the West Country in late 1822, before returning to its old headquarters at No. 14 Old Bond Street in London in February 1823.

Toby himself kept one step ahead of the butcher's knife for a few years longer. He was at Bartholomew Fair in 1823. Later the same year, he performed at a fair in Tetbury, being underbilled to a faked mermaid. In April 1825, he was back in London but had hit hard times. The Swinish Philosopher was under the management of a garrulous old woman, who failed to get sanction to exhibit her pig and mermaid in the Borough of Southwark when she applied at the Union Hall police-office.

Learned pigs were a staple item at country fairs in early Victorian times. They were almost invariably called Toby, and aping the tricks of their great predecessor from the 1780s. They were no longer a novelty, but could eke out a living for their masters, tramping round the countryside and performing at fairs and markets. No learned pig ever obtained even a fraction of the fame enjoyed by Bisset's original performer, and later by the first Toby in 1817 and 1818. By the mid-nineteenth century, learned pigs were getting out of fashion, and no longer fed their owners fat. An extreme example comes from 1844, when a showman named William Manley exhibited his learned pig about London in a caravan. In July that year, a hooligan cut off the pig's tail when the animal was taken for an airing. He was fined thirty-two shillings, but being unable or unwilling to pay, he was committed for ten days. From here onwards, things steadily got worse. In early 1845, the pig-trainer left London, pursued by his creditors. After the pig had died in Basingstoke, from unknown causes, he was chased out of town for trying to sell the bacon as prime meat. In April 1845, the pig-trainer's wife was found dead, presumably murdered, in Salisbury, and her absconded husband was the prime suspect. If he was caught, convicted and hanged, this ill-fated tour would have ended with 100 per cent mortality for its participants.

To leave my literary line
My eyes get red and leaky;
But Giblett doesn't want me *blue*
But red and white, and streaky.

So, which of all these learned pigs was the one to inspire Thomas Hood's poem? It may be that the first Toby played a part, since there are worrying signs that he may have come to a sad end back in 1825. But more probably, it was another Toby, exhibited from 1833 until 1835 in a small-time London animal show owned by a man named Mullins. Thomas Hood was a frequent visitor to circuses, fairs and markets, and the sights offered often inspired his poetic imagination: he wrote his *Ode to the Cameleopard* after seeing a giraffe exhibited, and another of his poems is dedicated to the famous clown Joseph Grimaldi. None of the available biographical works on Thomas Hood mention that he visited the pig, but it is still likely that he did so, and that he was later informed about the pig's sad fate through the newspapers. Few records have been kept about this Toby, except that he performed at Bartholomew Fair in 1833, and it is unlikely that his fame and skill compared favourably to those of his two great predecessors. While employed by a circus in 1833, Toby acted together with the manager's 'monstrously fat child'; this, again, indicates that he was a less attractive performer than the earlier learned pigs. When he failed to draw enough visitors, poor Toby was sold to the butcher Giblett, under the dismal circumstances detailed by Thomas Hood:

Old Mullins used to cultivate
My learning like a gard'ner;
But Giblett only thinks of lard,
And not of Doctor Lardner.

He does not care about my brain
The value of two coppers,
All that he thinks about my head
Is, how I'm off for choppers.

4

MUNITO,

THE

Wonderful Dog

Through great Spadille, or that famed Prince of Loo
All conqu'ring Pam, turn backward from his view, –
Swift in the noble chase, 'Munito' tracks
The Royal guests and Plebeian packs;
And though the cards in mixed confusion lie,
And mock the vigour of a human eye,
'Munito' still, with more than human art,
Knows Kings from Knaves, the Diamond from the Heart.

Winthrop Mackworth Praed, 'Munito', from *A Poem on Dogs*, 1844.

In late May 1817, when Toby the Learned Pig was at the height of his fame, there was a series of advertisements in the London newspapers that cannot have pleased Toby's manager Mr Hoare, since they announced that a formidable competitor had set foot, or rather paw, in the Metropolis:

The Celebrated Dog Munito
Signor Castelli having just arrived from Paris, begs leave to inform the Nobility and Gentry, that he intends to EXHIBIT the EXTRAORDINARY FEATS of his WONDERFUL DOG MUNITO at Saville-House, Leicester-Square; who will play at cards, write, and cast accounts with the most astounding accuracy.

Performing dogs were nothing new to the Londoners; in fact, acrobatic or dancing dogs had been a staple item at the old fairs and markets since medieval times. In his *Bartholomew Fayre*, first acted in 1614, Ben Jonson mentions 'dogges that dance the morrice'. It took much longer for any performing dog with intellectual pretensions to appear in London. The Chien Savant, or Learned French Dog, was quite a novelty when it made its debut in 1751. A small bitch of indeterminable race, this animal spelt out words in either French or English using cardboard letters. But when the French Dog set out to tour the provinces in late 1751, a usurper appeared: it was the New Chien Savant, or Learned English Dog, depicted on a print as looking rather like a border collie in size and colouring, and correctly spelling the word 'Pythagoras' with its cardboard letters. Apart from the obvious arguments of patriotism, the English Dog's master ceaselessly pointed out his charge's superiority over the French Dog: the New Chien Savant knew the Greek alphabet, answered questions in Roman, English and Sacred history, and performed various acrobatic tricks.

The French Dog made an attempt at comeback in late 1752, but failed miserably and had to return to France with the tail between its legs. Its trainer, M. le Moine, more than once threatened to return to London, with an even more sagacious dog and a troupe of learned birds and flying squirrels, but there is no record of him ever doing so. The English Dog now reigned supreme. In its showroom in Half-Moon Court, near Ludgate, the clever border collie entertained noblemen, ambassadors and various foreign magnates. In February 1753, there was once more competition, when Mrs Midnight's Animal Comedians came to town, performing at the New Theatre in the Haymarket. This was a large troupe of dogs and monkeys, some of them dressed in human attire, performing various amazing tricks, including a full-scale siege of a model monkey town, besieged by dogs. It has been claimed by some authors that Mrs Midnight trained these animals herself, but the truth would seem to be that the troupe of animal actors came from Italy, and were under the management of a foreigner named M. Billard. Mrs Midnight was a musician, not an animal trainer, and her only contribution to the shows was musical accompaniment.

The Learned English Dog and its master must have felt relieved when M. Billard returned to France in March 1753, taking his animals with him. The English Dog once more dominated London's animal amusements.

An advertisement pointed out that this sagacious animal had learnt a number of new tricks, including arithmetics, telling the value of coins, and answering questions in Ovid's Metamorphoses. Later in 1753, this dog toured Stafford, Shrewsbury, Hereford, Monmouth and Gloucester, during the Assizes at these places, before returning to London. One of the English Dog's 1754 advertisements told that the sagacious animal had been given a silver collar by a lady, for correctly predicting the time she would get married; another advertisement contained a poem beginning with the words

> Did souls through various bodies pass
> This dog might be Pythagoras...

The last we know of the English Dog is that it was performing at the Bull Inn, Cirencester, in early 1755. This clever border collie had no successor and it would not take long before any performing dog had similar success in Britain. A certain Mr Birbeck exhibited his Dog of Knowledge in the 1780s, but without being much of a competitor to Mr Bisset's original learned pig. But the supremacy of the pig in London's animal amusement world would soon be severely challenged by the arrival of Munito, the Wonderful Dog.

Munito was an instant success with the Londoners, although the shows, set at two and four on all weekday afternoons, cost as much as three shillings. Munito had complete knowledge of the alphabet and figures, played at dominoes in the most expert manner, and possessed other qualifications beyond the reach of most of his human contemporaries. In the evenings, Signor Castelli was always available if some wealthy gentleman wanted to entertain his guests with a private dog-show, to enliven an evening party. At these fashionable gatherings, both dog and master were at their best behaviour: Signor Castelli knew that if they did well, several guineas would change hands, and the Wonderful Dog knew that after the show, the ladies would like to pet him and feed him various delicacies. Munito was a pretty, affectionate dog, in size rather resembling a Large Poodle, but with shorter fur and a less pointed muzzle.

Later in 1817, Signor Castelli had to rent a larger exhibition room, at No. 23 New Bond Street, since their old accommodation in Leicester Square had proved far too small for the throng of people wanting to see

Munito perform. According to an exhibition poster, the shows were now on at three and seven in the afternoon and cost just a shilling. Castelli could brag that both the Prince Regent and the Duke of York, and a great number of the Nobility, had already beheld the Wonderful Dog with astonishment, and the most unbounded applause. This poster had a rather crude drawing of Munito making calculations at his writing desk.

Himself, Signor Castelli was something of a man of mystery. He was about fifty or sixty years old, rather shabbily dressed in foreign garb, and entirely unable to speak English. At the dog-shows, he gabbled away in Italian and bad French, languages he claimed that Munito knew perfectly. He was kind and attentive to his star performer, however, often taking Munito for a walk in the London streets. When they were strolling in Green Park, more than one passer-by remarked on the swarthy foreigner in his old-fashioned clothes, talking volubly to his pretty white dog, like if the two could really understand each other. We do not even know Castelli's first name, and this has led to speculation that he was identical to a showman of the same name who performed with his dogs at Sadler's Wells in London as early as 1783, and later at Smock Alley in Dublin in 1784. Other circus historians have suspected, quite possibly with some right, that he was identical to a conjurer named Castelli who performed quite widely in Italy, France and Germany since the late 1790s.

In September 1817, another exhibition poster announced that Munito was still performing in London, at three and seven every day. The Wonderful Dog was not too old to learn a few new tricks: in addition to spelling, counting and playing cards, he was now acquainted with the principles of botany and geography. A more elaborate illustration shows that Castelli had chosen to cut his dog's woolly fur into a rather primitive version of the lion-clip. The same illustration was used as the frontispiece of the *Historicall Account of the Life and Talents of the Learned Dog Munito*, published at about the same time and sold at the New Bond Street exhibition-room. According to this pamphlet, Munito was twenty-two months old and of a lively and caressing disposition. His father was a hound, his mother a water spaniel, but he resembled his mother most and was the size of a common water spaniel, rather tall and thin. His short, curly fur was all white except for a brown spot over the left eye.

Signor Castelli d'Orino, as the dog-trainer now styled himself, claimed to be an Italian gentleman who had devoted his life to the art of training animals. He recognised young Munito's matchless intellect at an early age, and educated him for thirteen months at an isolated country retreat in a village not far from Milan. The dog was always taught with mildness, Castelli insisted, and was never struck or spoken to angrily. The education was concluded when Munito was fifteen months old, at which time the pair set out on their travels through Italy and France.

In Paris, Munito performed at the Cabinet d'Illusions near the Palais Royal. According to an early exhibition pamphlet kept at the Bibliothèque Nationale in Paris, the Wonderful Dog was visited by many scholars and journalists, and was the subject of conversation in many salons. The Parisians were particularly fascinated by Munito's skills at dominoes. They bet bonbons or cakes in their games against the Wonderful Dog; a nobleman bet five louis d'or instead and lost them all.

Apart from his other superlative qualities, Munito was also very brave, the pamphlet claimed. Near Trier, Signor Castelli had lost all his luggage when the villainous carriage-driver had left them stranded. But after a while, Munito came running with a boot in his mouth, to make Castelli understand that he had found the thief. When the villain was tracked down inside a forest, Munito attacked him, seized him by the throat and forced him to confess in front of the local mayor. This tall tale leaves unexplained how the Wonderful Dog could have brought the mayor into the forest, or alternatively how he could have frog-marched the thief into the mayor's residence. A more sinister note is introduced by the claim that Munito had once performed an act of justice, by killing a large turkey-cock that had just pecked out the eye of a child. Coming too late to rescue the child, the Wonderful Dog had vented his rage on the wretched bird, tearing it to pieces.

Munito knows both French and Italian equally well, the pamphlet goes on to claim. He can play at cards and knows their colours and value. One of his tricks is to pick out a certain card from the pack, after it had been chosen by some person and the pack shuffled by others. The Wonderful Dog knows addition, subtraction, division and multiplication 'which many men will never learn, and which Munito performs with an astonishing quickness'. He can spell using cards with the letters of the alphabet on them, 'not being endowed with the gift of speech'. The Wonderful Dog also knows the art of palmistry: after gazing intently at some person's hand, he describes their character using his cards with letters on them. At the end of the show 'He plays a game of dominoes with whoever will condescend to procure him that little pastime'.

Munito remained in London until late in 1817, when he departed for France and Italy. The exhibition pamphlet was translated into French and several times republished. In the summer of 1818, the Wonderful Dog returned to his many admirers in London. It did not take long for him again to become headline news. On 2 October 1818, Signor Castelli was taking a walk round Green Park with his dog at nine in the morning. He could see a little girl screaming nearby, but due to his deficient grasp of English, he did not understand what she was saying. But then he saw that the girl was pointing toward the pond, where he could see a woman floating. The Italian acted with commendable resolution. Taking off his coat, he leapt into the pond and seized hold of the woman. But far from welcoming his intervention, the woman fought back fiercely. Castelli feared that they would both drown, but the faithful Munito saved the day, plunging into the pond and distracting the woman enough for Castelli to drag her onto dry land. She turned out to be quite deranged and intent on destroying herself; the little girl, her cousin, had followed her to try to make her return home.

Signor Castelli was awarded the Royal Humane Society's honorary medallion for his daring rescue. The Wonderful Dog also received a medal, as well as some useful further publicity: a newspaper article in Lysons's *Collectana* admires his sagacity and bravery, concluding that 'Munito continues to be one of the principal fashionable amusements. – The doors of the Exhibition Room are daily thronged with the carriages of the Nobility and Gentry who go to view his extraordinary performances.'

In the spring of 1819, Munito came back to London for a third spell, having spent some time in France, allegedly to finish his education. A new exhibition poster was printed to announce his return. It boasted that Munito was the same dog who last year obtained a medal from the Humane Society, having saved the life of a lady in the most extraordinary manner. To entice those who had visited the dog show in 1817 or 1818 to honour the Wonderful Dog with their company for a second time, it was pointed out that Munito had acquired vast knowledge in the sciences of geography, botany and natural history since he had last had the honour of performing before the Londoners. The showroom was now at No. 1 Leicester Square and the dog performed daily, every hour from twelve till five.

Munito remained in London until June 1819, before returning to the Continent. In 1820, the Wonderful Dog made an extended tour of France. There were new editions of the exhibition pamphlet printed in Paris, Nantes, Toulouse, Strasbourg and Lyons, as well as a Dutch translation published when Munito went to Utrecht in late 1820. In the Toulouse pamphlet, the dog-trainer provided some surprising information about his own background: Signor Castelli d'Orino claimed to be the former commander of the artillery train of the Kingdom of Italy, who had served his country for twenty years before being made redundant. In 1821 and 1822, Munito toured Germany, visiting Munich, Berlin and Augsburg among other places, before returning to Strasbourg in October 1822. In early 1824, he was performing in Mannheim before going to the Hague. But for several years thereafter, there are no records of the Wonderful Dog.

In early 1827, Munito resurfaced in Paris after several years away from the limelight. He was advertised as the same celebrated dog that had appeared all over Europe for more than ten years. But an engraving in the series *Le Bon Genre*, published in 1827, shows a startling development. Munito is no longer the rather large, muscular dog that had been performing in London ten years earlier, but a small poodle! Clearly Signor Castelli had trained another dog to take the place of the original performer. It would have been embarrassing for him if some sarcastic Frenchman had come up to him and pointed out that his dog must be wonderful indeed, to have shrunk in size in such a remarkable manner since his previous visit to Paris. But there is no record of any such untoward incident; in fact, the French nation once more took Munito to their hearts. As a schoolboy, a certain Eugène Muller, who would later describe the show in his book *Les Animaux Célèbres*, was taken to see Munito by his mother. Many years later, he could still well remember the beautiful white poodle in its elegant lion clip. On his own writing table with a green cover, Munito performed multiplication with the greatest skill, and told the time with his cards with numbers on them after having looked at a watch. He chose from twenty objects to find the one a certain spectator had named, before skilfully opening a wooden box with his teeth, having first turned the key. Then it was time for some acrobatic tricks, and a musical interlude where Munito kept time on a small drum using his paw, before the gallant Signor Castelli gave his dog a bouquet and invited him to bring it to a blonde lady in the audience. Madame Muller played a game of écarté against the Wonderful Dog, losing miserably to the delight of the rest of the audience.

In 1827, Munito toured Germany, before coming to St Petersburg later in the year. The Finnish nobleman C.G. Mannerheim saw one of the shows and wrote to a friend in Helsinki:

> This animal's highly trained instincts cannot be admired enough. All what I had read about it in the newspapers came true. What astounded me most was to see it perform multiplication of large numbers, always remembering what figure to carry over for the next calculation. It knows all the cards in a deck of playing-cards, and the spectators can order it to pick any particular card out. The dog never once failed to retrieve the correct one.

Mannerheim was fortunate enough to meet Munito and his master Signor Castelli when they took a walk around the block like any other dog-owner, and was impressed how kind the Italian was to his dog, and how well Munito was taken care of.

Munito then toured Russia and Poland, coming back to St Petersburg for a second visit before going to Austria. An exhibition poster for his visit to Vienna, dated 1 December 1828, boasts that the celebrated Munito had been praised by many Kings and Emperors all over Europe. The dog's accomplishments included addition, subtraction, multiplication, playing dominoes and knowing the playing-cards. The illustration again shows Munito as a much smaller dog than the one performing in London a decade earlier.

In April 1830, Munito came to Stockholm, Sweden, where the success story continued. In his *Gamla Stockholm*, August Strindberg wrote that 'a poodle-dog named Munito was very much noted for his great cleverness and unsurpassed skill in performing'. His exhibition room was at the Tawern inn in the Djurgården; the shows were on at five and seven each afternoon, and were quite expensive, costing about two shillings. An article in the *Stockholms-Posten* newspaper provides some further details:

> The dog Munito, who in just a few years has become so very famous, not just in Europe, but even in America, seems to deserve his great reputation, unlike

> many of the popular artists of this time, whether two- or four-footed. He is a beautiful white poodle of the smaller race. When he is not performing, he sits in a serious and pensive position…

The newspaper writer was impressed how fond the poodle was of his master: Munito seemed to enjoy the show, particularly the treats he was given after each trick was concluded.

The allegation that Munito had been to the United States is quite astounding, and does not occur elsewhere. There is a note in Ricky Jay's *Journal of Anomalies*, however, that a dog named Minetto performed at Peale's Museum in New York in May 1827. This would render it at least possible that the Wonderful Dog really crossed the Atlantic, although it should be kept in mind that several copycat learned dogs were active at the time. For example, the conjurer Mr Hoare, the former tutor of Toby the Learned Pig, had got a dog of his own, which he had the cheek to call Monetto!

During his sojourn in Sweden, Munito was taken ill. The people of Stockholm were very worried that he might expire, but the poodle recovered and again performed throughout June and July. As an added bonus, the 'Son of Munito, another poodle-dog', also took part in the shows. Was Signor Castelli grooming a successor already, in case he would once more lose his star performer? The dog-trainer's alleged military background was becoming increasingly colourful: he now claimed to be Captain Castelli d'Orino, a highly decorated war hero, who had fought in the Sardinian army in the battles of Marengo and Wagram. This was something that, if it was at all true, Castelli had kept very quiet about when he was in London in 1817 and 1818.

Munito remained in Stockholm for several months, before touring the provinces. A poster for one of the latter shows tells us that

> Many of the newspapers of Europe have unanimously lauded this Dog's rare and uncommon propensities, and expressed their admiration at the skill and cleverness with which Munito, also known as the LEARNED DOG carries out his tricks.
>
> The unprecedented feats of this Dog has secured him many accolades in Paris, London and Petersburg, among other capitals he has visited.
>
> The Tutor of this Wonderful Dog hopes that the Swedish people will give Munito the same encouragement and applause he has enjoyed elsewhere.

> This Dog understands the Italian and French languages, knows all colours, plays at Dominoes, can add, subtract, and multiply, can tell flowers apart, can perform the most remarkable acrobatic tricks; in other words, the only thing he fails to do, is to speak.

In September 1830, Munito performed in Helsinki, in the Sederholmska Huset near the Senatstorget. When taking Munito for a walk, Castelli met another spectator, Captain Charles Colville Frankland. In his *Narrative of a Visit to Courts of Russia and Sweden*, this gentleman described his visit to see the conjurer and his learned dog. Castelli was a funny old fellow, Frankland wrote, ugly and unfashionably dressed. His extensive travels around Europe had not improved his linguistic skills: he still spoke only Italian and bad French.

One of the Helsinki dog shows was described in the newspaper *Helsingfors Tidningar*. In one of his advertisements in the same newspaper, Castelli had waxed lyrical about his dog's superior intelligence, but the sceptical journalist was not quite disposed to agree. It was quite possible, he wrote, that Castelli directed his dog with minute movements of his hands and feet, or by certain cue words and signs; nor could it be ruled out that the cards used in the dog-show had been smeared with some substance.

In early 1831, Munito was back in St Petersburg. Later the same year, he returned to Paris, where Munito stayed for some considerable time, making occasional excursions to the provinces. In 1833, the dog show was described in a magazine article, illustrated with two amusing drawings, one of a bespectacled Munito spelling with his cards, another of a waistcoat-clad Munito playing dominoes with his master. A trade card for the Bordeaux firm Chocolats-Louit also depicts Munito wearing a red waistcoat, performing before a surprisingly youthful-looking trainer, but this card was probably printed quite a few years later.

It is not known exactly what year Munito held his farewell performance, nor whether Signor Castelli allowed his dog to enjoy a few years of retirement at the end of his career. The reason for this is the profusion of performing dogs at this time. It is recorded by Peter Bräuning, in his *Circus und autverwandte Künste*, that in 1830, when the original Munito was in Scandinavia, a certain 'Munito du Nord' had the cheek to perform at Munito's old exhibition room at Boulevard du Temple in Paris. At the same time, 'The Two Clever Dogs, Fido and Munito', were active in Mainz. In his *Anecdotes of Dogs*, Edward Jesse described Fido and Bianco, two poodles trained in Italy, performing in Paris in 1830. They spelt words with cardboard letters, read the striking of a lady's watch, and played écarté with each other. Fido was a steady, serious dog, but Bianco was giddy and frolicsome, sometimes pulling his companion's ears to make him come and play.

An obscure pamphlet entitled *Notice sur les chiens Munito*, published by a certain M.J.-F. Bertachon in 1836, may well provide some further clues about the later career of the Wonderful Dog. This pamphlet advertises two performing poodles, Munito and Young Munito, who were under the management of a certain M. Nief. These two dogs were dressed in red waistcoats and performed tricks that were exactly similar to those of Castelli's Munito, even down to the playing of dominoes. M. Nief had been a dog-trainer for many years, the pamphlet claimed. Old Munito, his first dog, had been born in Valencia in 1813 and had made his debut in 1817. They had visited many countries, always with success. The Princess Marianne had given Old Munito a silver collar and chain; the King of Westphalia had presented him with a silver cup and soup-bowl. This elderly dog was now retired and living in Caen, being provided with a pension of forty-five francs a month by the generous M. Nief. The current Munito was just as successful. The Queen of Spain had given him a pair of spectacles, which he sometimes wore during the shows. Munito was now nine years old and his son just two; an illustration depicts them both as poodles. Some months previously, they had performed before the King, Queen, Prince and Princesses of France, to their entire satisfaction.

It is of course possible that Nief's dogs were yet another set of imitators, but many details in the pamphlet agree with what is known about the original Munitos. The Bertachon pamphlet has induced some French circus historians to speculate that M. Nief was in fact the same person as Signor Castelli, having posed as an Italian to make himself seem more interesting. But the available information about Munito's early career clearly describes Castelli as an Italian, who could speak French only with difficulty. It would seem more likely that after touring with the three Munitos for more than fourteen years, the elderly Signor Castelli retired in 1831 or 1832 and sold his dogs to the enterprising M. Nief, who of course took the credit for having taught the animals himself.

The remainder of the nineteenth century saw performing dogs aplenty. The dancing poodle Pollux was a favourite in the 1840s, competing with

Herr Quincke's Dog Orchestra and Monsieur Leonard's dominoes-playing dogs Philax and Brac. In the 1860s, the poodle Bianca could translate and write in nineteen languages; in the 1870s, the Austrian Frans Patek's crossbreed Frieda could play 'God save the Queen' on the piano and sing parts from Italian operas. In the 1890s, a black poodle known as the Inimitable Dick became a major star in the Paris music hall. Dressed in fantastic garb, Dick waltzed on his hind legs, with powerful lighting effects illuminating his dress, and a bellows operating from underneath to make it billow out around his tiny body.

At the same time, Mr Lavater's Dog Orchestra were performing in London. They were a lower class of performers than the elegant Dick: six scruffy-looking mongrel dogs playing the big drum, little drum, cymbals, violin, bass and trombone, accompanying the dapper Mr Lavater playing 'The Girl I left behind me' and other popular tunes. When interviewed in the *Strand Magazine* of 1897, Lavater revealed a down-to-earth attitude to his trade: the reason he employed mongrel curs was of course that they were cheap and easily replaceable. The first drummer had to be gotten rid of because of his pugnacious disposition, his successor ran amok on board a ferry from Rotterdam to Antwerp, and the trombonist was sacked for his deplorable habit of stage-diving into the audience.

During the years, there has been a considerable debate about what breed of dog Munito belonged to. In several books on poodles, he is claimed as one of the most famous representatives of this breed ever. But we now know that there were actually not less than three Munitos. The first of these was quite a large dog, capable of tackling a robber and tearing to pieces a turkey-cock. There is no reason to disbelieve the statement in the 1817 exhibition pamphlet that he was the offspring of a hound father and a water spaniel mother, particularly as he was said to have resembled his mother most. The two breeds of water spaniels existing at the time were the Irish water spaniel and the European (or Portuguese) water dog. They were both quite poodle-like, although with shorter fur, generally coarser build, and less elegant head than today's poodles. The early drawings of Munito agree well with this description. Moreover, the primitive 'lion clip' boasted by Munito on the more elegant 1817 drawing agrees perfectly with the most commonly used trim for a European water dog at the time.

The career of Munito the water spaniel cross seems to have begun in early 1816, touring Italy and France. He went on performing until 1824, but after that year there are no further records of him. It has to be suspected that the ten-year-old dog expired at this time, and that Castelli had to train a successor. Munito the poodle appeared in 1827 and was still going strong in 1831. Whether the bespectacled, waistcoat-clad Munito performing in Paris in the mid-1830s was the same dog is not known with certainty, but from the Bertachon pamphlet, a moderately solid case can be made that the second Munito and his son continued their show business career under their youthful-looking new master M. Nief.

There were two good reasons for the nineteenth-century dog trainers to choose poodles as their performers. Firstly, canine psychologists have pointed out that certain breeds of dogs are cleverer than others. In their various investigations, the poodle and the border collie are consistent top performers, whereas the bulldog and the Afghan hound occupy the opposite end of the scale. The poodle is a natural performer, easy to teach, and keen to show off his tricks. Whereas young poodles are giddy and scatter-brained, older poodles also have impressive powers of concentration and attention, something that would have come in handy for Signor Castelli. Even so, it is amazing that he could make the dog perform five times a day without Munito getting bored with the whole thing. His strategy was probably to vary each performance, introduce new tricks with regular intervals, and to make sure Munito was always rewarded with some little treat after each successful trick. Secondly, poodles were very fashionable dogs at the time: expensive, elegant and sought after. Such a dog would draw more spectators than a common sheepdog that could be seen in every farmyard. The border collie has had its revenge, however, and is today a frequent and successful competitor in the agility and obedience events at various dog shows.

Having solved the mystery of the three Munitos, it is now time to address another problem, namely how the dog was trained. Here we are provided with some inside information by none less than Charles Dickens, who described his visit to one of the dog shows in his *All the Year Round* magazine in 1867. Forty-five years earlier, he had seen Munito, a clever French poodle, exhibited in Piccadilly. Munito was a very handsome dog, with a fine silky white woolly coat, half-shaved. During the show, Munito answered questions with his cards, some of which had letters, others figures. He could also pick out the card named – say the queen of clubs – when the pack was spread on the floor in a circle. Dickens noted that when Munito walked round the circle of cards, he had his nose down. He did not pick the card out as his eyes met it, but walked back and picked out, indicating that he was guided by smell rather than sight. When Signor Castelli walked past young Dickens, his waistcoat had an aniseed smell, leading Dickens to suspect that he put his thumb in his waistcoat pocket, impregnated with aniseed oil, and pressed it on the particular card Munito was supposed to pick out. Dickens waited until the performance was over and went up to speak to Castelli, who did not deny the discovery of his trickery.

Charles Dickens's discovery would certainly explain some of Munito's tricks, but hardly all of them. As suspected by the Finnish journalist in 1830, certain cue words or secret signs must have been used to make the dog deliver a bouquet of flowers to the right person, or to play dominoes. Other tricks used the dog's natural talent for acrobatics, and its propensity to learn to perform a sequence of events, like unlocking a box and opening its lid. An unanswered question is exactly what year Dickens saw Munito. We have to remember that he was born in 1812, and thus just seven years old when the first Munito left London for good. It is scarcely credible that a child of that age, however precocious, would be able to see through a quite accomplished performance that took in many adults. It may well be that the second Munito made a return to London some time in the late 1820s, to be seen by the teenage Dickens. After all, he described the dog as a pretty French poodle rather than a water spaniel cross.

Charles Dickens is not the only of Munito's 'literary kin'. The obscure poem by Winthrop Mackworth Praed that was used as an epigraph to this chapter compares Munito's ability to pick out the correct cards to that of a social climber preferring royal guests to the plebeian pack. In *My Novel*, Edward Bulwer Lytton made a joke about 'the dullest dog that ever wrote a novel', adding that 'we have a good many dogs among the fraternity that are not Munitos…' In *Le Boulevard du Crime*, his essay about the Boulevard du Temple in Paris, Mario Proth mentions the famous dog Munito who had his headquarters there for many years, playing games of arithmetic at his shows. In his essay *Le Chat*, the poet Théodore de Banville also discussed the famous dominoes-playing dog, performing tricks that no cat could ever be taught. Jules Verne, in his novel *A Captain at Fifteen*, also alluded to the Wonderful Dog. Like de Banville, Verne was just about old enough to have seen Munito perform in the 1830s. He gave a good description of one of the shows, with an explanation of his own: Munito's master snapped a toothpick in his pocket to make the poodle stop and pick up the correct card. The Norwegian novelist Henrik Wergeland may well also have seen Munito perform in 1830, since his play *Harlequin Virtuos*, published the same year, contains some references to 'the Divine Poodle Munito' that was clever enough to aspire to a university degree. Another unexpected reference to Munito appears in one of the early letters of Franz Liszt, where the future composer bemoans his precarious position as a virtuoso pianist, dependent on the plaudits of the fickle public just like a conjuror, or the learned dog Munito.

Like Mr Banks and Marocco, Signor Castelli and Munito have had many successors, although none of them have been able to dethrone the nineteenth-century canine superstar. In the early twentieth century there was a profusion of performing animals in Germany. One of them was Don, the Speaking Dog, who amused the spectators by barking out simple messages like 'Hunger haben!' (Hungry!) He was eclipsed by the Airedale terrier Rolf, who was active from 1913 until 1919. Rolf excelled in mathematics, solving complicated problems like cubic roots. Like Munito, he knew colours, botany and zoology, using his own alphabet to describe various objects. When a noble lady visitor asked Rolf what the dog would like her to do, the witty Airedale terrier responded 'Wag your tail!' Both Rolf and his equally gifted daughter Lola were studied by the canine psychologists of the time, some of whom were actually taken in by the dogs' antics, proposing that these two animals possessed superior intellects.

Rolf and Lola could also predict the future, particularly changes in the weather. The American crossbreed Chris, active in the 1950s, was even more remarkable. Not only could he count and spell, but he also showed amazing talents of telepathy, convincing some gullible American parapsychologists of the reality of extrasensory perception. Chris could also predict the future: after he helped a neighbour pick the winner in two consecutive horse races, his owners had to lock the dog up to protect him from enthusiastic betting men, and also from religious people who believed the dog was possessed by the devil. When a spiritualist medium asked Chris what kind of being he was, perhaps a reincarnated human genius or some ghostly spiritual creature, the modest crossbreed replied 'Clever dog!' Among Chris's predictions was the date of his own death, on 10 June 1962, but he actually died the day before.

Chris's psychic powers have been eclipsed by another strange canine performer, Oscar the Hypnodog. During the 1990s, this talented Labrador toured the United Kingdom and Europe with considerable success. His owner and manager, the conjurer and hypnotist Hugh Lennon, noted the fixed, dominant stare from his dog's large eyes, and decided to use Oscar in his own shows. Oscar seldom failed to put members of the audience to sleep, and was a particular favourite at the Cardiff Student's Union, where a pile of unconscious bodies on the floor marked his success. In 1994, Oscar disappeared when performing in Edinburgh, and a reward was posted for his return. Members of the public were warned not to look into his eyes, to avoid getting hypnotised. But a brave Scot found Oscar, avoided his hypnotic gaze, and collected a cash reward from a dog food manufacturer, as well as a keg of beer from the pub where Oscar was performing at the time. Sadly, Oscar has since died of old age, but Murphy the Hypnodog has succeeded him, under the same management.

5

Obituary

OF AN

ELEPHANT

Natures great master-piece, an Elephant,
The onely harmelesse great thing; the giant
Of beasts; who thought none had, to make him wise,
But to be just, and thankful, loth t' offend
(Yet nature hath given him no knees to bend)
Himself he up-props, on himself relies,
And foe to none; suspects no enemies,
Still sleeping stood; vext not his fantasie
Black dreams, like an unbent bow carelesly
His sinewy Proboscis did remisly lie.

In which as in a gallery this mouse
Walk'd and survey'd the rooms of this vast house,
And to the brain, the soul's bed chamber, went,
And gnaw'd the life cords there; like a whole town
Clean undermin'd the slain beast tumbled down;
With him the murth'rer dies, whom envy sent
To kill, not scape; for onely he that meant
To die, did ever kill a man of better roome;
And thus he made his foe, his prey and tombe;
Who cares not to turn back, may any whither come.

John Donne, *The Progresse of the Soule*

Elephants have, since ancient times, been used in the service of humankind, in war and for heavy labour as well as for show and entertainment. Already King Assurnasirpal II of Assyria, living in the ninth century BC, kept a zoological garden that contained, among many other animals, several elephants caught in Syria. The elephant entered the Western world with Alexander the Great, who brought several captured war elephants back with him as spoils of war; they became the pride of the Macedonian court. According to Pliny, the Romans saw elephants for the first time in the war against King Pyrrhus, calling them Lucan oxen because they were first seen in the province of Lucania. The Romans often used their elephants in ceremonies and victory parades. From the time of the Augustus onwards, it was customary for the Emperor to travel in a chariot pulled by four elephants during processions and triumphal festivities. In the gory animal baitings at the amphitheatre, elephants fought bulls or each other. When, during the second consulate of Pompey, a great entertainment was enacted, not less than twenty elephants fought a company of gladiators. The spectators considered it most amusing to see the great beasts fling the shattered gladiators up into the air with their powerful trunks. In the times of Claudius and Nero, the final battle in the arena was always between an elephant and a well-armed gladiator.

The Roman war elephants were trained to tread the enemy soldiers underfoot, or to throw heavy arrows at them with the trunks. In contrast, the ceremonial elephants were particularly docile. These beasts were trained to endure clamorous and noisy crowds without bolting; this was tested by keepers who sneaked up near the elephants during the solemn processions, blowing bugles or striking cymbals without warning. The rhetorician Ælian describes how twelve of the most accomplished elephants were marching in circle in a theatre, moving about with great precision and scattering flowers among the audience as they went. At the end of the performance, they lay down on great couches, stretched out their trunks, and feasted on a banquet of fruit and vegetables that had been laid out for them on an ornamental table. According to Pliny's *Natural History*, the Roman elephants were sometimes taught to dance or to imitate gladiators in the arena; once, a Roman impresario staged a comedy in which four elephants carried a stretcher on which lay a fifth, representing an expectant mother in childbed. Pliny also tells us that some of the most skilled elephants were actually trained to walk the tightrope, an accomplishment repeated by a late nineteenth-century circus elephant, a very thick rope, to be sure!

After the fall of the Roman Empire, the elephant disappeared from the Western world: some early medieval writers put it on par with the basilisk, the mantichora, the sphinx and other creatures of myth and legend. The two things every medieval bestiary reader knew about elephants were that they had no joints in their legs, which enabled hunters to capture them by cutting down the trees they were leaning against while they slept, and that elephants were often killed by mice crawling into their trunks, which communicated directly with the brain. This strange idea of anatomy, which would put the elephant in immediate danger of literally blowing its brains out when trumpeting violently, has remained widespread in folklore well into modern times, and the elephant and mouse motif is not infrequently met with in literature and poetry. In the year 797, Charlemagne received an elephant as a present from the Caliph of Baghdad: it crossed the Alps with its new owner and accompanied him on several of his later travels, until its death in 810. One of its tusks was made into an enormous hunting-horn; this famous 'oliphant de Charlemagne' is still kept, at Aachen. In 1254, an elephant from Palestine was given to King Henry III of England by St Louis of France; it was lodged in an elephant house near the Thames and immediately became one of the sights of London. A remarkable drawing of this elephant, by Matthew Paris, in the *Book of Additions to his Greater Chronicle*, is kept at the British Library. In 1514, the Portuguese Ambassador Tristan da Cunha brought an elephant to Pope Leo X's menagerie at the Vatican. When the rare beast was turned over to the Pope, under great festivities, the elephant bowed thrice at its keeper's command; this greatly impressed the Church dignitaries, who praised the creature's piety. The next moment, however, the elephant filled its trunk with water from a nearby trough and soused the assembled Bishops and Cardinals, not even excepting the majestic figure of the Pope himself.

During the seventeenth century, elephants became a more common spectacle in European cities. In Paris, the Versailles menagerie always kept one or two elephants. The most popular of them was an African elephant, which resided there from 1665 to 1681. With age, it became something of a gourmet, dipping its bread in huge pailfuls of soup with great relish. In 1679, Robert Hooke recorded in his diary that he had seen an elephant in London that could 'wave colours, shoot a gun, bend and kneel, carry a castle and a man etc'. Another elephant was on show in Dublin. When it was accidentally burned to death in 1681, the body was used for one of the earliest studies of elephant anatomy. Since the popular interest for this elephant dissection was immense, the proprietor had to employ a file of musketeers to guard the carcass until the skeleton was ready for inspection. The death of another elephant, while on exhibition in London in 1720, was attributed to the immense quantity of ale continually given to it by the spectators. No elephants reached the United States until 1796, when an enterprising sea captain named Crowninshield imported an Indian elephant whose name is unknown; there are several records of its appearance in various American towns.

The Exeter Change Menagerie

By the late eighteenth century, London had close to a million inhabitants, many of them with ample money to spend on amusements and an insatiable thirst for animal curiosities. An edict from 1697 had prohibited the exhibition of wild beasts in the London streets, since this was the privilege of the keeper of his Majesty's lions in the Tower. But this edict did not prevent showmen and monster-mongers from showing their beasts at fairs and markets, or clandestinely in the back alleys in the Metropolis. It was not until 1793 that any privately owned full-scale menagerie was established in London. The itinerant showman Gilbert Pidcock had purchased a large four-storey building in the Strand, called Exeter Exchange from having been built with material salvaged from the old Exeter House, which had stood at the same site in the Strand. It had once been some kind of 'exchange', or station for stage coaches. Since the house was of considerable size, it is likely that Pidcock first wanted it as winter quarters for his animals in between tours, but he soon realised that they could be profitably exhibited there all the year round. Gilbert Pidcock brought with him a rhinoceros, a zebra, a kangaroo, a lynx and a collection of rare birds; some years later, several tigers and elephants were purchased. The animals were all kept indoors, the majority of them on the first floor of the old house. The ground floor housed several small shops, flanking an arcade incorporating the Strand footway; the shop-owners must have become somewhat apprehensive when the rhinoceros shifted its weight upstairs. The cages and dens of the animals had been put in the ample parlours of the old house, whose walls had been decorated with murals of tropical motives – a sad reminder, for the wretched caged animals, of their faraway proper homes!

When the old Tower menagerie went into a decline in the late eighteenth century, Pidcock's Menagerie at Exeter Change usurped its position among the Londoners. Using ostentatious handbills and newspaper advertisements to attract public attention, it became extraordinarily popular, and was a lucrative business for many years. The money earned was cleverly invested by Pidcock and his deputy Edward Cross, and used to purchase a great variety of interesting animals, through contacts with sailors and animal dealers. It was an audacious, not to say unique, enterprise to establish a complete zoological garden in one of central London's most densely populated areas. Rather surprisingly, the civic authorities did not object to it, but there was a steady barrage of newspaper correspondence complaining about the disturbing jungle noises and noxious smells emanating from the old house. The early animal protectionists were also critical, rightly claiming that the cages and dens used at Exeter Change were far too small. Both Pidcock and Cross were skilled animal keepers, however. In a time not noted for humanity toward captive animals, they took good care of their beasts, some of which resided at Exeter Change for decades, and became well-known London favourites. Several lion and tiger cubs were successfully reared there. The exhibition catalogue of the Exeter Change menagerie was quite well written, containing lengthy quotations from the natural history works of Buffon and Oliver Goldsmith, as well as a dedicatory poem to the inhabitants of the menagerie:

> And if you would wish for an exquisite treat,
> At nine in the Evening the Wild Beasts all eat;
> Their dishes so various, substantial and good,
> That pleasure they give while enjoying their food,
> And wonder impress, both delightful and strange,
> On each one that visits famed *Exeter Change.*

In 1810, after the death of Gilbert Pidcock, another veteran menagerist, Stephen Polito, bought the whole establishment at auction.

When Edward Cross bought out old Mr Polito in 1814, and became the sole owner of the menagerie, one of his ostentatious newspaper advertisements likened him to 'that primeval collector of natural curiosities, Old Noah'. And the boastful menagerist was not far off the mark: the old house at Exeter Change contained a remarkable collection of animals, far outclassing any other British menagerie. The huge lion Nero was a long-term favourite among the Londoners, and the exhibition contained four other African lions and several tigers, leopards, jaguars and hyenas, as well as a boa constrictor, an orang-utan, and 'the greatest variety of Crocodiles ever exhibited'. Antelopes, camels, llamas, bison and sea lions were also kept. The huge collection of birds featured several African ostriches and five different species of eagles and vultures. Edward Cross corresponded with many of the leading anatomists and zoologists of London, like Sir Everard Home, Sir Astley Cooper and Joshua Brookes; he was also a patron of the arts, and several times allowed Sir Edwin Landseer and Jacques-Laurent Agasse to portray his beasts in various settings.

An Elephant in the Theatre

During the 1811 season, it was very fashionable to use animals in dramatic performances on the London stage: not infrequently, a well-trained dog, ape or horse received more accolades than the human actors and actresses. Mr Henry Harris, manager of the Covent Garden theatre, was one of the pioneers of English hippodrama: the use of horses in theatrical productions. Together with his partner John Philip Kemble, Mr Harris had hired horses and riders from Astley's circus to act in melodramas written particularly to suit the display of these equine performers. Some elderly purists were aghast at such novel vulgarities, which had usurped the place of Shakespeare's dramas at this venerable theatre. They suggested that the horses should be poisoned, before they poisoned the national taste, and described how Shakespeare's statue had groaned and shaken its head when being forced to endure these prolonged equine histrionics. But the majority of the Londoners, always eager for novel amusements, received the performing horses with rapture. Several other theatres had to follow suit and hire various animal actors.

In late 1811, Mr Harris wanted to outdo the competition once and for all, through recruiting an elephant and its keeper to perform in a pantomime version of *Harlequin and Columbine*. This elephant, a young

Indian male, was called Chunee; he had probably grown up in captivity in the Indian countryside. When just two or three years old, Chunee had been purchased by Captain Hay, of the East Indiaman *Lady Astell*. In July 1810, he took the elephant from Bombay to London. As soon as Chunee had disembarked, the elephant was purchased by Astley's circus, London's leading establishment of its kind. At the circus, Chunee was just another elephant until rented, for the huge sum of 900 guineas, by the Covent Garden theatre. Mr Henry Harris advertised his newly recruited elephantine actor widely, and at the sold-out premiere of *Harlequin and Columbine*, most people came to see the elephant. There was a general hush when the huge beast first set foot on the stage. The setting was that the Sultan of Cashmere was returning from a day's tiger hunting, seated in a howdah on the elephant's back. Just before the sultan in the procession was a slave carrying a bowl of strong rum punch, from which Chunee helped himself to a few mouthfuls, using the trunk. The Indian elephant-keeper from Astley's circus, who had joined Chunee in the elephant's theatrical career, was seated on the neck. But with some alarm, the audience noticed that this swarthy, turbaned fellow himself looked quite frightened, holding on for dear life as the elephant hastily walked toward the middle of the stage. Chunee was ordered to kneel, to enable the Sultan to dismount. After some reluctance the elephant obeyed the command. But when the enthusiastic audience cheered wildly, the clamorous sounds from galleries, pit, and boxes induced a severe attack of stage-fright: Chunee abruptly jumped to his feet and pushed his way out of the stage, driving the actors before him like a flock of cattle. The terrified sultan and elephant-keeper were desperately clinging to their seats, and only luck prevented them from being seriously hurt.

This dismal fiasco was much laughed at in the newspapers, but Mr Harris and his colleagues were undaunted: they kept the elephant in the cast, refusing to admit defeat and hoping that Chunee would, with time, get used to performing before a noisy crowd of people. Chunee's uncertain temper and lack of stage experience was a continual worry to them, however, and there were many other comic incidents, some of which would have broken the spirit of most theatrical managers. The flatulent elephant's nerves suffered from the shouts and clamouring of the audience: at regular intervals, Chunee's thunderous farts resounded in the theatre hall, and there were frequent calls of 'Shame!' and 'Off! Off!' from the pits. After being a witness to one such performance, a reviewer in *The Times* suggested that the purchase of a wooden elephant with wheels would have been more suited to the dignity of the theatre.

The Indian elephant-keeper was a brutal rascal, who punished Chunee with his sharp iron goad when the elephant had been disobedient. Chunee returned his dislike fully: whereas the elephant was docility itself when ridden by the theatre's leading lady, the beautiful Mrs Henry Johnston, the Indian was frequently thrown from his seat, or given a resounding box on the ear from Chunee's powerful trunk. These burlesque additions to the pantomime's subject matter were greeted with cheers, applause and catcalls by the rowdy audience, which jarred Chunee's sensitive nerves further. After a run of forty nights, the play closed and Chunee retired permanently from the stage; the manager and actors probably breathed a sigh of relief to get rid of the unruly beast. The director of Astley's circus was not particularly interested in using Chunee in his own shows. He struck a deal with the Exeter Change menagerie, where Chunee took up residence in a purposely built elephant den on the first floor. It has not been recorded how Mr Polito and Edward Cross managed, some time in 1812, to get Chunee up the groaning wooden stairway of the old house.

London's Favourite Elephant

From 1810 to 1826, the Exeter Change menagerie was very popular indeed, and an extremely lucrative business. This was largely due to Chunee the elephant: along with the lion Nero, he was by far the most famous inhabitant of Exeter Change. The menagerie was open between nine in the morning and nine in the evening; it cost a shilling to see each of the three main apartments, or two shillings to see them all. The façade toward the Strand was decorated with colourful drawings of various animals, and a large sign: 'Edward Cross Dealer in Foreign Birds and Beasts'. A gigantic doorman, dressed as one of Henry VIII's Yeomen of the Guard, stood at the entrance, handing out descriptive bills to passers-by and describing the living wonders awaiting them inside in a stentorian voice. Above him, a similarly noisy and gaudily coloured macaw sat perched on a swing. The animals within supplied their own exotic sound effects, sometimes frightening passing horses in the Strand and making them bolt.

The animals were all fed at eight in the evening, at which time the whole place was crowded with spectators. The journalist William Clarke wrote in his *Every Night Book* that the Lords of Parliament and the lions of Exeter Change all dined at about eight; the journalists reporting from Parliament thus had ample time to visit the menagerie on the way home. Himself, he vastly preferred to see a beautiful Bengal tigress and a noble African lion gruffly debating over a bone, than to hear an Earl and a Viscount doing the same over some boring political question. Chunee the elephant rang a large bell, hanging from the roof of the den, as a signal that food was on its way. On 14 November 1813, Lord Byron visited the menagerie to watch the lions, tigers and panthers 'growl over their grub'. In his diary, he recorded that the sloth much reminded him of his own valet, both in appearance and in habits. Lord Byron was much amused to see the elderly Exeter Change hyena Billy's great affection for his keeper, but the sight of the camel made him pine for Asia Minor. He also wrote that the face of the hippopotamus looked very like that of the Prime Minister, Lord Liverpool. This is a remarkable observation, since there is no record of the Exeter Change having a hippopotamus at this time. The menagerie had got a rhinoceros, however, and it may be that Lord Byron's poetic imagination got the better of his zoological knowledge; the existing portraits of Lord Liverpool give no hints either way. Lord Byron also saw Chunee perform. The keeper Alfred Copps had taught the unruly elephant a bag of tricks, and Chunee gently returned a coin Lord Byron had tossed into the den. Chunee then removed his tall hat and gingerly put it back in his head. The elephant was on its best behaviour throughout his visit, and Lord Byron joked that he would like to employ it as his butler.

Chunee had an impressive memory, always remembering some person that had shown him kindness on previous visits. During the elephant's tempestuous theatrical career, Chunee had made friends with several of the actors. One of them, Charles Mayne Young, had a life ticket to the menagerie, and when he visited the elephant, Chunee always recognised him. The great tragedian Edward Kean was another of Chunee's old friends. Once, when returning after a lengthy tour to the United States, he doubted whether the elephant would remember him. But as soon as Chunee had heard his voice, the elephant turned round in amazement and welcomed him with many caresses. Thomas Hood, the poet of the Learned Pig, was also an avid visitor to the menagerie, and a particular friend of Chunee:

I was the Damon of the gentle giant,
And oft has been,
like Mr Kean,
Tenderly fondled by his trunk compliant.
Whenever I approached, the kindly brute
Flapped his prodigious ears, and bent his knees...
I bribed him by a apple, and beguiled
The beast of his affection like a child;
And well he loved me till his life was done
(Except when he was wild).
It makes me blush for human friends, but none
I have so truly kept or cheaply won!

Edward Cross was a clever, observant man. Although he lacked a formal education, his knowledge in practical zoology was considerable. He was known and respected by many of London's anatomists and zoologists, and a particular friend of the surgeon Sir Everard Home, who was a copious writer on comparative anatomy and physiology. Home was often consulted when men or beasts belonging to the menagerie were taken ill; in return, all dead animals of comparative anatomical interest were taken to Home's headquarters at the Royal College of Surgeons in Lincoln's Inn Fields, to be dissected and prepared for the famous Hunterian Museum. Sir Everard was something of an elephant enthusiast, and visited Chunee many times. He was particularly interested in the elephant's power of digestion. In 1823, Sir Everard wanted to investigate whether the elephant was capable of appreciating music. Cross was easily persuaded to assist him, and recruited a pianoforte tuner to bring his instrument to Chunee's den. Sir Everard accompanied him on a French horn when they started playing, and Chunee seemed to appreciate their impromptu concert: 'He brought his broad ears forward, remained evidently listening, and he made use of sounds rather expressive of satisfaction than otherwise'. For a lark, they also played for the lion Nero, which stood glaring at them when the high notes were sounded. As soon as the flat notes were played, however, the lion sprang up, lashed his tail, roared fiercely, and endeavoured to break free, to the alarm of the female spectators and the amusement of Sir Everard Home.

Big Trouble at Exeter Change

Each day, Chunee consumed more than eight hundred pounds of hay, corn, straw, carrots, mangelwurzel and biscuit. The elephant grew at an astounding rate. In 1820, when a new den had to be built to accommodate the huge beast, Chunee had more than doubled his size in a little more than eight years. When Mr Cross published a new guidebook to Exeter Change in 1820, he proudly declared that Chunee was Europe's largest elephant, being more than ten feet in height and weighing about five tons; 'familiarly speaking, he may be called an animated mountain'. In spite of his huge size, the elephant was timid and easily frightened, or at least so Mr Cross claimed. Once, when quite young, the elephant had been terrified by a large dog leaping forward; now, it was enough that Mr Cross's fierce little fox terrier ran into the den for Chunee to cower into a corner, trumpeting with fear. In his guidebook, Mr Cross advised the visitors not to try to pat or fondle the elephant; he had received many complaints from ladies whose white gloves had been ruined by the smelly oil rubbed into Chunee's coarse hide by the keepers. Other well-intentioned advice was that the ladies should not stand too close to the cage of Ould Bill, the orang-utan, since he liked to dash forth and grab hold of their long skirts. All visitors were strongly recommended to get out of the way pretty sharply when the llamas cleared their throats to spit.

In his pamphlet, Mr Cross boasted of Chunee's docility and great affection to the keeper, but he neglected to mention that there had been several violent incidents at Exeter Change, all involving the elephant. Chunee's keeper Alfred Copps long seemed capable of controlling his charge. Several visitors to the menagerie, Lord Byron among them, had even been quite impressed by the elephant's obedience and sagacity. But one day, in early 1815, Chunee attacked Copps without warning and gored him into a corner of the den with great force; it was fortunate that the tusks went on each side of his body. When Copps fell senseless to the floor, Chunee throttled him using the trunk. A bystander alerted Mr Cross, who valiantly ran into the den and struck Chunee with a pitchfork. As the elephant turned and attacked Cross instead, the senseless Copps, who had 'scarce any breath remaining in his body', was pulled out through the bars.

Rather understandably, Alfred Copps did not dare to enter Chunee's den again. He left Exeter Change for good, later to become head keeper of the Tower menagerie. A young man named George Dyer was appointed in his place. This individual had little previous experience of animal keeping, and had probably never seen an elephant before. Since he completely lacked the skill to control the unruly beast, Chunee's behaviour went from bad to worse. The gentlemen who let Chunee act the part of their valet sometimes received their hats back in a flattened and dirty condition, or covered in elephant dung. When Dyer objected to this latter outrage, and struck Chunee with a poker, he was soused with dirty water from the elephant's trunk. The wretched man had his own bedroom next to the elephant den, which is unlikely to have benefited his night's sleep. Chunee could easily reach into his room with the trunk, and once tore up the keeper's entire wardrobe.

George Dyer complained to Mr Cross, who, rather surprisingly, did not fire this bungling youth; instead, an experienced animal keeper named John Taylor was employed as his assistant. According to a newspaper clipping, Taylor was a former circus artist, who had really dedicated his life to animal keeping. Although a lion had once torn off his right arm and eaten it in front of his eyes, he had not despaired of the inherent docility of the brute creation. The one-armed old keeper was no fool, however, and it was clear to him that Chunee had been ill treated by his brutal and inexperienced attendant. By adopting a policy of kindness, and constantly staying with the elephant, Taylor had considerable success, and Chunee's behaviour steadily improved. After the Battle of Waterloo, the patriotic Mr Cross invited a large force of soldiers and Bow Street constables for a free showing of the menagerie. One of the policemen was unwise enough to tease the elephant with grimaces and threatening gestures. Chunee suddenly grasped him with the trunk and tried to pull him through the bars of the den; if Taylor had not been quick to intervene, the man might have had to pay a high price for his jokes.

One evening, George Dyer went to a masquerade at the English Opera House. He returned early in the morning, having eaten and drunk well. He was dressed in an extravagant devil's costume, and imprudently went into the elephant house to reach his own quarters behind it. The startled elephant did not recognise him, and Dyer received a violent blow from the trunk, which disfigured him for life with a pugilist's nose. After the enraged Dyer had punished the elephant severely, Chunee took an even more determined dislike to him, frequently striking at him with the trunk or squirting him with water, and refusing to take any food from him. George Dyer again complained to Mr Cross about the many hardships of his hazardous employment, but since old Taylor had pointed out his shortcomings to Mr Cross, the result was that Dyer was unceremoniously discharged. In his place, Taylor was promoted to head elephant-keeper, with a German youth named Johann Tietjen as his assistant. John Taylor was skilled in handling all kinds of animals, and his reign as elephant keeper would have been a happy and peaceful one, had his promotion to head keeper not given him a taste for office intrigue. He seems to have been a small-minded, gossipy character, who was not above calumniating his colleagues to gain favour with Mr Cross. Later in the same year, when he gained further promotion, and became deputy to Mr Cross, the other keepers had had enough of him. They threatened to resign if Taylor was kept on the establishment, and after a tempestuous meeting, Mr Cross sacked the one-armed old man, on the spot.

A man named Richard Carter (or Cartmell) was appointed as elephant keeper in his place. In his autobiography, John Taylor spared no invective in describing the sloth, wrong-headedness and cruelty of this individual, whose only previous merit was a very short tenure at the Tower menagerie. Other sources agree that Carter was a coarse, brutal character, and unable to manage the elephant in any degree. When Taylor visited Exeter Change four months after being fired from his position, he was sad to see that Carter was threatening Chunee with a sharp spear to make the elephant perform the usual tricks. When Chunee confidingly stretched out his trunk to Taylor, the keeper saw that it had a lump the size of an egg from a thrust of the spear. Taylor expostulated with Carter and Mr Cross, but received gruff replies. Later, he wrote to William Tyler, a veteran animal keeper who was the deputy to Mr Cross, pointing out Carter's incompetence and demanding to be reinstated as elephant-keeper in his place, but his lengthy missive was not even answered. Carter's ill treatment of the elephant led to further trouble at the menagerie, particularly during the musth, the elephant's annual period of heat. In India, the elephants were sometimes let loose in the forests during this period, but it was of course impossible for Mr Cross to let the ungovernable elephant roam the streets of London at will. Richard Carter and Mr Cross had a theory that libido and constipation could be treated by the same means. They mixed large amounts of calomel, Epsom salts, syrup and croton oil into poor Chunee's molasses; it was recorded that this dose of laxatives would have purged some six thousand human beings. The treatment had the desired effect, and one would not envy the keepers whose duty it was to clean out the den after this elephantine purgation. Carter believed that Chunee had been somewhat calmed by this unsavoury physic, which had to be repeated every year during the rutting season. Modern zoologists would not agree with him, but the dosages used were extremely high, and might well have killed a less hardy beast; the peristaltics of the bowels continuously operating at maximum velocity might well have a fatiguing influence even on an ungovernable elephant.

The German keeper Johann Tietjen had remained as Carter's assistant. The reason, according to the scurrilous John Taylor, was that Carter was quite incapable of handling the elephant himself. On 1 November 1825, Tietjen entered the elephant house early in the morning. Since a few spectators had already gathered outside, the German wanted to show off his mastery of the huge beast. After the previous incidents, Mr Cross had ordered that the keepers always had to enter Chunee's den in pairs, one of them flourishing a twelve-foot spear to keep Chunee in check while the den was cleaned. Tietjen told Carter to drop the spear, however, since he trusted the elephant fully. Chunee took the spear in his trunk and playfully whirled it round, to the terror of Carter, who was standing nearby. Being told to do so by Tietjen, Chunee obediently dropped the spear. Mr Cross was just then passing by; he teasingly called out to Tietjen: 'Don't go near him, John, or perhaps you may have your sore foot trod on!' since earlier the same morning, one of the gnus had trod painfully on poor Tietjen's toes. The German was cleaning the elephant with a broom and told Chunee to turn round. The elephant did so very sharply, thrusting his tusk through Tietjen's ribs. Carter screamed and rushed out of the den, but the valiant Mr Cross, who had heard the horrid sound, rushed back to pull the lifeless keeper out through the bars. Chunee did not try to attack him or to trample on Tietjen's body; indeed, the elephant stood quite still, seemingly aghast at what had occurred. A medical practitioner was called, but Tietjen was stone dead. According to the old-fashioned British laws, the elephant was summoned before the coroner's jury, since it had caused the death of a man. At the inquest, the keepers testified that the elephant had always seemed quite attached to Tietjen, and the spectators affirmed that immediately after the fatal blow, the elephant had hastily withdrawn to a corner, trembling all over. The verdict was death by accident, and the jury laid a nominal deodand (or fine) of one shilling on the elephant. There was much writing in the newspapers about this 'melancholy occurrence'. The old elephant keeper John Taylor put the blame on Carter's ill treatment of the elephant. Carter himself (probably erroneously) suspected that Chunee had not recognised Tietjen, since the accident-prone German had spent the previous three weeks in bed, having been badly torn up by one of the leopards.

The Destruction of Chunee

Throughout the early 1820s, Chunee kept his position as London's favourite animal. A whole generation of English children was taken to see the elephant, Princess (later Queen) Victoria, Charles Dickens, Captain Marryat and Robert Browning among them. Another early visit to Chunee was described in Douglas Jerrold's *Punch's Letters to his Son*: a young boy threw a halfpenny coin to the elephant, and Chunee seized it with an elegant curve to the trunk, to give it to the cake-seller outside in exchange for a small biscuit, which was at once put into the capacious mouth. In the hot summer evenings, many strollers on the Strand stopped by to see their old friend the elephant, but even more of them went on to the English Opera House nearby, where the popular actor Charles Mathews held his popular 'at Home' entertainments. In July 1825, Chunee's friend Thomas Hood published another comic poem in the *London Magazine*, in which the elephant, envious of his rival's fame, suggests to Mr Mathews that they should perform in the same show instead of competing.

Mr Cross had been severely shaken by the death of poor Tietjen. He swore that the elephant would one day be the death of him and declared that he would have it destroyed before it caused any more mischief. When a visiting American offered him 500 pounds for the elephant, Taylor suspected that Mr Cross would have accepted the offer, had not the negotiations stranded due to difficulties in getting Chunee downstairs, and the reluctance of any American sea captain to transport a five-ton elephant across the Atlantic. Mr Cross's worst nightmare was that the elephant would break free in central London, causing carnage in the Metropolis. In Venice, six years before Tietjen's death, an elephant belonging to a Swiss lady, Mlle Garnier, had killed its keeper and held the city under a rule of terror for more than a day. Chunee's old friend Lord Byron, who was in Venice at the time, amused himself by watching, from the safe distance of his gondola, the enraged beast flinging great beams of wood into the water. When the elephant charged, the Venetian soldiers dropped their muskets and ran. The conclusion was that, in the rather flippant words of Lord Byron, 'the elephant dispersed all his assailants and was at last killed by a shot in his *posteriore* from a field-piece brought from the *Arse*-nal on purpose'. Another elephant, under the management – or rather lack of management, it would seem – of the same lady, broke free in Geneva the year after. It roamed the streets at will and, after attempts at poisoning it had proven futile, was also killed by a well-aimed cannon shot. Some Swiss gentlemen urged Mlle Garnier to devote her energies to matters more suitable for the female mind than elephant-keeping, before her gunned-down elephants would clutter the streets of every European capital.

Mr Cross was well aware of the risk of the elephant breaking loose, but he believed, or perhaps rather hoped, that the huge beast was secure up in his den on the first floor. Since Chunee kept his popularity among the Londoners, Cross was loath to have the leading light of the menagerie destroyed or removed. On Sunday 20 February 1826, Chunee again showed signs of anger and irritation, goring the walls of the den until the floor was covered with plaster and mortar. Carter tried his old trick of mixing a strong dose of laxatives into the elephant's gruel, but this time the medication seemed wholly ineffective. To speed up the actions of this 'opening medicine', Carter offered Chunee a large tub full of strong, hot ale. The elephant had grown suspicious of his keepers, and it was not until Carter himself had drunk a jug of the ale that Chunee emptied the tub, with audible satisfaction. The ale seemed to have had some calming influence on the elephant, but on Wednesday, Chunee was more furious than ever. The den had been constructed by the master builder Mr Harrison, who had ensured Mr Cross that it would withstand the assault of any animal without even being dented. It was unfortunate for Cross that this guarantee had not been put in writing, since on Wednesday morning, the elephant again battered the sides of the den, cracking a thick wooden beam and pulling down parts of the roof. Mr Cross and the keepers feared the worst when they saw the infuriated state of the elephant. If the great beast broke free and shook the entire building down, several lions, tigers, crocodiles and boa constrictors would be liberated, to wreak havoc among the Londoners. After a brief council of war, they decided to kill Chunee by poison. Carter the elephant keeper vigorously seconded this motion, but poor Mrs Cross, who was very fond of Chunee, wept bitterly.

At Wednesday noon, Edward Cross went to the pharmacy to purchase all potent poisons in the premises; the startled apothecary first refused to sell him anything, believing him to be an intended mass murderer. After finally making the purchase, the keepers mixed corrosive sublimate into the elephant's hay, but Chunee refused it; nor did he touch a trough full of arsenic and gruel. Mr Cross then tried another ruse: he persuaded a boy, who was not connected in any way with the menagerie, to pose as a visitor and to give the elephant several large buns, one of which was filled with poison. Chunee eagerly took each of the buns until handed the poisoned one; the sagacious beast dropped it and trod it underfoot, afterwards taking no food from anyone. Some hours later, Chunee again attacked the wall of the den, cracking another wooden beam and weakening some of the others; bricks and mortar rained from the roof, and the whole building shook, as if hit by an earthquake. Pandemonium broke out at Exeter Change: the few remaining spectators were hastily evacuated, and the keepers armed themselves with cutlasses, bayonets and harpoons. Mr Cross ordered his deputy, William Tyler, to secure the sagging walls of the elephant house with some strong rope and to lash down the gate of the den. Himself, he dashed off to call in the police and the military. Only the part of the floor directly under Chunee's den had been reinforced to support the elephant's weight, and the rest of the decayed flooring would immediately collapse under Chunee's weight. This would cause the elephant to fall into the arcade below, along with many of the other animals residing on the first floor. Their dens would present but feeble barriers to Chunee's great strength. Outside the gates to Exeter Change, an eager mob was gathering, alerted by the elephant's trumpeting and the deafening roars of the lions and tigers. They were speculating that the whole place would be shaken down and that the entire company of animals would come bursting out through the great gate into the Strand, the elephant leading the assault.

Mr Cross first ran to the Paddington police station, where his brother-in-law Mr Herring and two other members of the Bow Street patrol seized their truncheons and marched toward Exeter Change. When they arrived, the whole place was in confusion, with a crowd of people milling about, and the animals most uproarious. According to an eyewitness, 'the combined roaring of the Lion, Elephant, Tigers, and other enraged animals was dreadful'. As the elephant's furious assault shook the foundations of the old building, the keepers desperately tried to reinforce the broken bars of Chunee's den with rope. Mr Herring now understood that the situation was a precarious one, and that their truncheons were useless against such a formidable opponent. Some rifles were fetched, and as the three policemen advanced upon the elephant, Carter called out 'Chunee, Chunee, Chuneelah!' to make the elephant present a favourable target to them. The policemen fired their rifles, expecting the elephant to drop dead on the spot, but Chunee instead gave a furious hiss, dashed after them and struck at them with the trunk, narrowly missing Mr Herring.

In the meantime, Mr Cross was visiting his old friend, the anatomist Joshua Brookes, who was at that moment delivering a lecture to his medical students at the Marlborough Street anatomy school. When the pale-faced, distraught menagerist ran into the theatre, calling out 'Sir, a word with you, if you please, immediately: I have not an instant to lose!' every one present knew that some momentous happening was afoot. Both Joshua Brookes and his students listened with rapt attention while Mr Cross explained his extraordinary predicament. Brookes went with Mr Cross to advise the policemen how to aim for the balls to hit vital inner organs. The students ran through London in the direction of Exeter Change, whooping and carousing to celebrate their unexpected half-holiday, and spreading the news of the berserk elephant to all passers-by. Mr Cross had also called in a troop of soldiers from the Somerset House military depot, and they elbowed their way through the crowd outside. After the civilian firing squad had failed in its mission, the soldiers knelt before the den, and discharged an uneven volley from their muskets, which was barely noticed by the elephant. These soldiers were no hardened veterans from the Battle of Waterloo, but rather a troop of raw recruits with hardly any training; many of their shots actually missed the elephant, since Chunee dashed about the den 'with the speed of a racehorse, uttering frightful yells and screams, and stopping at intervals to bound from the back against the front'. These bungling recruits had only three cartridges each, and they rammed such generous amounts of gunpowder into their muskets that the barrels would have burst, had not the policemen intervened and loaded their weapons for them.

Mr Herring sent for all the powerful rifles and muskets in Mr Stevens's gunsmith's shop in High Holborn. These weapons were distributed among the policemen, soldiers, keepers and other individuals having sufficient courage to remain in the room; in all, fourteen people were armed. Outside, the crowd was held back by two other patrols of Bow Street officers, who were offered bribes of one, or even two, guineas, by rich snobs who wanted to see the elephant being killed. When Mr Herring and his men had fired upwards of fifty rounds, Chunee suddenly fell to his knees with a groan. Herring dashed forth, brandishing a harpoon, calling out 'He's down, boys! He's down!' But when he tried to climb through the broken bars of the gate, he had difficulties getting into the den. This turned out to be very fortunate for him, since Chunee rapidly leapt up again, and made another furious assault on the gate. The remaining bars were broken and the entire door lifted off its hinges with great force; Mr Herring, who had not been able to release his hold of it, was catapulted out into the room like a rag doll. Had the door not been secured with powerful ropes and chains, nothing would have prevented Chunee from bursting out into the room.

The riflemen kept up their barrage of fire, and the keepers tried to thrust spears and harpoons into Chunee's flanks, but with little effect on the furious elephant's onslaught. Being aware of the means of destroying Mlle Garnier's beasts in Venice and Geneva, the distraught Mr Cross dashed off to a nearby military depot to fetch a cannon. Since Chunee was turning about at great speed, the riflemen were unable to take a steady aim for the windpipe, eye and ear, according to Joshua Brookes's instructions. But using the same commands as during the shows, Carter the elephant-keeper ordered Chunee to kneel. Nobody expected the elephant to obey, but Chunee really knelt. Carter then thrust a long bayonet into Chunee's flank, and Herring fired his powerful rifle at the ear at short range. With a furious roar, Chunee thrust his weight against the front of the den in a final, desperate bid for freedom; the door was once more lifted from its hinges, and only held by the ropes and chains securing it to the gates. Chunee reeled into the centre of his den and slowly sank to the floor, motionless although his puny assailants fired their rifles at short range, and thrust harpoons and spears into the elephant's unprotected flank. When Mr Cross returned a few minutes later, with a cannon and artillerists in tow, the pride of Exeter Change had already breathed his last. During the mêlée, not less than 152 projectiles had been fired.

Chunee is Used Up

Poor Mr Cross was seized with despair when he saw the horrid spectacle: the lifeless elephant lying in its blood-spattered den, and the exulting killers, Herring and Carter, congratulating themselves that the furious beast had not broken free. This dismal scene was accompanied by the thunderous roaring of the other animals and the shouts of the populace outside. Chunee lay fallen like a mountain, his sinewy proboscis remisely outstretched among the blood and gore; around the great carcass, the triumphant human mice were cavorting about. Yet the names of these elephant killers lay hidden in the faded pages of old newspapers, but the name of Chunee would remain a household word in London for many years.

Only with the greatest difficulty could Tyler and Carter persuade Edward Cross to open the gates to the menagerie and let in the noisy crowd waiting outside in the Strand. Cheering wildly, the rowdy mob broke past the policemen and ran upstairs; they then stopped short, in spite of themselves, at the awe-inspiring sight of the fallen giant in the blood-spattered, broken den. Although they were charged the ordinary entrance fee, more people visited the menagerie that evening than during an entire normal week; due to the objections of the crowd, Mr Cross could not close the doors until midnight. In the following days, the dead elephant had as many visitors. The wretched Mr Cross, who was pondering how best to dispose of the five-ton cadaver, was somewhat consoled by the cash flowing in. Sir Humphry Davy, President of the Royal Society, the legislator Lord Stowell, and the Bishop of London all honoured the elephant's lying-in-state with their presence. Chunee's old friends from the theatre grieved him bitterly, as did Thomas Hood, who visited Exeter Change shortly after the elephant was killed:

> The very beasts lament the change like me.
> The shaggy Bison
> Leaneth his head dejected on his knee;

The Hyæna's laugh is hushed; the Monkeys pout;
The Wild Cat frets in a complaining whine;
The panther paces restlessly about,
To walk her sorrow out;
The lions in a deeper bass repine;
The Kangaroo wrings its sorry short forepaws;
Shrieks come from the Macaws;
The old bald Vulture shakes his naked head,
And pineth for the dead;
The Boa writhes into a double knot;
The Keeper groans
Whilst sawing bones
And looks askance at the deserted spot...

Less sentimental individuals made offers to purchase parcels of elephant meat, and the *Mirror* newspaper published a series of recipes for elephant steaks and stew. Every medical student in London wanted to be present at the dissection of the elephant, and the shrewd Joshua Brookes charged them a considerable fee for this privilege. At this time, phrenology, a pseudo-science claiming that the individual's character was determined by the shape and irregularities of the skull, was in its heyday. One of the practising phrenologists in London, a certain Mr Deville, must have considered veterinary phrenology as one of his sub-specialities, since he wanted to try his art on the elephant's head. After a huge craniometer had been applied to the prostrate Chunee's head, Deville wanted to take a mould of it, to produce a cast of the elephant's skull for his private museum. The mould was taken from the head to the shoulders, and seven and a half hundredweight of plaster of Paris was required. Mr Deville's conclusion was that the 'bump of fury' on the elephant's head was extremely well developed. He hinted to Mr Cross that he might – for a small fee – examine all the other animals to find out if any of them had any violent tendencies, but Cross was a down-to-earth man, who distrusted this modern, unproven branch of science. Another phrenologist, the well-known Dr Spurzheim, wanted to purchase Chunee's brain for dissection, but Cross was again unresponsive, since he wanted to keep the skull intact. Chunee's old friend Sir Everard Home, who had examined the elephant several times during life, was allowed to take several specimens of muscle from the elephant, for use in his experimental studies on the structure of muscular tissue of various animals.

Mr Cross left the elephant on its bizarre *lit de parade* for several days, until the overpowering stench from the cadaver prevented all but the most hardy Londoners from paying their respects. In the meanwhile, the neighbouring houses had been evacuated by their furious tenants, who threatened Cross with criminal prosecution. The shops on the ground floor, immediately below the putrid elephant, were deserted by their owners. The animals also suffered: it is recorded that one of the tigers residing in a room next to Chunee's den fell dangerously ill and was carried away on a stretcher. On Saturday 4 March several blocks in central London had become uninhabitable. Sir Richard Birnie, one of the Bow Street magistrates, sent a message to Cross 'that, unless the body was removed by Monday morning, Mr Cross would hear from Sir Richard, in a way he would not like'. This thinly veiled threat had the desired effect. Two huge pillars were erected on each side of the battered den, to support a huge cross beam, from which a pulley capable of raising ten tons was suspended. The body was first turned by ropes that had been fastened to all four legs. Then the trunk was cut off and the eyes gouged out, since these parts had been sold to gentlemen within the audience. Joshua Brookes made a deep incision through the abdominal wall, and the entire contents of the abdominal and pelvic cavities were taken out. The elephant's body was again lifted, and nine butchers worked day and night to flay the enormous cadaver. On Sunday morning, Chunee's entire hide (save the trunk) was dragged to the residence of a certain Mr Davis, who had purchased it for fifty guineas. The entire intestinal tract of the elephant had also disappeared by this time; there were dark rumours that Cross had had it dumped into the Thames from Waterloo Bridge, under the cover of the night.

On Sunday morning, Joshua Brookes started the dissection, assisted by Dr Spurzheim, the zoologist Mr Ryals, and several other anatomists; more than 100 medical students were also present. The educational value of this spectacle was debatable, however, due to the putrid state of the animal, and the extreme speed at which the dissection was performed. Joshua Brookes was egged on by Edward Cross, who wanted to avoid criminal prosecution at all costs. According to an eyewitness who wrote one of the many pamphlets about the elephant's violent demise, the sight was not a prepossessing one: 'A number of medical men were hacking most furiously at the enormous carcass of the animal, cutting away pieces of flesh that weighed at least ten or twelve pounds each. It stunk most intolerably, and was getting putrid and black.' The groaning medical students carried huge burdens of meat down into the entrance to the Strand, where slaughtermen were busy cutting it into smaller pieces. According to a contemporary account, the dirty, exhausted, cursing butchers cutting into the putrid meat presented a particularly disgusting appearance; this did not prevent them from being closely surrounded by a curious crowd. Newspaper men were shocked to detect several ladies among them, 'eager to witness the pleasing *sight* and *smell*, certainly a delectable spectacle to *delicate* minds'. It had been suggested to Mr Cross that the elephant meat was to be used to feed the other beasts at the menagerie, but he did not allow this, probably less due to sentimentality than to the extremely unwholesome aspect of the meat and grease. Instead, the meat was hauled off by an endless caravan of carts, to be delivered to various purveyors of cat's meat. The elephant beef Mr Cross had considered too seasoned for his big cats at the menagerie thus had to make do for their smaller cousins on the streets of the metropolis.

During the dissection, Joshua Brookes found nothing remarkable, except that Chunee's entire body was riddled with bullets. The elephant's heart was nearly two feet long and eighteen inches broad. When the pericardium was opened, it was observed to contain about five gallons of blood, the effusion of which had been caused by one or more sharp objects penetrating the heart. Several of the anatomists and zoologists present remarked that the state of the body, in all particulars, denoted the most perfect health, as could be expected from a twenty-year-old Indian elephant in the prime of life. Chunee would, under normal circumstances, have had many years left to live.

What Happened to Chunee's Remains?

Although both British Museum and the Royal College of Surgeons were reported to have shown some interest to purchase Chunee's mounted skeleton, Mr Cross eventually decided to keep it. This is likely to have been a clever move, since Chunee continued to serve him well: there was, for several months, a steady flow of visitors coming to see the skeleton standing in the battered den as a memorial of the death of the martyred elephant. Several people tried to persuade Edward Cross to get a replacement for Chunee, but he remained most reluctant to keep another elephant indoors. Chunee's martyrdom was in fact a close harbinger of the end for the old menagerie house. In 1828, the Strand was to be widened as a part of the urban improvement scheme leading to the construction of Trafalgar Square, and the Exeter Change building was marked down for demolition. Mr Cross remained convinced that it was quite possible to keep a complete indoor zoo within a central London building, and his animals were moved to another Noah's ark, situated a few blocks away, at Charing Cross. His old friend Thomas Hood commented on this in another poem:

> Let Exeter Change lament its change,
> Its beasts and other losses –
> Another place thrives by its case,
> Now *Charing* has two *Crosses*.

On the way to Charing Cross, an antelope and a hyena escaped, but Mr Cross and the keepers were able to recapture them after a furious chase through the London streets. The great procession of animals, and the playful fugitive hyena, inspired another broadside print, called *An Uproar on Change or a Trip from Exeter to Charing Cross*. This fanciful aquatint depicts the animals galloping off to their new abode, led on by the hyena and antelope; even the elephant skeleton is to be seen, walking out through the side door of the old Exeter Change building. But Chunee's remains did not stay long at Charing Cross. In 1829, the mounted skeleton was sold to the itinerant showman Mr Bentley, who took it on tour to the provinces. Advertisement posters from Manchester and Liverpool both reproduce an engraving of the skeleton once made at the orders of Mr Cross, to be sold at the menagerie. It shows not only the impressive proportions of the skeleton, but also that Mr Cross had equipped it with two new tusks. One of Chunee's original tusks had been injured in some way when the elephant was quite young, and the other was completely broken off during the final assault on the elephant house. Bentley seems to have been more of an enthusiast than a businessman, and the tour was a fiasco. In 1830, the skeleton was lent to London University for a niggardly sum. Bentley eagerly sought another buyer, but there were few prospective purchasers capable of finding accommodation for a skeleton this size. Bentley had himself paid 300 pounds for it, but was now prepared to accept 200 pounds. In May 1831, he contacted William Clift, the Conservator of the Hunterian Museum of the Royal College of Surgeons at Lincoln's Inn Fields. Clift recommended the Trustees of the Hunterian Collection to make the purchase, and 200 pounds was voted to Mr Bentley, on condition that he himself made sure that the skeleton was mounted in the main hall.

William Clift, who was an expert zoologist, examined Chunee's skeleton thoroughly, particularly the short, broken original tusks, which Bentley delivered in a separate parcel. One of them showed signs of an advanced state of inflammation of the large matrix of the tusk, also engaging the jaw skeleton. This must have been exceedingly painful, and likely to have contributed to Chunee's paroxysms of fury. The eccentric naturalist Frank Buckland, who had also examined the skeleton, was even more outspoken. In his *Curiosities of Natural History*, he wrote that the barbarous murder of poor Chunee at Exeter Change remained an everlasting disgrace to the individuals involved in the slaughter: 'This poor elephant was mad, but he was *mad with the toothache*'. He claimed that if an incision had been performed, down to the root, the pus would have been allowed an outlet, and the intense pain would have been greatly relieved. Frank Buckland had no suggestion how such an incision should have been performed, before the age of anaesthetics, on an elephant furiously dashing about in its den and striking at people with the trunk.

Several pieces of Chunee's anatomy, like the eyes, the trunk and the heart, were preserved during necropsy, but no trace of these specimens remain today. Nor is it known what happened to the elephant's hide, which was purchased by Mr Davis in 1826. Three years later, when resold at auction in London, it was stated to be thirty feet in length. It was again put on the market in 1832, and fetched thirty-two pounds, twelve shillings and sixpence. According to a note in *The Times* of 9 October 1832, the hide weighed 269 pounds and that it had been tanned at Greenwich. A small piece of Chunee's hide was presented to the Saffron Walden Museum in 1837 and is still there, raising the possibility that the 1832 buyer divided it into smaller souvenirs of the famous elephant.

For many years, Chunee's skeleton remained at the Hunterian Museum. In a late nineteenth-century drawing of this museum, reproduced in my book *Cabinet of Medical Curiosities*, it is seen towering over all the other animal and human specimens, in the middle of the great exhibition hall. During the London Blitz of 1941, the Royal College of Surgeons building was struck by several German bombs, and the elephant skeleton was blown to smithereens. It is commonly believed that no fragment of it was saved: at least no exhibit related to the elephant's skeleton is present at the Hunterian Museum today. There are rumours among some historians of zoology, however, that part of one of Chunee's tusks, perhaps the one with the marks of the fatal abscess, was salvaged by a fireman; it is reported to belong to a private collection in London. In another collection, I have seen an old elephant's tooth with a mark from a bullet that might have been Chunee's; for many years, it had been the property of an Eton schoolmaster.

The Immortal Chunee

One of the purposes of an early nineteenth-century zoological garden was to serve as a demonstration that man could shape nature after his own mind: the wild beasts were kept in cages along a pleasant walk, decorated with exotic plants and shrubberies. The Exeter Change menagerie was a further travesty of nature: the animals were kept indoors in the old house's apartments, and the tropical plants were kept in pots or painted on the wall murals. The tame lion Nero was allowed to walk at will among the visitors. Everyone was allowed to handle or feed the beasts, at their own risk. Chunee resided at Exeter Change for not less than fourteen years; his size and fame grew simultaneously, and in the 1820s, he had become something of a national institution. The news of 'the Destruction of the Berserk Elephant' came as a shock to Chunee's many friends in London. There were several prints depicting the gory details of Chunee's battle for freedom, and at least four pamphlets describing the life and death of the noble elephant.

After Chunee's tragic demise, elephant mania ruled among the London journalists. All the papers, *The Times* not excluded, ran detailed reports of the elephant's last days. Tough, unsentimental reporters, who used to chronicle the latest murders and rapes of the Metropolis with gusto, now composed tear-jerking stories about the martyred elephant. One sentimental poem began with the words: 'Farewell, poor Chuny! generous beast, farewell!', and another newspaper writer solemnly hoped that God would smite the wretched keeper who had harpooned poor Chunee after the elephant martyr had obediently knelt in front of him. In his dedicatory poem to Chunee, Thomas Hood mocked these sentimental excesses, comparing the elephant's death to the mass murder in the Ratcliffe Highway, where the entire Marr family had been butchered in cold blood by an unknown attacker:

When, like Mark Anthony, the keeper showed,
The elephantine scars! –
Reporters' eyes
Were of an egg-like size;
Men that never wept for murdered Marrs!
Hard-hearted editors, with iron faces
Their sluices all unclosed
And discomposed
Compositors went fretting to their cases!

Several newspaper writers criticised Edward Cross for his, in their opinion, premature decision to have the elephant shot, and some busybodies suggested medication or laxatives that should have been tried instead. The old elephant keeper John Taylor wrote a lengthy pamphlet, depicting himself as Chunee's last loyal friend among a crowd of villains, fools and incompetents; the later keepers were roundly accused of having precipitated the cataclysm through ill-treating the favourite of all Londoners. Taylor was still jobless and in dire financial straits; the title page of his memoirs stated that it was published 'for the benefit of the author, a person deprived of one arm'. Since Taylor's stories were avidly picked up by the press, both Mr Cross and Carter the elephant-keeper were booed by the mob when they entered Exeter Change. Their ally, the controversial anatomist Joshua Brookes, was also slandered in the newspapers. Brookes was well known to supply his large anatomy school with corpses through certain unscrupulous 'body-snatchers', who robbed fresh graves in the churchyards. These outrages had, rather understandably, made him somewhat unpopular among the Londoners. There were allegations that he had staged the murder of the elephant martyr only to get the chance to dissect a recently dead elephant. Another rumour stated that Joshua Brookes had cut out several beefsteaks from the elephant's rump, one of which he had eaten for dinner. Even *The Times* repeated this story, but the enraged anatomist, seconded by Mr Cross, wrote a letter to the editor to deny these allegations, and to inquire how a respectable newspaper could carry such calumnies. The editor's only defence was that 'the paragraph came from an Evening paper'! In a popular play, Joshua Brookes was further mocked. It began with a quiet chorus:

If the elephant you'd see
Pray walk in, sir – pray, walk in, sir,
Press among the company,
And dash through thick and thin, sir,
Now you'll see a sight so rare,
Spurzheim and Deville are there,
And Joshy Brooks with arms all bare,
Hacking at the skin, sir!

Later, a chorus of the Exeter Change animals responded hollowly:

The deed, alas, is done
Accomplished is our fear
Great Chuny's soul is gone.

The cruel Joshua Brookes answers, whetting his scalpel:

Yes, but his *trunk* is here!

Later in the play, an indignant chorus of men and animals repel the rapacious anatomist's assault on the elephant martyr:

O, Joshua Brooks, turn out – turn out –
Joshua Brooks, turn out –
Do you want to make beef
Of poor Chuny you thief
Fie, Joshua Brooks, turn out!

Another play, entitled *Chuneelah; or, the Death of the Elephant of Exeter Change*, was staged six months after the elephant's death, at Sadler's Wells Theatre, with considerable success.

Already in the 1820s, most zoologists considered it cruel and inhumane to keep large wild animals locked up in small cages in an indoor zoo. They harshly criticised Mr Cross and pointed out the small private zoos of certain British noblemen, and the Jardin des Plantes in Paris, as model establishments of their kind. When, in 1829, it was decided that the condemned old house at Charing Cross was to be razed, to provide a site for the National Gallery, Cross and his animals were homeless once more. He offered the entire stock of the menagerie, with his own services included, to the newly raised Zoological Society of London, but the zoologists wanted nothing to do with a mere showman. The resourceful Mr Cross had a surprise in store for them, however. He obtained several impressive backers, among whom were Queen Adelaide, the Archbishop of Canterbury, and the Duke of Devonshire. They supplied him with money to purchase thirteen acres of land at Walworth, a couple of miles outside central London, where he opened his new Surrey Zoological Garden in 1831.

When he retired at the age of seventy, in 1844, Mr Cross's new zoological garden was a both successful and respected establishment. It boasted a rhinoceros, several beautiful giraffes, a giant tortoise big enough to be ridden by children, many boas and pythons, and an aviary of eagles and vultures donated by Joshua Brookes. Although a catalogue mentions two 'dwarf' Asian elephants, there is no record that he ever got a successor to Chunee. According to some correspondence in the Fillinham Collection at the British Library, it would seem as if Cross briefly had another elephant, also named Chunee, in the late 1820s, but this animal was not part of the menagerie. He sold this second Chunee to a certain Mr Massey, who went on to exhibit the elephant in Oxford and other places. In April 1831, Massey wrote to Mr Cross for advice since Chunee was very ill with a broken tusk. The elephant regained its health, however, since a print in the same collection depicts 'Kiouney', Mr Massey's Performing Elephant, during their tour of France a few years later.

After the retirement of Mr Cross, the Surrey Zoological Garden was taken over by William Tyler, who had been one of the men present at Chunee's death. He had worked at Exeter Change for many years, and must have been quite an old man; during his reign as director, the zoo went rapidly downhill. Public interest was low, and the animals old and infirm. In 1856, the Surrey Zoological garden was closed and the entire stock of animals sold at auction, fetching niggardly sums. A group of monkeys could be bought for ten shillings and two jackals for twenty-four shillings. It is sad to contemplate that the bears were all purchased by a hairdressing firm, to be made into 'bear's grease' for balding pates. The remaining giraffe was purchased by a continental zoo, but when hoisted on board ship, it fell and broke its neck.

As one is standing at the present-day Strand, surrounded with buses, cars and motorcycles, it seems marvellous that this street had, 160 years ago, contained a complete menagerie, with lions, tigers, apes, crocodiles, a rhinoceros and an elephant. Not a trace of the actual Exeter Change building has been preserved to posterity; today, the Strand Palace Hotel is located at its former site. A more apposite monument to Mr Cross and his beasts can be found in the nearby Trafalgar Square, where the lions at Lord Nelson's column are the work of Sir Edwin Landseer; he may well have used his drawings of Nero, the Exeter Change lion, while sculpting them.

6

JUMBO, *KING OF* Elephants

When people call this beast to mind,
They marvel more and more
At such a LITTLE tail behind
So LARGE a trunk before.

Hilaire Belloc, *The Elephant.*

The elephant later to become known as Jumbo, and one of the world's most famous animals, first came into contact with human civilisation in 1861, when it was little more than a year old. While taking a stroll along the bank of the Settite River in Abyssinia, the elephant calf was caught unaware by a party of Arab hunters, who soon secured their prey, using their clubs and nets to good effect against the startled animal. Jumbo was, at this time, about three and a half feet tall. The Arabs transported the elephant calf to the coast, where it was sold to the German big game hunter Johann Schmidt. Early in 1862, it was sold on to the zoological garden of the Jardin des Plantes in Paris, where it was to reside for three years. During this time, nothing unusual was noted about its growth and general behaviour. In 1865, there was an exchange of animals between the Jardin des Plantes and the London Zoological Gardens: the young elephant crossed the channel together with two spiny anteaters, being traded for a rhinoceros. For the elephant, this is likely to have been a fortunate turn of events. During the German siege of Paris in 1871, the starving Parisians raided the zoo for all its edible inhabitants; the most startling dishes were on the restaurant menus at this time, and Jumbo may well have escaped ending up as *ragoût d'éléphant*.

Jumbo at London Zoo

At this time, Mr Abraham Dee Bartlett was the superintendent of the London Zoological Gardens. He was the son of a hairdresser who had his salon in the Strand, near the Exeter Change menagerie. Young Abraham frequently visited Mr Cross and his beasts, and this early experience was instrumental in arousing his lifelong passion for practical zoology. He became an expert taxidermist, but this trade was not lucrative enough to support him. He was apprenticed to his father, and attended to the hair of the living by daytime and the fur of the dead by night. In 1851, he won a prize at the Great Exhibition for a display of stuffed animals, and was appointed naturalist to the Crystal Palace exhibition, to take charge of the stuffed animals exhibited among the plants in these huge greenhouses. The beasts rotted quickly in the humid atmosphere, however, and the appointment was an unhappy one. Bartlett decided to devote his energies to living animals instead of stuffed ones, and succeeded in obtaining a position as naturalist, and later superintendent, of the London Zoological Gardens. He was quite an eccentric: his usual dress, even when tending the animals, was a tailcoat and a tall top hat. His skill in handling large and dangerous animals was unsurpassed. Once, he was able to saw off the damaged and malformed horn from a female rhinoceros, an operation taking ten minutes, the animal not objecting in any way. Another time, he pulled a broken tooth from the mouth of a large hippopotamus, using a two-foot pair of tongs. When two young rhinoceroses were to be moved from one enclosure to another, Bartlett ran before them, his long white beard and coat-tails fluttering, and dropped bits of bread to guide the rhinoceroses on their way to their new quarters. Not less than twenty-four keepers were pulled after the animals by strong ropes fastened to the beasts' harnesses, in order to slow them down.

Once Jumbo had been installed at the London Zoo, Mr Bartlett appointed Matthew Scott, one of the Zoo's veteran keepers, to take care of the young elephant. Scott was normally a keeper of antelopes, but the eccentric Bartlett considered this an advantage, since he would be more attentive to the directives of the superintendent if he lacked preconceived ideas about how to handle pachyderms. The young elephant needed much attention during its early stay at the zoo, since it had not been well taken care of in Paris: its hide was ingrained with filth, and the feet were overgrown. Mr Bartlett and Matthew Scott took good care of their young charge: the hide was washed and brushed, the feet filed and pared, and nourishing meals administered thrice a day. The elephant's name, Jumbo, is likely to have been chosen by Abraham Bartlett. It had not been previously used for elephants. The word 'jumbo' had belonged to the slang language since the early nineteenth century, being used to mock clumsy, thick-set and corpulent individuals; the elephant was thus given its name rather due to its (presumed) clumsiness than its size. According to another interpretation, the elephant's name was derived from 'mumbo-jumbo', the name of a powerful African supernatural being; the adherents of this theory are supported by the fact that Bartlett later named an African gorilla Mumbo. There are also several other derivations of the word that might explain its use as the name of an African elephant, like that the Zulu word 'jumba' means a large packet, and that the Angolan vernacular name for elephant is 'jamba'.

Jumbo was the London Zoological Gardens' first African elephant (*Loxodonta africana*). The elephants of this species are considerably larger than their Indian cousins (*Elephas maximus*), and are further distinguished by their huge ears and the cloven end of their trunks. Mr Bartlett was also well aware that African elephants were considered to be more temperamental than Indian ones, and that some zoologists considered them wholly untameable. From the very beginning, however, he was favourably impressed by Jumbo's intelligence and great affection for his keeper. Since Jumbo needed his daily exercise, he was used to give rides to little children in a large howdah strapped onto the elephant's broad back. Jumbo seemed like an ordinary African elephant until the age of seven. At that time, Matthew Scott noticed that Jumbo's appetite increased dramatically: the elephant daily consumed two hundred pounds of hay, two bushels of oats, a barrel of potatoes, several quarts of onions, and between ten and fifteen loaves of bread. Matthew Scott often gave Jumbo a bucket of strong ale, and sometimes even a bottle of whisky. Some teetotallers were concerned about this, but Matthew Scott claimed that the whisky was an elixir of health to Jumbo, and that the ardent spirits aided his prodigious growth.

Jumbo grew in proportion to his intake of food, and he was soon Europe's largest elephant. For many years, he was the foremost attraction of the London Zoo: innumerable children, including the Prince of Wales, had ridden on his broad back. Young Theodore Roosevelt had seen Jumbo when he visited London, and Winston Churchill had had his picture taken with the famous elephant. The elephant rides were supposed to be free, but it was good manners to hand a shilling or two to Matthew Scott when Jumbo returned. If this sum is multiplied with twelve (the number of children Jumbo could carry in his howdah) and then with four (the number of elephant rides each day), it is easy to understand why Matthew Scott wanted to keep his sole rights to the elephant riding at the Zoo. Matthew Scott's prestige at the Zoo increased with the fame of his charge; he was soon known as 'Jumbo's keeper', and at the pub, the other keepers respectfully made way for him when he came to have a pint of bitter to refresh himself in between elephant rides.

Throughout the 1870s, Jumbo grew at a steady rate. He was established among the sights of London, and the favourite of the Royal Family. Queen Victoria never failed to visit him when visiting the Zoo, or to give him a loaf of bread. In 1880, Jumbo was nearly eleven feet tall at the shoulder and weighed six tons; with his seven-foot trunk, he could reach objects twenty-five feet above ground level. That year, the previously docile elephant showed his first signs of temper: he gored the iron cage-doors with such force that both tusks were broken near the jawbone. The tusks then grew into the jaw, and a painful abscess was formed. Bartlett made the correct diagnosis, however, and ordered a long harpoon to be sharpened. Together with Matthew Scott, he went into the elephant house and, without warning, thrust it into the swollen jaw, causing the effusion of a large amount of very offensive pus. Jumbo uttered a tremendous roar, but did not attack them. The next day, Bartlett could incise the other abscess in the same way, without the elephant objecting in any way.

After these successful operations, Jumbo's health improved rapidly, and his broken tusks once more grew through their proper apertures. For several years to come, however, he periodically became aggressive and difficult to handle. No one but Matthew Scott had the power to calm Jumbo down during these paroxysms of rage; as soon as he went into the elephant den or took Jumbo for a walk, the elephant's fury abated. Scott was a stubborn, difficult character, however. He persistently refused to

Bartholomew Fair.

THE Greatest Wonder in England IS

THE LEARNED CATS!

SIGNOR CAPPELLI

(Previous to his leaving London) begs leave most respectfully to inform the Visitors and Inhabitants of the Metropolis, that having met the most flattering encouragement while in Regent-street, London, Brighton, Bath, Cheltenham, Manchester, Liverpool, Dublin, Edinburgh, &c. &c. where he has been patronised by the Nobility and Gentry, will now exhibit his WONDERFUL AMUSEMENTS,

Performed by Cats,

At 19, GILTSPUR STREET,

EVERY DAY

DURING THE FAIR.

The Entertainment will commence with an Exhibition of some extraordinary manœuvres of

SLEIGHT of HAND

By Signor Cappelli, the Inimitable Tuscan;

Executed in a style the most remarkable and unknown in the country. The Cats will then be introduced, and their performance will be, to beat a drum, turn a spit, grind knives, play music, strike upon an anvil, roast coffee, ring bells, set a piece of machinery in motion to grind rice in the Italian manner, with many other astonishing exercises. One of the Cats, the cleverest of the company, will draw Water out of a Well, at her Master's command, without any other signal being given than the sound of the voice; this command being pronounced both in French and Italian. All who have witnessed her prompt obedience, have expressed themselves at once astonished and delighted at the prodigy.

The Wonderful Dog

WILL PLAY ANY GENTLEMAN AT DOMINOES THAT WILL PLAY WITH HIM

Gentleman 4d.—Working People 2d.

Printed at the Literary Saloon, 11, Holywell-street, Strand.

1 An 1829 handbill advertising Signor Cappelli's cats, when they performed at Bartholomew Fair. A similar handbill, advertising one of the Regent Street shows, is reproduced in Ricky Jay's *Extraordinary Exhibitions*.

2 Another image of one of Cappelli's cats, ringing a bell in a small belfry.

3 The Clever Cats: a troupe of acrobatic felines performing at the London Pavilion in 1888.

4 Mr Banks and his horse performing; a woodcut from the pamphlet *Maroccus Extaticus*, which was later reissued as a print.

5 Performing horses at the Circus Ambassadeur in Paris. One of them has the doubtful distinction of being ridden by a bear.

6 Professor Bristol's Equescurriculum: other late nineteenth-century rivals of Mr Banks and Marocco.

7 The Gastronomic Horse takes a meal of beef, potatoes and beer at this German circus in 1827.

8 The Arab stallion Zarif is being taught by his stern German schoolmaster Karl Krall. Note the blinkers, used to focus the horse's attention on the blackboard.

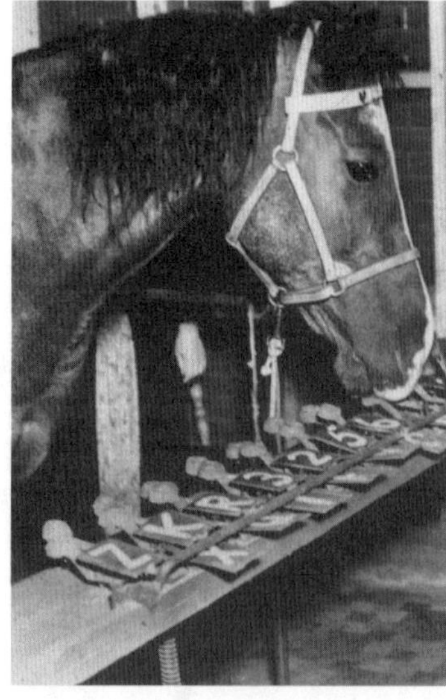

9 An old photograph of an American learned horse, probably the mare Lady Wonder.

THE WONDERFUL PIG. Publish'd by S.W. Fores No. 3 Piccadilly April 12 1785

Above: 10 The original learned pig performing in London, as drawn by Thomas Rowlandson in 1785.

Right: 11 Sheet music praising the virtues of the Wonderful Pig, issued in 1785.

The Downfall of TASTE & GENIUS or

The WORLD as it goes.

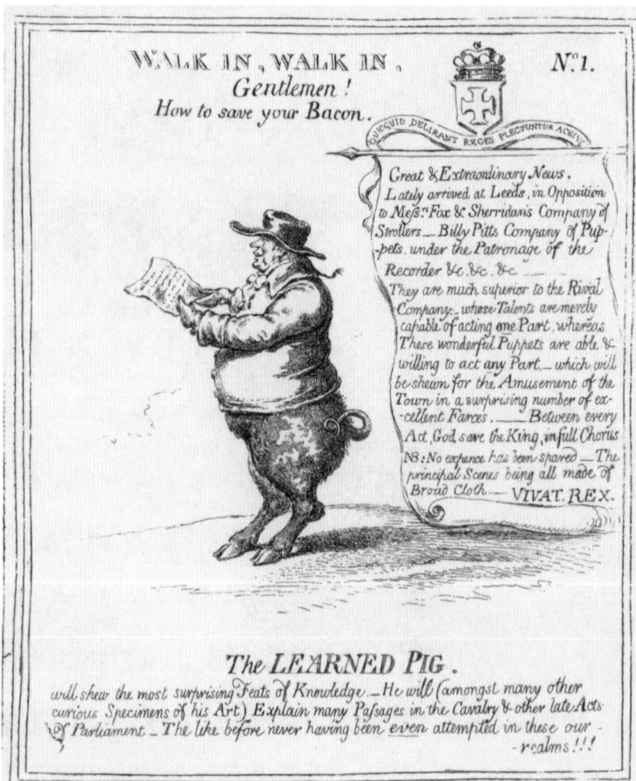

Above: 14 The frontispiece of Toby's autobiography.

Right: 15 A Gloucester advertisement for Toby's 1818 tour.

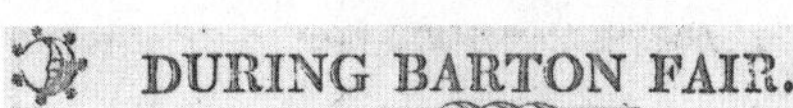

DURING BARTON FAIR.

MOST

Extraordinary Novelty!

THE WONDER OF THE PRESENT AGE!

Under the Patronage of the ROYAL FAMILY, and the First of Nobility,

TOBY!

THE

SAPIENT PIG,

From the Royal Promenade Rooms, Spring Gardens, London.

He is in colour the most beautiful of his race; in symmetry the most perfect, and in temper the most docile.—He far exceeds any thing ever yet seen, for his intelligent Performances It is impossible to form an adequate idea of the surprising sagacity of this Animal; in him the power of Instinct is so extremely striking, that it seems superior to reason in many instances, and to some Persons it may have the appearance of romance; but the curious may form some just idea of his extraordinary capacity from the following particulars:—

THIS MOST SURPRISING CREATURE WILL

SPELL AND READ,

CAST ACCOUNTS,

Tell the Points of the Sun's Rising and Setting.

Any Lady or Gentleman may put Figures in a Box, and make what numbers they please, and then shut up the Box, and this wonderful Pig absolutely will tell what number is made before the Box is opened.

He will tell any Person what o'Clock it is to a Minute, by their Watch;

TELL THE AGE OF ANY ONE IN COMPANY;

AND WHAT IS MORE ASTONISHING,

HE WILL DISCOVER A PERSON'S THOUGHTS!!

And when asked a Question, will give an immediate Answer. In fact, he is beyond every conception, and must be seen to be believed. He is the only Scholar of his Race ever known or heard of in the world.

Those Ladies and Gentlemen who please to honour MR. HOARE with their presence may depend on witnessing the greatest prodigy in existence.

An Elegant Place is prepared for the Scene of his Exploits, adjoining the Turnpike Gate, Barton-Street, Gloucester:—To commence each Day during the Fair at the following Hours:—viz, One, Two, Three, Four, Five and Six.—*Admittance One Shilling.*

[W. Price, Printer, Gloucester.]

Opposite above: 12 The caricature *Downfall of Taste and Genius*, or *The World as it goes*, by Samuel Collings, depicting the muses of art and music being assaulted and trodden underfoot by a host of trained animals, clowns and burlesque comedians; the Learned Pig is leading the charge.

Opposite below: 13 One of the many caricatures mocking Prime Minister William Pitt as the Learned Pig.

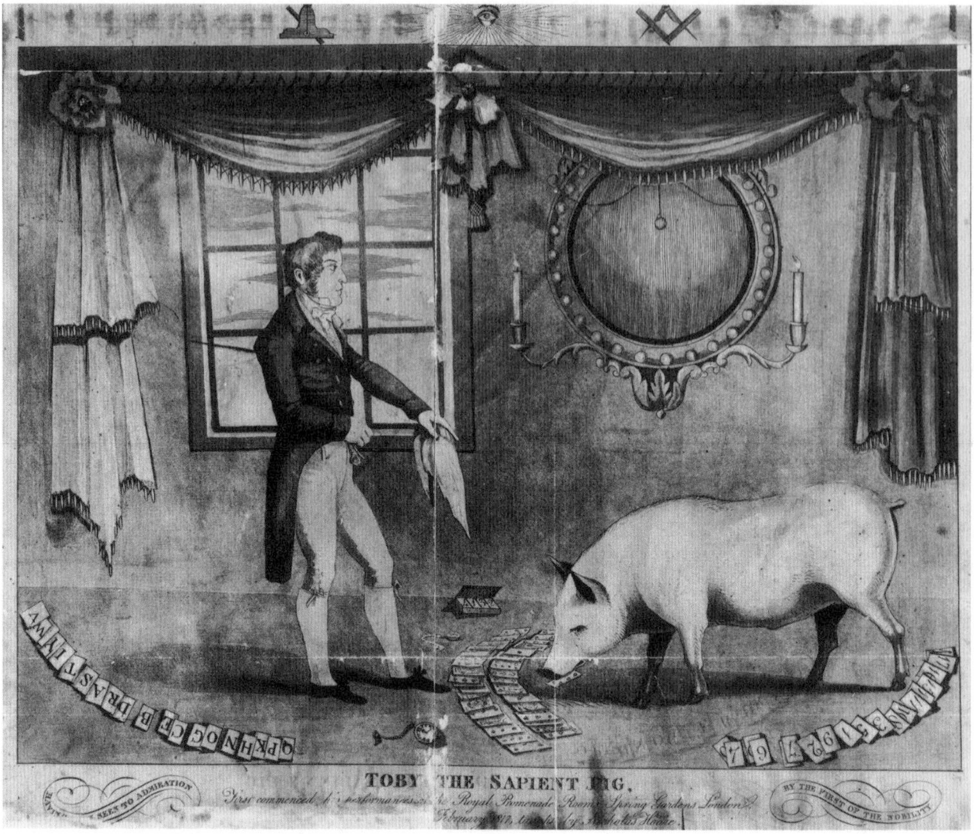
TOBY THE SAPIENT PIG.

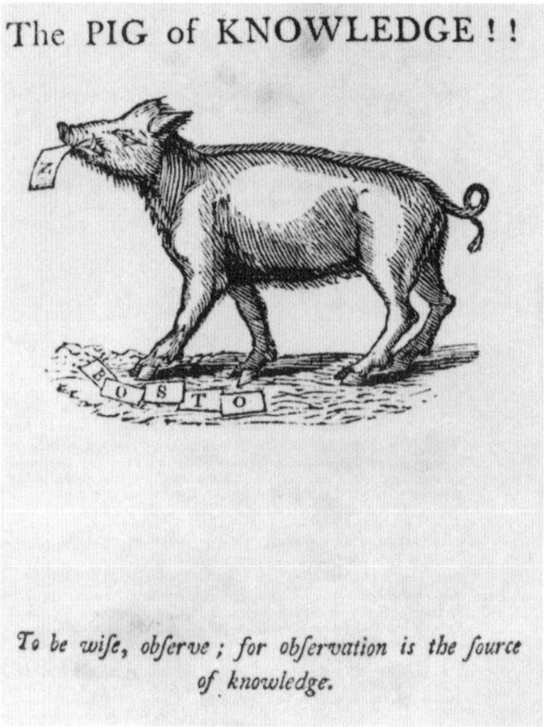
The PIG of KNOWLEDGE ! !
To be wiſe, obſerve ; for obſervation is the ſource of knowledge.

Above: 16 A very good drawing of Toby performing, from the Fillinham Collection of Cuttings from Newspapers.

Left: 17 The conjurer Pinchbeck's learned pig.

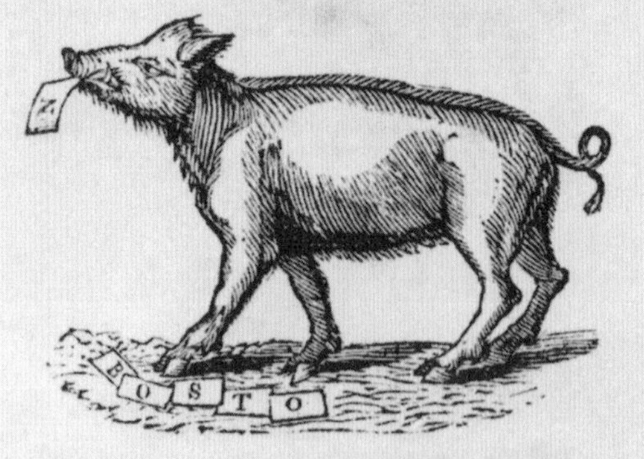

18 A French circus poster from the beginning of the last century, depicting various animal amusements, including a pig being ridden by a monkey.

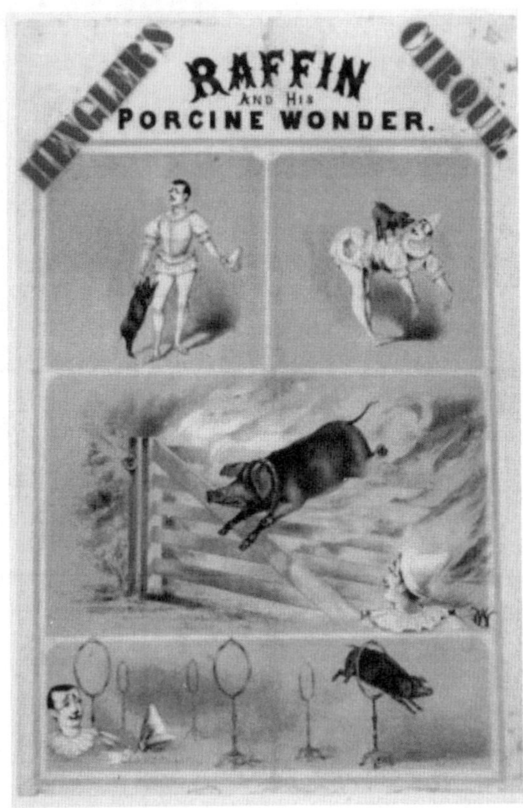

19 The clown Raffin and his Porcine Wonder performing in 1882.

20 The learned pig seen by Thomas Hood.

The new CHIEN SAVANT, or LEARN'D DOG, that reads, writes, & casts Accomps &c. &c

Nicholls pinxit 1752

F. Morellon la Cave fecit

Behold (what patroniz'd the Old Disputes
Of human Souls Transition into Brutes)
A Dog that mouths all Language by the Roots!

Publish'd according to Act of Parliament and to be had at all the Print Shops, and at the Place where the Dog is exhibited

21 Munito's best-known predecessor, Le Chien Savant, an engraving from 1752.

Right: 22 Mrs Midnight's Animal Comedians: a monkey town besieged by dogs. From Chambers' *Book of Days*.

Below: 23 A very early drawing of Munito, from his first 1817 London poster.

Above left: 24 A scarce handbill advertising Munito later in his 1817 sojourn in London. Note the different drawing of the dog.

Above right: 25 Munito's 1819 London advertisement poster, boasting of his success at the Humane Society.

26 A French caricature of Munito from the early 1830s, from an unknown magazine.

Mit Allerhöchster Bewilligung

wird

heute Montag den 1sten Dezember und die folgenden Tage

eine Abend-Unterhaltung

mit dem

einzig berühmten Hunde Munito

gegeben werden.

Herr Castelli d'Orino, der schon früher das Glück hatte, mit seinem berühmten Pudel den Beyfall der höchsten Monarchen Europas zu erhalten, wird nichts verabsäumen, damit ihm auch hier das nämliche Schicksal zu Theil werde.

Dieser Hund addirt, subtrahirt, multiplizirt, spielt Domino, und erräth alle Karten durch den Geruch.

Bey einer jedesmaligen Vorstellung werden auch andere Stücke gewählt werden, um das Publikum angenehm zu unterhalten.

Der Eintritts-Preis ist 24 Kreuzer.

Der Schauplatz ist in der goldenen Ente bey Herrn Teufelhart in der Windenmachergasse über eine Stiege. Der Anfang ist täglich um 6 Uhr.

Right: 27 Munito in Vienna in 1828; again note the size of the dog.

Below: 28 A French drawing of Munito II, depicting a much smaller dog, and issued as a part of a series called *Le Bon Genre* in 1827.

Left: 29 An advertisement card for a French chocolate firm, depicting Munito performing under the direction of Signor Castelli.

Below: 30 The usurper dog Monetto, with his trainer Mr Hoare.

Första gången i Åbo!
I Hotell Post, Östra Auragatan N:o 3
gifvas
FÖRESTÄLLNINGAR
med de tre verldsberömda hundarna
SCHNAPSL, FRIEDA och DIANA.

DIANA
uträknar med största färdighet hvarje af publiken gifven uppgift i addition, subtraktion och multiplikation, angifver besökarens ålder, äfvensom noggrannt timslaget och urskiljer alla nationalfärger.

SCHNAPSL, alla hundars konung,
som urskiljer mynt, klädesstycken och andra saker, kommer att spela kortspelet "Stukulka".

FRIEDA
hopsätter hvarje af publiken uppskrifvet ord och spelar domino med hvem, som det önskar, utför pa pianoforte tyska och engelska folkhymner samt sjunger ur noter italienska operor.

Undertecknad har haft äran att under det största bifall gifva föreställningar med sina fyrfotade artister vid hofven i BERLIN och WIEN, äfvensom många förnäma hus i ST. PETERSBURG, MOSKWA och AMSTERDAM samt under utställningstiden sex manader i Kristallpalatset i LONDON. Om så önskas gifves föreställningar inom familjer.

Above left: 31 The German dogs Schnapsl, Frieda and Diana in Finland in 1874.

Above right: 32 Hermany's aeronautic cats and dogs.

Below: 33 An early twentieth-century German learned dog rehearsing with his master, from an old photograph.

34 The old house at Exeter Change housing Mr Cross's menagerie; note the advertisement with the elephant in centre.

Left: 35 The entrance of the Exeter Change menagerie.

Below: 36 The interior of the menagerie; a drawing from one of Edward Cross's catalogues.

37 An engraving from George Cruikshanks's drawing of Chunee's destruction.

Left: 38 Another, less skilled anonymous engraving of the elephant's last struggle for freedom.

Below: 39 *Uproar on a Change*, an engraving of the fugitive animals leaving their new Noah's Ark at Charing Cross.

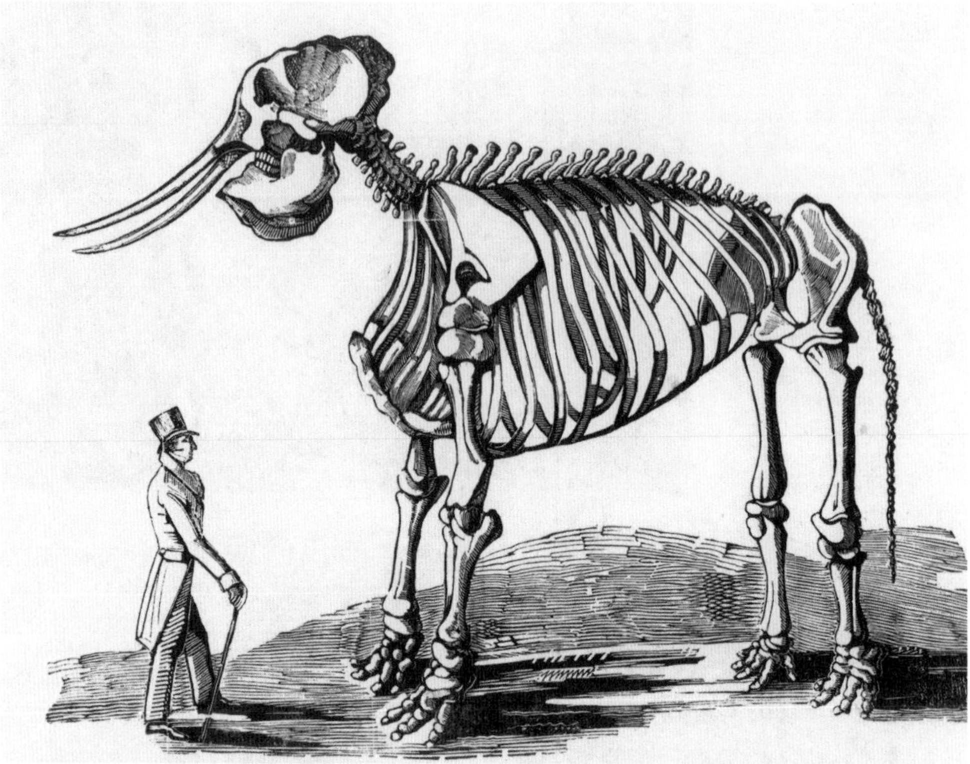

40 Chunee's skeleton in 1829, from a drawing commissioned by Edward Cross.

41 The remaining piece of Chunee's hide.

Above: 42 Jumbo and Matthew Scott in 1865.

Right: 43 Some officials of the Zoological Society of London take a ride on Jumbo in the late 1870s. The man in a grey bowler hat holding the elephant's trunk is Matthew Scott.

44 The caricature *Arcades Jumbo*, published in 1882. Mr Punch suggests to P.T. Barnum that he should bring the politician Charles Bradlaugh, who is depicted in the guise of a pig, with him to the United States, instead of Jumbo, whose back is cluttered with grieving British children.

Right: 45 Jumbo being taken up Broadway.

Below: 46 Scenes from the Life of Jumbo.

47 A coach drives under Jumbo's belly in this exaggerated advertisement.

let any other person handle Jumbo, and particularly objected to having a deputy elephant-keeper under him, since this would have meant that he had to share the earnings from the lucrative elephant rides. In his youth, Bartlett had been one of the horrified witnesses to the destruction of Chunee in the Exeter Change. With these tumultuous happenings in mind, he gave orders to purchase an elephant gun, to be used if Jumbo ran amok at some time when Scott was away. Bartlett believed that Jumbo's occasional paroxysms of fury were due to the periodic insanity of bull elephants during the rutting season, and this diagnosis is by no means impossible, since he was an expert zoologist with previous experience of elephants. Some zoologists have advanced another theory, however, after studying casts of Jumbo's teeth. In the upper jaw, the teeth are abnormally developed and severely maloccluded, and Jumbo's periods of fury started just as the fifth molars were erupting in each jaw.

P.T. Barnum Intervenes

After Phineas Taylor Barnum's American Museum had been destroyed by fire in 1865, this clever and active showman had entered the circus business with considerable success. After joining forces with his colleague James A. Bailey, he became the owner of America's leading circus. Barnum & Bailey's Greatest Show on Earth employed 370 circus performers, and had a huge menagerie with 20 elephants, 338 horses and 14 camels, in addition to many zebras, lions, leopards, hyenas and large snakes. For some time, Barnum had coveted Jumbo, but he had considered it highly unlikely that the Zoological Society of London would even consider selling this famous elephant. In January 1882, Barnum's London agent once more approached Mr Bartlett about Jumbo. Initially, the London zoologists were reluctant to sell Jumbo, but when Barnum offered 10,000 dollars (2,000 pounds at the time) for the elephant, they changed their minds and promised that the Board of the Zoological Society would debate the matter. At first, not even Barnum believed that the deal would go through, but after two days of debate, the zoologists decided, by a small majority, that the elephant was to be sold. The cause was officially stated to be Jumbo's uncertain temper, and it was also claimed that his size was making him impossible to ride. Many people presumed, however, that the considerable sum of money offered was instrumental in prompting the sale, since the financial state of the venerable Zoological Society was not strong. Because of Jumbo's immense popularity, the zoologists were unwilling to break the news to the press and the British public, who would not, they knew, take it kindly that their great favourite was being shipped to America. The news leaked to the newspapers, however, probably through the agency of the publicity-minded P.T. Barnum, and a national furore arose when it became known that Jumbo was to be sold.

Many Britons at first believed this tale of Jumbo being sold to a vulgar American to be some kind of tasteless joke, but the Secretary of the Zoological Society of London reluctantly had to confirm to the Press that Barnum had really bought the elephant. This 'outrageous sale of a national character' disgusted many people whose children had once ridden on Jumbo: hundreds of vituperative letters flew to the offices of various newspapers. The children themselves wrote sentimental letters to the Queen or to Prime Minister Gladstone, begging that the wicked Barnum would not be allowed to take their beloved Jumbo away from them. Queen Victoria, the Prince of Wales, and the aesthete John Ruskin together wrote an appeal to the Zoological Society, urging the zoologists not to let Barnum have Jumbo. The Queen would pay any costs incurred by this breach of contract.

Despite his Yankee bravado and business-like attitude, P.T. Barnum had always had a secret admiration for Britain: its glorious past, historical monuments and famous writers and poets. Although some of his biographers have depicted him as a coarse, illiterate, boorish man, Barnum, albeit no scholar, was well read in the English classics, and even staged Shakespearean dramas at his American Museum. His admiration for Britain and its national treasures sometimes inspired him to attempt business deals that did not at all amuse the jingoist Britons, who viewed this exuberant Yankee with great scepticism. Barnum had once very nearly succeeded in purchasing the cottage in which William Shakespeare was born, in Stratford-on Avon. He intended to have it carefully dismantled and shipped to New York for reassembly. At the very last minute, a consortium of public-minded Englishmen managed to outbid him, turning the building over to the Shakespeare Trust. According to rumour, another audacious transaction had nearly deprived London of one its prime attractions, Madame Tussaud's Museum at Baker Street, which narrowly escaped being shipped to America. The furore caused by these attempts to remove traditionally British monuments was nothing, however, to the nationwide fury caused by Barnum's attempt to kidnap Jumbo to the United States. Lord Winchilsea must have expressed the opinion of many Englishmen when he suggested that the Prime Minister, William Gladstone, should be shipped to America in Jumbo's stead:

But since in England's fallen state
She owns two things supremely great,
Jumbo and Gladstone – (each we find
The most prodigious of their kind) –
And one won't budge. Then, Barnum, make
A fair exchange, for quiet's sake!
Take the Right Honourable, and go!
He'll make the better raree show!
Leave Jumbo.

Jumbo-Mania

Next to P.T. Barnum himself, the obvious target of abuse for patriotic Englishmen was Mr Sclater, Secretary of the Zoological Society of London. After surreptitious attacks in the Press, this gentleman had to write a rebuttal, emphasising that Jumbo had, in later years, seemed excitable and easily enraged; several experienced zoologists had feared that Jumbo would have had to be shot if he had gone berserk within the zoo. Mr Sclater pointed out that this, and not the monetary aspect, was the cause that Jumbo had been sold. In America, Jumbo would not be used as a riding elephant but only be shown during circus performances. Mr Sclater was particularly offended by the allegations from several journalists, that Jumbo would be badly treated in the United States. He pointed out that Barnum & Bailey had more than twenty elephants in their circus, and that one of them had recently had a calf, something that happened only rarely among elephants in captivity. Mr Sclater was sorry to announce that both he and Mr Bartlett had received many threatening letters, in which they were, with suitably zoological metaphors, called 'skunks', 'reptiles', and 'craven beasts'. Poor Matthew Scott had, by another earnest letter-writer, been likened to Judas Iscariot, since he had basely betrayed Jumbo to his enemies.

Mr Sclater's defence did not impress Jumbo's many friends. If Jumbo was dangerous and vicious, why had he been allowed to consort with young children just a few days earlier? And if Jumbo was dangerous, would it be morally correct to sell him off to the United States, thereby valuing American children's lives lower than English ones. The editor of *The Daily Telegraph* sent a telegram to Barnum in the name of the British nation:

> Editor's compliments. All British children distressed at elephant's departure. Hundreds of correspondents beg us to inquire on what terms you will kindly return Jumbo.

Barnum immediately sent a telegram in return, but its contents did not please Jumbo's many friends:

> My compliments to Editor *Daily Telegraph* and British nation. Fifty millions of American citizens anxiously await Jumbo's arrival. My forty years' invariable practice of exhibiting the best that money could produce makes Jumbo's presence here imperative.

It thus seemed as if Jumbo could not be saved for the British nation. The *London Standard* compared the act of separating Jumbo from his British friends to a southern slave-owner selling the members of a black family separately at auction. In the *London Telegraph*, the avaricious American was solemnly cursed, and poor Jumbo's future among the Yankees bemoaned:

> No more quiet garden strolls, no shady trees, green lawns, and flowery thickets. Our amiable monster must dwell in a tent, take part in the routine of a circus, and, instead of his by-gone friendly trots with British girls and boys, and perpetual luncheon on buns and oranges, must amuse a Yankee mob, and put up with peanuts and waffles.... We fear, however, that Jumbo will never come back to us alive. His mighty heart will probably break with rage, shame, and grief; and we may hear of him, like a another Sampson [sic], playing the mischief with the Philistines who have led him into captivity, and dying amid some scene of terrible wrath and ruin.

The editor of the *Vanity Fair* weekly started a fund for the preservation of Jumbo, himself donating £5. He wrote that since an elephant could become more than 120 years old, Jumbo was likely to survive the fall of the British Empire. Although the editor's political intuition was thus more highly developed than his zoological knowledge, the readers of *Vanity Fair* contributed considerable sums of money, although far from enough to outbid P.T. Barnum. A poor old lady, who had no money to give, instead donated her sewing machine to save the elephant.

Jumbo appreciated his many visitors, and particularly the buns, cakes and fruit baskets they had brought with them. People had rather confused ideas what an elephant liked to eat, however. After an animal cruelty inspector had stopped an individual who tried to feed Jumbo a leg of mutton, one of the keepers was posted on guard outside Jumbo's den to stop people from giving him kippers, bones, beefsteaks, oysters, whipped cream, or other food wholly unsuitable for an elephant's diet. An old lady bringing Jumbo a box of sweets and hothouse grapes was confounded when the elephant instead seized a basket of flowers, which he was meant to smell, and devoured it whole, ribbons and all. Once, a kind-hearted visitor gave a loaf of bread to the completely neglected Indian elephant in the den next to Jumbo's, but the huge neighbour put his head into the den, stretched out his long trunk, and seized the loaf. Every day, a well-dressed old lady stood in front of Jumbo's den, distributing hand-written pamphlets containing a prayer that the Lord would forgive the heretical scoundrels who had sold Jumbo to the American barbarians, and that He would intervene to stop Jumbo being moved to the United States. Three times a day, she herself knelt opposite the elephant house to personally present the elephant's case before the Lord.

Thousands of buns were sent to Jumbo by children from all over Britain. Other individuals sent the elephant an amazing variety of gifts: fruit, sweets, puddings, cakes and sandwiches arrived at a steady rate, and a gardener sent a huge prize pumpkin, which Jumbo devoured with relish. Eccentrics sent bottles of wine, champagne, beer and whisky, and cases of snuff and cigars; Matthew Scott cautiously stated to the Press that these gifts 'were put where they would do more good'! A well-wisher sent a huge night-cap to Jumbo, for him not to catch a cold while crossing the Atlantic. Another odd present was a huge crate of pills against seasickness. Alice, the African cow elephant known as 'Jumbo's wife', although the two animals seldom met and showed no interest in each other, was given a widow's cap to wear while mourning her departed husband. Innumerable letters were addressed to 'Jumbo, Zoological Gardens'. Most of them were from children, containing sentimental verses or phrases like 'Jumbo don't go' or 'Jumbo come home for Christmas'. Many children sent Jumbo locks of their hair; they probably imagined that Jumbo would treasure these mementoes of his little friends, and paste them into an album along with the sentimental poems.

In the London shops, Jumbo hats, Jumbo coats, Jumbo cravats and Jumbo fans had a roaring trade. At the restaurants, Jumbo soup and Jumbo stew were served, although neither of these dishes was actually made from elephant meat. The colour *à la mode* for the satin dresses of the fashionable ladies was a dark grey, also named after the famous elephant. Many books, broadsheets and music-books featuring Jumbo were avidly bought by the public. In the *London Fun*, it was suggested that the lion in the British coat of arms should be changed into an elephant, with the accompanying device *Dieu et mon Jumbo*! Americans were quite unpopular in London during this time, and the US Ambassador James Lovell remarked that 'the only burning question between the two nations is Jumbo'.

But although the odds were against them, Jumbo's friends did not give up. Egged on by the Queen and by several influential politicians, a group of dissidents within the Zoological Society of London, led by Sir George Bowyer and Mr Berkeley Hill, asserted that the sale of Jumbo was in disagreement of the original charter of that society. Not only was it morally wrong to sell a dangerous animal, but the sale of this huge elephant, a type specimen of its kind, to a mere showman would seriously hinder the study of zoology. They took the Zoological Society to court, and the trial began before Mr Justice Chitty on 9 March 1882. All the newspapers published lengthy accounts of this trial, delighting their patriotic readers with pro-Jumbo editorials. But the Zoological Society soon gained the upper hand by conclusively proving that according to their charter, the board had the authority to sell any animal without consulting all the Fellows. Sir George Bowyer compared the sale of Jumbo to the governors of the British Museum selling off the Magna Charta or the Codex Alexandrinus to the highest bidder. He argued that Jumbo was just as important for the study of zoology as these documents were to the study of history, and that the Society had no right to sell 'any article valuable for the study of natural history'. The Zoologists again objected that they had sold animals before, in particular a gnu for $750.

The dissidents replied that although less valuable animals could be sold, Jumbo was a type specimen of what was presumed to be a newly discovered, larger form of African elephant. Another argument was that African elephants had been so heavily decimated by the ivory trade, that many zoologists feared that they would soon only be met with in zoological gardens. Mr Justice Chitty's verdict was that the sale of Jumbo broke no law, and that the elephant now was the property of P.T. Barnum. In his summing up, the Judge lamented that during this trial, he had received an unprecedented amount of sentimental and threatening letters from the public; like the editor of *The Times*, Mr Justice Chitty hoped that this final sentence would end the Jumbo-mania that had affected all Londoners.

Jumbo Leaves the Zoological Gardens

Together with Matthew Scott, Barnum's agent tried to lure Jumbo into a cage with wheels under it, inside which the elephant was to be pulled down to the London Docks. They had considerable difficulties in handling the elephant, however, since Jumbo proved to be quite restive and timid once he had been removed from his habitual surroundings inside the Zoological Gardens. He was very frightened by horses and sat down and remained seated as long as any member of the equine race remained in view. Barnum's agent reported to his boss that the morose little Matthew Scott was far from co-operative. Barnum replied that help was on its way: as soon as the Zoological Society had agreed to sell the elephant, William Newman, one of Barnum & Bailey's most skilful elephant keepers, had been dispatched across the Atlantic to bring Jumbo back with him. After Newman and Scott had made plans, another attempt was made to lure Jumbo into the cage, which resembled a very large horse-box. Although Jumbo was put in chains by Newman, he refused to mount the ramp up to the crate. The next day, when Jumbo was led toward the cage, he lay down on the ground and refused to go near it. The spectators applauded and sang 'He's a jolly good fellow!' 'Elephant Bill' brought out his long pike staff, which he used to discipline his elephants back in the United States, but a stalwart animal cruelty inspector forbade him to use this weapon. Jumbo had chosen to lay down just outside the parrot house of the London Zoo, whose denizens let out a communal shriek when they were excited by Jumbo's trumpeting, the curses of the keepers, and the hearty cheers of the spectators. The other zoo animals also contributed various sound effects, and even the stolid elephant cow Alice trumpeted loudly.

As soon as the furious Newman had given up, ordering that Jumbo was to be taken back to his enclosure, the elephant promptly rose at Matthew Scott's command and plodded back to the zoo in his footsteps. The journalists threw themselves into their hansom cabs and rushed back to the headquarters of their papers to report the latest news: like a true Englishman, Jumbo refused to go to the United States, and his faithful wife Alice wept and called for him to come home! Barnum's agent wired his boss to inform him that Jumbo would not budge, but the clever showman replied that he was allowed to lie there as long as he wanted to – 'it is the best advertisement in the world'. 'Elephant Bill' Newman was less amused by Jumbo's peccadilloes, however, and according to a (probably exaggerated) newspaper report, he even had declared that he had the right to shoot Jumbo if this proved necessary: 'Living or dead, Jumbo is to go to New York!' This declaration is unlikely to have added to his popularity among the Londoners.

These dramatic occurrences at the zoo were given as much attention in the newspapers as a recent attempt to assassinate Queen Victoria. This sentimental story of the poor elephant objecting to be exiled to the United States, and triumphing, as a honest British underdog, over the Yankee vulgarians sent to remove him, arose much interest. One Londoner sent a wreath of flowers to Jumbo 'as a trophy of triumph over his brutal owners and American kidnappers' and a fashionable young lady who had just got married sent half her wedding-cake as a present to the elephant. One newspaper leader compared the sight of Jumbo in chains, to be delivered up to the Americans, to Mr Selby disposing of the honest, uncomplaining Uncle Tom. A young boy, writing to the *Vanity Fair*, was very much disappointed with the elephant cow Alice, who 'did not look miserable at all' at the prospects of losing her dear husband. Entire schools of children petitioned the Zoological Society, and Barnum claimed that hundreds of children had written to him, begging that Jumbo should be spared. He reproduced one of these pathetic letters, allegedly written by 'A young English girl', but the style, and Americanised spelling, would suggest that it had been written by himself or by some unscrupulous journalist in his employ.

A sentimental poem, written at the height of the Jumbo craze, and illustrated by a drawing of Jumbo and Alice at the Zoo, contained the following words:

When quite a baby I came here, and now to London folk I'm dear
They'll try to keep me yet, I know, from Barnum and his travelling show.
It grieves me sadly to be sold for just two thousand pounds in gold,
And could I talk I'd quickly say, 'I'm treated in a shameful way.'
They chained me up one day, to be shipped across the raging sea,
But I, your faithful friend Jumbo, did not just feel inclined to go.
Again they tried the nasty chain, but all their efforts were in vain,
For with a very angry frown upon the ground I laid me down.
I love the brave old British flag, of it, my boys, I'll always brag,
And you must clearly understand, I do not care for yankee land.
Leave me with Alice kind and true, leave us together in the Zoo,
And let our friend Squire Barnum know, I can't go with him in his show.

The editor of *Punch* did not take part in the rampant Jumbo-mania. He instead pointed out that while ample funds were available to keep Jumbo on the right side of the Atlantic, a mission dedicated to giving a dinner of Irish stew to the starving children of the East End on every Wednesday was failing due to lack of funds. In the accompanying poem, a forthright East Ender gives his views on the Jumbo controversy, contrasting the lot of the pampered elephant with that of the stunted, filthy children of his own class:

We can feel the gnawing hunger and *we* never gets our fill,
No columns in the TELEGRAPH when TOM or DICK falls ill.
There's no national subscription to keep us over here –
No! It strikes me they're uncommon glad when outward bound we steer.
Bu then *we're* not all elephants, we're only rags and bone,
To be gathered by the dustman, and left unfed, alone;
To be cast upon the gutter, and to grovel in the slums;
To never have a decent meal, and raven for the crumbs…

The clever Mr Bartlett had carefully observed the futile attempts to get Jumbo into the cage. He had seen that at the same time Matthew Scott called out to the elephant to rise, he clandestinely made a sign to his great charge to remain in a recumbent position. The sly old 'Scotty' had wanted to keep his old job as elephant-keeper at the zoo, to earn ample money from the elephant riding and hobnob with the nobility and gentry who wanted to see Jumbo. His immediate rapport with Jumbo had been noted by Bartlett many years earlier; it had been further strengthened as the years went by, and Scotty could direct Jumbo only by signs and gestures. He had played the fool before the Americans, who had not seen through his deception. Mr Bartlett called Matthew Scott to his office and reproached him for his disloyal behaviour, which was seriously threatening the zoo's agreement with P.T. Barnum. Bartlett saw no possibility of keeping the disobedient Scott within his establishment if he did not agree to accompany Jumbo to Barnum & Bailey's Circus, where he would retain his position as Jumbo's keeper, at a good salary. Although Matthew Scott was dismayed to be put under the command of an American, he grudgingly agreed to this offer. In the meantime, Elephant Bill had ordered a wheeled elephant cage equipped with two large gates to be shipped across the Atlantic. It arrived just in the nick of time, when Jumbo had become considerably more docile after Scott had ceased his subversive actions. The elephant was led through the crate on several occasions, and when the time was right, the two gates were slammed shut and Jumbo's legs were chained. For an hour, the elephant struggled furiously to get free; the whole cage shook, and each time a plank was torn loose, a rowdy mob outside cheered and exulted. It was feared that Jumbo would be able to tear the chains asunder, but Barnum's strong ironware was hardy enough to confine even a furious elephant. Elephant Bill and his colleagues could finally nail a sign with the address 'Barnum & Bailey, New York, USA' to the crate, this probably more owing to advertising purposes than fear that it would be sent to the wrong address.

Ten great draught horses were hitched onto Jumbo's crate and pulled the elephant out into Regent's Park without difficulty. The London zoologists had warned Elephant Bill that the wheels of the trolley were likely to be too narrow to carry Jumbo's bulk over the gravelled walks of Regent's Park, but the American had not heeded their advice. As soon as the elephant was hauled out into Regent's Park, the wheels sunk into the earth. Only through jacking and digging the wheels out at regular intervals could Jumbo be kept moving. When Jumbo's crate was negotiating a steep, grassy mound near Regent's Canal, the police and keepers guarded its path and egged the horses on, dreading a stop at this point, where the ground was exceedingly soft. Just as they thought they were clear, some mischievous person in the crowd loudly cried out 'Whoa!', and all the ten horses obediently stopped short. Before the team of horses could be persuaded to get moving again, the axles and wheel had sunk into the earth. It took many hours to dig them out and to lever planks under the wheels, and it was not until just after midnight that Jumbo's crate was finally moving forward again. In spite of the early hour and the cold, drizzly weather, a rough crowd had assembled before the gates of the Zoological Gardens, singing 'Rule Britannia' as Jumbo was slowly approaching, pulled by the ten big, steaming horses.

The progress was swift through the silent streets of sleeping London; at regular intervals, the party had to stop to refresh the horses and to pour water over the steaming wheels. Elephant Bill and Matthew Scott, who rode on a platform in front of the elephant's crate, were probably grateful that Jumbo was moved just after midnight. Had such a conspicuous procession taken part by daytime, the elephant's progress would inevitably have been impeded by a large and rowdy mob, and Jumbo's attendants would have been in immediate danger of lynching. Even at this hour, a crowd of 200 people were running along with the elephant crate, and a few journalists were pursuing it in their hansoms. At the military barracks of Albany Street, the guard turned out and shouldered arms to the passing elephant. Initially, Jumbo had taken things quite calmly, comforted by Scott, who stood just before the elephant, fondling the trunk. At one occasion, however, Jumbo stretched out his trunk and tweaked the tails of the horses. Later, he took hold of the reins of the cart, to the delight of the crowd, who shouted out that Jumbo was driving himself!

At seven o'clock in the morning, the whole company had breakfast, and Jumbo was given two dozen oysters and a bowl of champagne by an eccentric peer. At St Katherine Docks, Jumbo's crate was unloaded and hoisted over to a large Thames barge. Later in the morning, Jumbo's crate was hoisted onto the *Assyrian Monarch*, a large steamer used to ship immigrants to the United States. Once on board, Jumbo had many visitors. Barnum's agent staged a gala luncheon on board, to which many noblemen, politicians, socialites and newspaper men had been invited. The American consul general gave a speech, expressing his hope that the anti-American sentiments that had been aroused by the untimely selling of the elephant would abate as soon as Jumbo had been freighted across the Atlantic, and that the great elephant would one day unite Britain and the United States in unanimous sympathy. Elephant Bill was, at the same ceremony, awarded the gold medal of the Zoological Society of London for his skilful handling of the elephant during its transport from Regent's Park to the docks. As Jumbo's last visitor on British soil, the Baroness Burdett-Coutts boarded the *Assyrian Monarch*, along with a distinguished party of noblemen and ladies. She gave the elephant a last bun and shook hands with his keepers Scott and Newman. No one noticed the 400 poor Russian Jews who had bought their cheap third-class passage on the *Assyrian Monarch*; compared to Jumbo, they might just as well have been fleas on the coat of a prize dog. Nor did any one care about the 200 further emigrants who had been displaced by the elephant. When the Baroness Burdett-Coutts graciously spoke to some of the less unattractive children, they knelt down before her and kissed the hem of her gown, since they believed her to be Queen Victoria who had come to say farewell to her beloved Jumbo.

When the *Assyrian Monarch* hove to at Gravesend, the men-at-war manned the rails to honour the elephant, and at every pilot cutter in British waters, communiqués about Jumbo's state of health were carefully deposited. The elephant was mightily seasick during the first few days afloat, since the ship was struck by a storm while out into the Atlantic. At many London churches, prayers were said in favour of animals and men in peril on the sea, after some disreputable newspaper had spread the untrue rumour that Jumbo's ship was in danger of sinking. The storm calmed down, however, and after a fifteen-day journey, the *Assyrian Monarch* lay to in New York; during the following months, the Jumbo-mania slowly abated.

Jumbo as a Circus Elephant

When Jumbo went ashore in New York on 10 April 1882, P.T. Barnum was at the quay to receive the most recent – and valuable – addition to his circus. He was deeply touched when he saw the gigantic animal, which he had paid 30,000 dollars to purchase and transport across the Atlantic. In meandering detail, he described to a crowd of newspaper men how he had, several years earlier, ridden on Jumbo's back together with his tiny protégé, the famous midget General Tom Thumb. Some of the journalists, themselves already the worse for drink, decided to enliven the occasion by pouring a couple of bottles of whisky down Jumbo's capacious trunk. P.T. Barnum objected to their intoxicating his elephant, but the merry newspaper men did not heed his warnings and continued their horseplay. One of them admiringly remarked that Jumbo was able to swallow down a bottle of whisky in one single gulp, and to drink a bucket of beer as a 'chaser', just like a human being. During the welcome ceremony that had been arranged for Jumbo, the elephant was pulled through Broadway in a cart pulled by sixteen horses and pushed by two other elephants. P.T. Barnum's three brass bands played rousing music at a deafening note as the parade was approaching the Madison Square Gardens, and the throng of inquisitive people was frightening poor Jumbo, who was used to his tranquil life at the London Zoological Gardens, out of his wits.

In the circus flyers and handbills, Jumbo's proportions were greatly exaggerated: 'His trunk is the size of an adult crocodile, his tail is as big as a cow's leg, and he makes footsteps in the sand of time resembling an indention as if a very fat man had fallen off a very high building'. It was also hinted that Jumbo had nearly caused a war between Britain and the United States, and that the dastardly Brits had attempted to feed Jumbo poisoned buns just before his removal to America, believing that their darling elephant would prefer death to slavery among the vulgar Yankees. A witty columnist in the New York Times decided to improve on Barnum's flights of fancy. He remarked on P.T. Barnum's remarkable self-restraint in not mentioning several remarkable facts about the elephant's life in London. It was well known in Court circles, he asserted, that from her earliest years, Queen Victoria had been accustomed to play and romp with Jumbo at the Windsor Castle Park, making the elephant fetch and carry like a dog, and rolling and tumbling with him on the turf. Later in her life, when the Royal veterinary advisers had tactfully pointed out that the risk of her Majesty accidentally rolling upon Jumbo and seriously injuring the poor animal was too obvious to be disregarded, the stoutly built Queen had to be satisfied with keeping Jumbo indoors like a well-trained poodle, and to have him sit at her side and 'beg' for sugar-lumps at tea-time. After Lord Beaconsfield had procured for the Queen the title of Empress of India, she became very fond of riding Jumbo around the back yard of Buckingham Palace. Lord Beaconsfield used to sit on the elephant's neck to act as a mahout. This practice was, of course, carefully hidden from the liberal statesmen of the time. It might never have been known outside the Palace, had not Jumbo entangled his trunk with one of the Royal clotheslines one Monday morning, and bolted across the yard, throwing both the Empress and the mahout. P.T. Barnum was delighted with this clever spoof of his own advertising pamphlets. In a letter to the editor, he replied that it could now not be doubted that all the stories about Jumbo's loving intimacy with Queen Victoria were true – 'We all know that the Queen's attachment to Jumbo was so ardent that for years there could be no sleep on the Royal couch until Jumbo had sounded his trumpet 'good night' from the Windsor Park or the back yard of Buckingham Palace…'.

After some months, Jumbo became used to circus life. When Barnum & Bailey's Greatest Show on Earth performed, Jumbo took precedence over all other two- or four-legged artists. There was a general hush when the ringmaster shouted out:

> The Towering Monarch of his Mighty Race, the Colossus of Elephants, The Biggest and Most Famous Animal in the World, ridden upon by Queen Victoria, the Royal Family, and more than a million Children – just arrived from the Royal Zoological Gardens, London – JUHUMBO!

When the line of nearly thirty elephants trudged into the ring, led by the mighty Jumbo, the crowd was dazzled by their size and power. At the tail of the parade went two elephant calves, which were the objects of much sentimental affection. Jumbo usually walked together with a small 'clown elephant' called Tom Thumb, to further accentuate his own great size. Tom Thumb later performed a comic show with the circus clowns, pretending to steal bottles of liquor from them and get more and more drunk. Other elephants stood on their forelegs, played on the seesaw, or balanced on barrels. Jumbo himself was too old a 'dog' to learn new circus tricks, and during the actual shows, he dignifiedly stood to one side, watching the cavorting of the other elephants with an air of slight boredom.

Jumbo was the largest, as well as the most famous, immigrant into the United States. Just like in Britain, the elephant became quite a media personality. Cigars, crocheted potholders, and a particularly big sewing machine were all named after Jumbo. The use of Jumbo in advertising was quite extraordinary, even by American standards. Baking powder, sewing-thread, soap and tooth-powder were advertised using the famous elephant's image on the trade-cards. An astonishing drawing depicts

Jumbo stampeding through a desert landscape, wearing patent boots with clinching screw fasteners; the caption was 'The two biggest things on earth: the Clinching Screw and Jumbo!!!' The sun shines benignly upon the great, well-booted elephant as he runs by, carrying a banner emblazoned with the words 'For Hard Work & Constant Use give me the "Clincher"'; a party of Arabs reverently stand aside when the elephant pounds by them in his ungainly footwear. Another, even more far-fetched advertisement depicts Jumbo feeding an elephant calf castor oil, as an advertisement of the laxative Castoria; it is accompanied by the following deplorable poem:

From peasant nurse to high-born lady
All mothers know what's good for baby, CASTORIA.
While Jumbo, too, though not a lady
Follows suit and feeds the great baby CASTORIA.

Jumbo proved one of P.T. Barnum's most shrewd investments ever. In just two weeks, the elephant had repaid the 30,000 dollars consumed by its purchase, transport and advertisement campaign, with a twenty per cent interest. In his first season at the circus, Jumbo was taken on a thirty-one-week tour from coast to coast, which earned 1.7 million dollars. Jumbo travelled in a specially built railway car called 'Jumbo's Palace Car'. It was richly decorated in red and gold and was mounted on two six-wheeled bogies, with double entrance doors in the middle, reaching almost down to the track. Matthew Scott had his quarters in the same railway car, and when on tour, both he and Jumbo lived, ate and slept there. Although Bailey and the circus elephant-keepers were quite unimpressed with the gloomy, truculent Matthew Scott, the clever Barnum observed Scotty's almost hypnotic influence on Jumbo and signed a long-term contract with him. Jumbo's attacks of fury, which had alarmed Mr Bartlett and the other attendants at the London Zoo, completely ceased when Jumbo had been moved to the United States. This would favour the hypothesis that Jumbo's bad temper was associated with the emergence of his molars. The long-time companionship of Matthew Scott certainly had a calming influence on the elephant. Through his great stubbornness, he managed to launch a scheme of elephant riding at the circus that benefited both Jumbo, who needed his daily exercise, and Scotty's own purse.

P.T. Barnum rightly asserted that Jumbo continued to grow during his sojourn with the Greatest Show on Earth. In 1884, the elephant was more than twelve feet tall and weighed about seven tons. Once, as a publicity stunt, Barnum arranged that Matthew Scott was to lead Jumbo across the newly built Brooklyn Bridge. The bridge withstood this test of its strength, although it vibrated for each of Jumbo's footsteps. Jumbo became the favourite of the American public, just as he had once been the darling of all Londoners. There were many sentimental pamphlets, books and poems about Jumbo, in which the great elephant was anthropomorphised to fit the nineteenth-century idea of how an elephant ought to behave. The Americans were much impressed by Jumbo's majestic, yet gentle demeanour, his impressive memory, and his kindness to little children.

During Jumbo's first three years at the circus, the elephant brought in earnings a hundred times in excess of the price for which he had been bought from London. Barnum was well aware that a tour to Britain with Jumbo and chosen parts of the circus would prove a very lucrative enterprise. In 1885, he was busy making plans to cross the Atlantic and to restore Jumbo, at least temporarily, to his little friends in London. Jumbo still had a long career in front of him: in captivity, African elephants may well reach the age of sixty or even seventy years.

Jumbo's Death

On 15 September 1885, the Greatest Show on Earth was visiting St Thomas, Ontario, during its Canadian tour. After the show, when all the other elephants had been loaded into their railway cars, a railwayman was escorting Matthew Scott, Jumbo and the dwarf elephant Tom Thumb along the track toward 'Jumbo's Palace Car'. Suddenly, a train could be heard rapidly approaching from behind them, and a powerful whistle sounded. The horrified railwayman ran toward the train, a long express goods train, hauled by a powerful Grand Trunk Railway locomotive. The train-driver probably received the shock of his life when he saw the frantically waving railwayman, and, behind him, Jumbo's immense shape looming up in the locomotive's searchlight. He threw the engine into reverse and sounded three short blasts on the whistle as a signal to have the brakemen apply the brakes, but the distance was far too short.

As the train approached them, Matthew Scott jumped down the railway embankment and called Jumbo to follow. The elephant was first frightened of the slope, but when suddenly facing the locomotive's powerful headlamp and piercing whistle, Jumbo ran down the embankment, trumpeting loudly. The sheer impetus of Jumbo's seven tons took him far beyond Matthew Scott, however, and the elephant nearly ran into a high fence. This made Jumbo panic and run back up on the railway track. Matthew Scott desperately tried to drive Jumbo toward an opening between two railway cars. Trumpeting loudly and lifting Scotty, who was hanging on to the elephant by a strap, high into the air with each step, the huge beast ran past them, again from sheer impetus. It is not easy for a seven-ton elephant, running at its utmost speed, suddenly to stop or to turn round. The train first hit the dwarf elephant, which was thrown down the embankment like a football, and then rushed on toward Jumbo, with the brakes shrieking and sparks issuing from the wheels.

Just before the collision, Jumbo uttered a tremendous roar; during all their years together, Matthew Scott had never heard anything like it. The locomotive struck Jumbo from behind, wedging the elephant's body half over, half under one of the railway flatcars; the force of the collision derailed both the locomotive and the coal tender. The driver and the stoker both threw themselves from the locomotive as soon as they realised that a crash was inevitable, and their lives were saved. Jumbo lay on the railway track with severe internal injuries, blood pouring from the mouth and trunk. In spite of his terrible injuries, Jumbo could still recognise Matthew Scott, and when the keeper spoke to the stricken giant, the trunk sought his hand. Clutching Matthew Scott's hand, the elephant died some minutes later. Poor Scotty wept bitterly, and could only with difficulty be persuaded to let go of the elephant's corpse.

Before the circus people had presence of mind enough to post a guard on Jumbo's huge body, it was attacked by rapacious souvenir hunters, who cut off hairs from the tail and filed the tusks, like a flock of harpooners pitching into the body of a huge, dying whale. According to one source, there were attempts to cut off both the tail and the trunk, as well as to cut chunks of meat out of the flanks. When poor Matthew Scott, who had fallen asleep beside the huge carcass, exhausted by grief, finally awoke from his slumber, he became hysterical when he saw that a huge slice had been cut out of one of Jumbo's ears. The St Thomas police went out in force to prevent further outrages of this kind, and a policeman was posted to guard the elephant night and day.

Barnum and Bailey were of course most annoyed when they heard that the star of their circus had been killed in a railway accident. They accused the railway of negligence, but the officials of the appositely named Grand Trunk railway asserted that anyone leading their unruly beasts along the railway had to watch out for themselves, since if there were railway tracks on the ground, it was likely that trains would run on them. There was a story at the time that a young boy, who had been sent to St Thomas in order to warn the stationmaster that the extra goods train would pass through the station, had stopped for doughnuts on the way and arrived too late. If true, this tale does not inspire confidence in the Grand Trunk railway's signalling system.

As befitting one of the world's most famous animals, Jumbo's strange death gave rise to a great variety of lurid tales and oddball theories. According to Barnum's own version, Jumbo died a hero's death, to save his little friend Tom Thumb. Sacrificing his own life, Jumbo had snatched the dwarf elephant with the trunk and pulled it away to safety, moments before being hit by the train. Some writers of popular books on the American circus have claimed that Jumbo died through mere stupidity, and that the elephant had charged the train, bellowing with rage. Another, more lurid version stated that Jumbo had been more than usually addicted to his rations of ale and whisky on that fateful day, and that the huge beast had reeled toward a drunkard's death.

Just two weeks after Jumbo's death, a remarkable conspiracy theory was advanced by a hack journalist named C.F. Ritchel, writing in the Hartford *Sunday Globe*. He asserted that Barnum had deliberately planned Jumbo's death, since he knew that the elephant was badly ill with tuberculosis. A dramatic accident would generate a furore of publicity, which would benefit the circus. After reading this calumny, Barnum immediately sued the publisher for 50,000 dollars. The editor of the *Globe* went to Barnum's headquarters in Bridgeport and obtained testimonies from Matthew Scott and several independent eyewitnesses who had been present when Jumbo died. When the irate editor returned, Ritchel was sacked on the spot, and the next issue of the *Globe* contained a mealy-mouthed apology to Barnum.

Another, even more daring conspiracy theory was advanced in the 1960s. Jumbo's incredible flatulence had 'stunk up' the entire circus, and out of sheer embarrassment, Barnum had decided that he must go. An unscrupulous English animal keeper turned assassin was instructed to shoot Jumbo with a powerful pistol, while Barnum himself supervised the elephanticide from a safe distance. Jumbo was shot in the eye and fell upon the dwarf elephant, nearly crushing it to death! The circus train had started moving just at that moment, in order to cover the sound of the shot, and to Barnum's chagrin, Jumbo fell between two of the cars, damaging the skull. The cunning showman had arranged for Jumbo's hide to be stuffed in advance, and the taxidermists were standing by.

All these fanciful tales are nothing but lies, and cannot be reconciled with the actual events of that fateful evening in St Thomas, as testified by several independent eyewitnesses, including Matthew Scott himself. A later re-examination of the elephant's skeleton further implies that Jumbo was most probably hit from the back, and that the cause of death was internal injuries caused by the impact of the locomotive, and that the head was wedged between the engine and a railway car with great force. Nor was any trace of projectiles found when the skeleton and body were examined.

Jumbo is likely to have been the only animal whose death became front-page news like the demise of a prominent politician or royal personage. The news of Jumbo's tragic death was telegraphed all over the world, and many newspapers printed lengthy obituaries of the King of Elephants, often with many sentimental comments, fetched from Barnum's untruthful account of Jumbo's heroic death. An editorial in the *Spectator* emphasised that 'It was his destiny to attract more attention than any other elephant which ever existed, and it pursued him till his death. Alone of his race he has been killed by a railway locomotive.' In the *Daily Mail*'s obituary, Jumbo was eulogised as:

> The pillar of a people's hope,
> the centre of a world's desire.

Mr Punch, with his usual attitude of cheerful, materialistic unconcern, mockingly wrote:

> Alas, poor Jumbo! Here's the fruit
> Of faithless Barnum's greed of gain.
> How sad that so well trained a brute
> Should owe his exit to a train!

Jumbo's Widow

Although Jumbo's sudden death was a severe shock to P.T. Barnum, the farsighted showman had made plans how to handle such an emergency long before it occurred. For several years, he had co-operated with Professor Henry Ward, of the Natural Science Establishment in Rochester, New York, who used to mount and stuff those deceased circus animals that Barnum saw fit to have preserved for future generations. In 1883, Barnum had written to Ward, and a contract had been drawn up that he was to stuff Jumbo's skin and mount the skeleton if the famous elephant was to expire. It took the professor and his nine assistants two days to dissect the elephant and to prepare the hide and skeleton. A man named Peters, who was appointed to perform the 'inside work', likened himself to Jonah inside the whale. At regular intervals, he had to crawl out to get some fresh air, 'looking a little white around the gills'. Jumbo's stomach was found to contain an amazing collection of objects: a huge lot of coins, gold, silver, and copper, of both British and American coinage; a policeman's whistle; a toy pistol; a bunch of keys; several nails, tack, and buttons; and the brass figure of a pig.

An American wrote to Barnum, desiring to buy Jumbo's eyes, another wanted to purchase a barrel of elephant's grease, for use against rheumatism. Jumbo's heart was purchased by Cornell University, where it was preserved for posterity at the Veterinary College. When, in 1986, Dr J. Shoshani tried to trace it, the Cornell veterinarians could only produce an empty glass jar in which it had, according to the labelling, once been kept. One of the veteran veterinarians could recall that he had, forty years previously, seen Jumbo's heart in this jar. Whatever had happened to it in the meantime is uncertain, but it remains a distinct possibility that the specimen dried out after the fluid (spirits) in which it had been kept had evaporated.

Professor Ward and his men toiled for six months to mount Jumbo's skeleton and prepare and stuff the enormous hide. Barnum ordered that Jumbo's hide should be stretched during mounting: 'By all means let that show as large as possible. It will be a grand thing to take all advantage possible in this direction! Let him show as a mountain.' It was soon apparent to Henry Ward that the business-minded Barnum had made another clever deal when he drew up the contract to have Jumbo's remains preserved for posterity, since his own salary of 1,200 dollars was not even enough to pay for the costs in stuffing and mounting materials. Professor Ward wrote to Barnum to ask for more money, but although he gave Mrs Barnum an inscribed slice of one of Jumbo's tusks, he received none. Instead, Barnum cashed out on a grand party for politicians and journalists, during which the two Jumbos were uncovered amidst thunderous applause. Small fragments of Jumbo's tusks had been ground and mixed into a jelly which was consumed by the journalists, politicians and socialites invited by Barnum; to actually eat parts of the body of the guest of honour was a novel event even at an American society banquet.

P.T. Barnum took both versions of Jumbo on tour with the circus for several years. The famous elephant's power of attraction to the public was nearly as great as during his lifetime. Furthermore, Barnum had bought the stolid old elephant cow Alice, known as 'Jumbo's wife' during their time together in London. In 1886, a grand parade was arranged at Barnum & Bailey's Greatest Show on Earth. While a huge brass band played funereal music, Jumbo's skeleton and stuffed body slowly travelled round the arena, standing on two large carts driven by morticians dressed in deep mourning, and pulled by horses with black capes. Then came the grieving widow Alice, wearing a widow's cap which was an exact copy of that of Queen Victoria, although of course several sizes larger. Then came the other circus elephants, which had been taught to hold black-edged handkerchiefs in their trunks, and to wipe their eyes with them at regular intervals. This orgy in vulgarity, staged by Barnum himself, was repeated many times, and always greeted with enthusiastic cheering and applause. Late in 1887, the Bridgeport winter quarters of the circus were ravaged by fire. The two Jumbos were saved just in the nick of time, but poor Alice expired in the flames.

The Immortal Jumbo

After a few years, P.T. Barnum became aware that Jumbo was losing his value as a popular attraction; furthermore, the stuffed elephant gradually became the worse for wear as a result of travel on the railways. In his old age, Barnum had become a wealthy and generous patron of the arts and sciences: in 1889, he donated Jumbo's skeleton to the American Museum of Natural History in New York, and the stuffed elephant to Tufts College. The latter seat of learning was much supported by Barnum, who had a seat in its board of directors. P.T. Barnum had kept the right to take the two Jumbos with him on tour again, however, and later in 1889, both versions of the famous elephant accompanied the Barnum & Bailey circus on its tour to England. At Olympia, the circus was visited by 15,000 people each day; many of them, like Queen Victoria and the Prince of Wales, paid their respects to the immortal Jumbo. The innumerable children who had once said their prayers every night to save the elephant had probably never expected that their prayers would be fulfilled in this dismal way, and that their beloved Jumbo would be returned to them in duplicate.

Barnum had feared that the Jumbo incident would have made him permanently unpopular with the British nation, and that he would be blamed for indirectly causing the elephant's death, but this was not the case. The only untoward incident occurred when Barnum was viewing a display of the Horse Guards. During a pause in the ceremony, the Prince of Wales sent him a note that he had observed Barnum's enthusiasm for the performance of the Horse Guards, and that he sincerely hoped that the showman would not purchase them and take them with him to the United States.

After the British tour, the two Jumbos were returned to the American Museum of Natural History and Tufts College, respectively. Old Matthew Scott accompanied the stuffed elephant to Tufts College, where Barnum paid him a modest salary for keeping it clean and tidy. With time, the hunched, lonely figure of the old elephant-keeper became increasingly pathetic: he sat by the huge, stuffed elephant, dusting it with a broom and speaking to it as if it had still been alive.

P.T. Barnum died in 1891. During his early career in show business, he had been quite a rogue, but in his old age, he became a wealthy and generally respected magnate. Circus historians have agreed that he was the greatest American showman of the nineteenth century, who shaped the popular entertainments in that country even more strongly than Walt Disney did the century after. For some reason, Matthew Scott had expected to get a legacy from Barnum. He was left a fine brass chest, but when opened, it only contained a signed copy of Barnum's autobiography. This was a severe disappointment to the gloomy little elephant-keeper, who became increasingly odd in his old age. In spite of his earlier claims to have supported teetotalism, his habits became increasingly dissipated. The circus continued to employ him as a keeper of various small animals well into the twentieth century; he never returned to his native land, but died at the Bridgeport almshouse in 1914.

The stuffed Jumbo remained at the Barnum Museum at Tufts University for many years. The elephant became something of a mascot to this seat of learning: it was depicted on the college flags and on the shorts of the football and athletics teams. According to an old tradition, a coin dropped into Jumbo's trunk just before an examination was said to ensure top grades. Jumbo remained the pride of Tufts University until 1975, when the Barnum Museum was gutted by fire; the flammable stuffed elephant literally went up in smoke. The students mourned it bitterly, and it was remarked that college life would never be the same again without Jumbo. Although the fire had destroyed values for more than two million dollars, it was the old stuffed elephant that was missed most sorely.

Jumbo's skeleton was exhibited at the American Museum of Natural History for many years, before being taken to the museum stores in 1977. But in 1993, Jumbo's skeleton reclaimed its position in the open exhibition when the American circus celebrated its 200-year anniversary, and it was seen by millions of spectators, just like in the old days. The lower parts of the skeleton shine like polished, from having been touched by innumerable spectators. Jumbo's skeleton is today, together with the slices of the tusks that are kept at various museums, the only memorial of what was perhaps the world's most famous animal ever.

In several languages, the name Jumbo has since been used as a denominator of elephants in general. Already in the early twentieth century, the word 'jumbo' also signified an unusually large object within its category. In both Britain and the United States, particularly large garden products were thus called jumbo cucumbers and jumbo pumpkins. This usage has since become widespread all over the globe, and the ghost of the famous elephant has been invoked in the most unexpected combinations. Those Americans who wish to commemorate the famous elephant could have a celebratory dinner might dine on Jumbo prawns served with Jumbo peanuts and Jumbo olives, before the main course of a Jumbo-burger, served with a Jumbo Martini.

There is no doubt that in his time, Jumbo was the largest elephant in captivity. P.T. Barnum never allowed any outsider measure or weigh

Jumbo, and the estimates of the elephant's size given to journalists were considerably exaggerated. Nor did Barnum consent to Jumbo being photographed in a way that divulged the animal's correct proportions. In the circus drawings, Jumbo was depicted as a monstrously huge caricature of an elephant, who could reach the roof of a three-story building with the trunk. Barnum even published a print depicting a coach being driven under Jumbo's belly. In the circus advertisements, it was sometimes speculated that Jumbo belonged to a novel species of elephant. Strangely enough, the British zoologist Richard Lydekker advanced a similar hypothesis in 1907, suggesting that Jumbo belonged to a novel subspecies of the African elephants, called *Elephas africanus Rothschildi*, and distinguished by its uncommonly tall stature and the size and shape of its ears. Later zoologists have not agreed with Lydekker's hypothesis, however. The modern opinion is that there are only two subspecies of the African elephant: the bush elephant and the forest elephant. Jumbo is considered as a particularly large example of the former subspecies (*Loxodonta africana africana*).

Jumbo's huge size was not the only reason for his astonishing worldwide fame: in modern terms, the great elephant might be called a media product, created by P.T. Barnum's genius for advertisement and publicity. The characteristics attributed to Jumbo bore the stamp of the anthropomorphizing of animals that was common among nineteenth-century journalists. The life of the famous elephant became a fairy tale created by Barnum's craving for publicity and the newspapers' need to sell copies; in that respect, Jumbo was a worthy forerunner of the present day TV pseudo-celebrities. If Jumbo had evaded capture when he encountered the Arab hunters during his stroll near the Settite river on that fateful spring morning in 1861, his life would have been completely different. Instead of embodying the late nineteenth-century idea of how an elephant was to act and behave, he would have lived out the natural existence of his species, until it would have been ended by old age or by the bullet of an ivory-hunting sniper. If he had remained in Africa, Jumbo would not have been as large, since an elephant living in the wild rarely reaches the size of one leading an inactive life in a zoological garden with ample provisions of food. He would nevertheless have been a better representative of his species than the pampered circus elephant, who was forced to enact many undignified spectacles, both before and after death.

7

Animals *ON* TRIAL

On 17 August 1487, several peasants and landowners complained before Monseigneur Jean Rohin, Cardinal Bishop of Autun, that a multitude of slugs was devastating the young crops in their fields. The cardinal bishop was much angered by this unprovoked invasion of his diocese. He ordered that public processions were to be held for three days in every parish. Three times, the slugs were solemnly requested by all the vicars and curates to leave the diocese of Autun; if they ignored this warning, the cardinal bishop would excommunicate them and smite them with his anathema. Faced with this lethal threat to their future existence and wellbeing, the slugs rapidly made themselves scarce, and a thanksgiving was held in Autun to celebrate this triumph for the holy church.

Some years later, another danger threatened the diocese of Autun. A host of field-rats was laying waste the vineyards and barley-crops, and the peasants again turned to the cardinal bishop. This time, prayers and processions did not affect the havoc wrought by these voracious rodents. For their defiance, the rats were summoned before the ecclesiastical court of Autun by the bishop's vicar general. A young lawyer named Barthélemy Chassenée was employed as their defence council. He probably realised that he was facing a particularly difficult task when he saw the pompous clerics, dressed in their best habits, elaborate at length about the bad character and notorious guilt of the accused rodents, before a vast crowd of peasants listening to their tirades with rapt attention.

When Chassenée was asked why his clients did not attend the trial, he cleverly pointed out that the rats lived dispersed throughout a large part of the diocese, and dwelt in many villages. A single summons was not enough to call them all to the cathedral, and there were precedents that people who had not been summoned to appear at a trial in a fully correct manner could not be prosecuted in their absence. The prelates had to adjourn the court, since they could not contest this argument. Every vicar and curate in the entire diocese was ordered to read the summons to the rats, both from the pulpit and in the fields, while the churchwardens frantically rang their bells. At the new trial, Chassenée again sat alone at the bench of the accused. When asked why these disobedient rodents had again failed to appear in court, he replied that they had not been able to reach the cathedral in safety, since their sworn enemies, the cats, had been lurking in the hedges and passages, intent upon their lives. He argued that there were precedents that a person cited to appear in court, who cannot come without risking his life, was not to be punished in his absence. After this point had been argued at some length, the outcome was again that the court was adjourned, and the rats saved.

The Barrister of the Rats

According to tradition, Barthélemy Chassenée's skilful defence of the rats of Autun attracted the interest of his superiors; from that day onwards, he enjoyed a meteoric career as a consulting lawyer. Although he was once or twice consulted about animal trials, he preferred having noblemen and wealthy merchants as his clients, rather than destitute rats and insects. He amassed a considerable fortune during his long and distinguished career within the French legal system, ending up as president of the *Parlement* of Provence. He was an opponent of the persecution of the Waldensian heretics, and did not give his consent to these unfortunates being summarily arrested and executed. According to a defender of the Waldensians, he ironically said that if even the rats of Autun had been given a fair trial, then there was no reason to deny that right to these heretics.

This defiant statement did not endear Chassenée to the authorities, and it seems as if one of his old enemies saw an opportunity of settling the score once and for all. He sent Chassenée a bouquet of flowers which had been soaked in a powerful poison; after smelling the beautiful flowers, the Barrister of the Rats fell to the floor, stone dead. His contemporaries were unanimous that he had been poisoned, since he had previously seemed to be in excellent health; even his debunking biographers, Messieurs Bouhier and Pignot, consider it likely that he had been deliberately murdered. These two gentlemen have doubted, however, that Chassenée had really been involved in the trial against the rats of Autun, particularly since the trial is not mentioned in his own writings. M. Bouhier believed that Chassenée had instead, under similar circumstances, defended a party of flies, which had destroyed some vineyards near Beaune. In spite of these objections, many scholars have repeated the tale of the Barrister of the Rats, and it rests upon relatively strong authority: the works of the eighteenth-century Judge Auguste de Thou.

For a modern reader, the tale of the Barrister of the Rats would appear like some bizarre farce, in which animals are transformed into human beings. But the truth is that in late medieval and early modern continental Europe, people found it nothing but reasonable to bring a lawsuit against weevils, take voles before an ecclesiastical court, or have a pig executed in public for biting a child. One of Barthélemy Chassenée's legal *Consilia* deals with the formal requirements in animal trials. If the accused beast had spilt blood during its criminal act, it was to be tried by a secular court; otherwise, it was to be punished through the agency of the Church. The secular animal trials, against goring bulls and vicious boar-pigs, were usually summary processes, ending with the ignominious death of the animal in question. The ecclesiastical animal trials were directed against a large flock of animals or an entire species: rats, insects or other vermin. They were much more elaborate procedures: the president, or judge, was usually a senior cleric, and the defending and prosecuting council were qualified lawyers. If the animals in question were convicted, they were threatened with excommunication if they did not promptly leave the territory in question.

From the Annals of Animal Trials

The medieval people had an immense trust in the bishops and other men of the Church. The authoritative prelates were considered almost as demi-gods, able to conjure demons, to make rain, and to appease hurricanes and thunderstorms. The medieval hagiographers could tell the most astounding tales about the ability of holy men to conquer nature. In the late ninth century, Rome was invaded by swarms of locusts. The civic authorities decided to give a reward to any person who could show them a certain number of dead locusts, but this measure did not affect the rapid propagation of the insects. After the secular extermination patrols had thus failed ignominiously, Pope Stephen VI took charge of the campaign against the locusts. He had prepared vast quantities of holy water over which a solemn malediction against all kinds of imps, phantoms and satanic pestilence had been read. After an army of clerics, deacons and choirboys had sprinkled the fields and meadows all around Rome with this holy water, the locusts immediately disappeared. Another holy man, St Agricola, was responsible for the cursing and burning of storks at Avignon in the year 666. A disgruntled anchorite, known as John the Lamb, once cursed the fishes, which had incurred his anger in some way or other, with results similarly disastrous to the finny tribe.

More laudable acts were the expulsion of venomous reptiles from the island of Reichenau by St Perminius in 728, and the appearance of St Augustinus in the sky near Toledo in 1286, where he threw a plague of locusts into the river Tagus with the sign of his cross. It is told of St Bernard that once, when he visited the abbey church of Foigny, both the priests and the worshippers were complaining bitterly about a plague of flies infesting the church; their loud buzzing made the entire building reverberate like a beehive. When St Bernard excommunicated the offending insects, the buzzing immediately stopped; the next morning, the grateful clerics had to throw the heaps of dead flies out with shovels. Another authoritative prelate, Bishop Egbert of Trier, was much irritated by having to share his cathedral with numerous colonies of swallows, which were fluttering about and disturbing the services with their chirping. After the birds had committed the additional offence of defiling the bishop's head, mitre and vestments with their droppings, when he was officiating at the altar, he solemnly forbade them to enter the cathedral again, on pain of death. It is still a saying in Trier that if a swallow ventures into the cathedral, it immediately drops dead.

For the curse against the offending animals to have its full effect, the entire tribe of animals had to be tried and convicted by an ecclesiastical court. A few of these ecclesiastical animal trials took place already in the thirteenth century, but they became increasingly frequent during the following 200 years. In 1338, a kind of beetle caused much devastation in the fields near Kaltern in the Tyrol. The beetles were tried, convicted, sentenced and solemnly cursed in the name of the Holy Trinity. It is recorded that, due to the sinful lives of the people in these parts, the beetles did not heed this anathema until several years had passed and the people had repented their wicked ways.

In 1479, another famous animal trial took place in the court of the Bishop of Lausanne. This time, the inger were on trial for damaging the young crops in the fields. The prosecutor brought forward some cunning arguments to denigrate the defendants. They had not been present on Noah's Ark, but had been hovering above it, defying the anathema of God; he also claimed that the inger were not animals, but imperfect, spontaneously generated creatures bred from putrefaction. The defendant of the inger was powerless to prevent that his clients were excommunicated by Monseigneur Benedict de Montferrand, Bishop of Lausanne, using a solemn malediction beginning with the words: 'Thou accursed, infernal foulness, thou inger, which shalt not even be mentioned among the animals...'.

The defence had as little success in a trial against the field voles that took place in the Tyrol in 1519, in which the rodents were sentenced to eternal banishment from the territory in question. The only leniency achieved by their council was that the expected mass migration of voles should be granted a safe-conduct from cats and dogs, and that, in the name of humanity, pregnant females and their young were to be given two more weeks to prepare their move.

During the heyday of ecclesiastical animal trials, it was commonly believed that Satan could inhabit the bodies of animals and control their actions. Already the Bible had provided a drastic example of this: the Gadarene swine, which were possessed by the devils that Christ had exorcised from an insane man, and threw themselves down a high precipice into a lake. From the protocols of the animal trials, it is sometimes apparent that the snails, rats or insects at the bar were considered as the Devil's disciples; the ceremonies used to expel them from a certain territory resembled the curses of exorcism of devils from a possessed human being.

The Weevils of St Julien

Perhaps the best known of all animal trials was held in 1587. In the famous wine district of St Julien, the young crops in the fields were ravaged by a species of greenish weevil, called *charançon* by the locals. On 13 April 1587, the insects were summoned before the tribunal of the Prince-Bishop of Mauricenne by the syndics and procurators of St Julien. An experienced lawyer, Antoine Filliol, was selected as their defence council, with a certain Pierre Rembaud as his assistant. The prosecuting council, M. Petremand Bertrand, pointed out that God had created the animals before man, and that their purpose in life was to serve the Lord of the Creation as loyal, uncomplaining minions. The animals that were wilfully disobeying God's directives, like these gluttonous, criminal weevils, deserved to be severely punished, whether they acted on their own accord or had been seduced by the Devil.

The barrister of the weevils denied that his clients had anything to do with the fiend below; instead, they had been sent by God as a scourge for the sinful inhabitants of St Julien. To punish these innocent messengers would bring down the wrath of the Almighty in earnest. Antoine Filliol then quoted the famous lines from Genesis that every thing that creepeth upon the earth was given the green herbs for meat. If the court denied the weevils the sustenance allotted to them by God, how were these poor insects expected to be fruitful and multiply? That these hapless insects happened to have been created before Man did not give this court any authority to sentence and excommunicate them without reasonable cause.

The prosecution side was seriously shaken by these clever arguments. The trial was adjourned several times, and it almost looked as if the weevils had gained the upper hand, but Petremand Bertrand and François Fay, the procurator and advocate of the plaintiffs, thought of a way out. On 29 June, the church bell was rung and all the inhabitants of St Julien were called to a public meeting. Facing the crowd of grumbling *vignerons*, Fay had to admit that the outcome of the trial was very uncertain indeed, and that the weevils had several arguments speaking in their favour. He recommended a compromise: if the court was to banish the weevils from the vineyards, a parcel of land on the village commonage had to be given to these insects, as their private reservation, where no human was to disturb them. After much discussion among the vine-growers, a territory called La Grande Feisse was selected as the future home of the weevils. It was inspected by the advocate and procurator, and declared to be fully adequate for them. The council then drew up a formal agreement of lease, allowing the insects sole right to all pasture within La Grande Feisse in perpetuity, but reserving for the villagers the rights to pass through this territory, to make use of its springs of water, and to work the mines of ochre and other mineral colours found there.

When the trial was resumed on 24 July, Petremand Bertrand called everyone's attention to this generous offer, as he called it, but Antoine Filliol cautiously requested everything in writing, and good time for deliberation, before he passed his judgement on this novel proposal. When the legal wrangling was restarted on 3 September, Filliol declared that his clients turned this rascally compromise down, with scorn, since the reservation allotted to them was far too small, and barren of vegetation. The weevils demanded a full pardon, with costs, and an ample fee for their own lawyer. Bertrand maintained that the insect reservation was amply provided with delicious plants and herbs; the disgruntled *vignerons* probably uttered the French equivalent of 'Hear! Hear!' as he pointed out that the wretched insects could hardly expect to be given an entire vineyard of their own, with a comfortable *château* to sleep in! To resolve this stalemate, the court president ordered a committee of impartial experts to inspect the intended insect reservation, and submit a written report about its suitability. The trial did not come to an end until 20 December 1587, and thus lasted more than eight months. The final outcome of this exciting courtroom drama is unknown, although the legal proceedings are still kept; the sentence could have been either way. It may be speculated that the weevils were not satisfied with the verdict, however, since the final page of the records has been destroyed by insects!

Murderous Sows

Throughout the middle ages, it was customary in most European towns that pigs were allowed to roam the streets at will. Hundreds of hungry, filthy, leprous-looking pigs were grubbing about in the sewers and heaps of offal; even the fashionable high streets smelt like a pigsty. It was of infrequent occurrence that any one actually fed these pigs; they were left to fend for themselves, fighting with the street mongrels for the possession of offal and filth from the gutters and refuse heaps. A desperate, starving sow with small piglets could not afford to be fastidious in her choice of victuals; every animal smaller than herself was in constant danger of being attacked. Playing little children were by no means safe from these ravenous swine, and the street-pigs not infrequently fell foul of the law.

There are records of more than forty pigs being prosecuted for attacking human beings, the earliest of them from the thirteenth century. In 1386, an infanticidal sow was tried and convicted in Falaise. Since it had bitten the child in the face and arms, the barbaric sentence was that it should be mangled and maimed in the head and forelegs, before being garrotted and hanged at the scaffold. This macabre ceremony was enacted before the Vicomte de Falaise and more than 500 pious Frenchmen, who had gathered to see the murderous sow pay for her evil deeds. The execution of the sow was depicted in a fresco in the Church of Holy Trinity in Falaise, made at the order of the Vicomte himself, who was probably proud of the part he had played in teaching the criminal elements of the porcine tribe a hard lesson. An engraving of this extraordinary scene, made when the fresco was still in existence, depicts the hangman and the torturer garrotting the wretched animal to death. The sow is wearing a waistcoat, breeches, and white gloves. The Vicomte, seated on his horse and wearing a plumed hat, is smugly looking on.

A particularly difficult animal trial took place in 1394, at Mortaign in France. A sow stood accused of blasphemy: during its desperate scavenging for food, it had roamed into a church and eaten a wafer left lying about on the altar. The priests debated whether this act had transubstantiated the sow's flesh into that of Christ: should it be slaughtered or revered, and should the wafer be honoured even inside the pig's stomach? Finally, they decided to execute the pig: there was general relief among the *curés* when no trace of the wafer was found within the swine's intestinal canal; in that case, they would have had to eat it, in order not to show the Saviour disrespect.

In 1403, another murderous sow was executed in Mantes. The civic archives still keep an elaborate bill for its upkeep in jail, the cost of cords to bind and hale it, and the hire of a carriage to take it to justice. A separate account was the salary due to the hangman or 'Master of High Works', as he was called; to be able to leave his task with unsullied hands, he was also provided with a pair of new white gloves. The records of the execution of another pig, hanged in Pont de Larche five years later, are even more elaborate. It is recorded that the cost of the pig's daily upkeep in jail was equal to that of a human prisoner. On another occasion, a pig that had killed and ate a small child was convicted not only for murder, but also for the sacrilegious crime of eating meat on a Friday. In 1572, an infanticidal pig was actually given a privilege not granted to human prisoners. From time immemorial, the prisoners to be executed at the order of the Lord Abbot of Moyen-Montier had to be naked when mounting the gibbet. The pig was to be led by a rope around its neck, and could thus not be considered as completely naked. After due consideration, the Lord Abbot allowed the rope, but it was emphasised that no precedent was to be created, and that no two-legged malefactor was to lay claim to clothing on his last journey.

If the owners of these murderous swine could at all be traced, they assumed no responsibility for the actions of their beasts. Occasionally, they were fined for having let dangerous animals run wild, but more commonly, they were paid compensation by the court, allowing them the sum their executed pig would have fetched if sold on the marketplace. In fifteenth-century Paris, a thoroughbred horse suddenly kicked out and killed a young man. The local court summoned the animal to appear, to be tried for murder, but the horse's owner, who was apparently quite fond of his charger, moved the horse to a stable outside the court's jurisdiction. For this offence, he was severely fined, and the money was used to fabricate the effigy of a horse, which was hung by its neck at the scaffold; the medieval prosecutors of animals certainly did nothing by halves!

Although the pigs were by far the most common animal to appear before the bar in secular courts, many other species occurred in the court-rooms: kicking horses and mules, goring bulls, snappish dogs and butting billy-goats. One or two rams and asses were also executed, as well as a cat that had badly scratched the face of a small child. The reader of Victor Hugo's famous *Nôtre-Dame de Paris* will recall that when the unfortunate Esmeralda is charged with murder, her trained goat Djali also faces trial, accused of witchcraft and sorcery. After the goat had demonstrated its ability to count by stamping its hoof, the judge and jury are convinced of its guilt, and it is sentenced to death along with its mistress. Esmeralda is saved by the agile Quasimodo, who swings down in a rope and snatches her from the scaffold. The death-defying hunchback has no opportunity to bring the goat along as well, but the learned animal has intelligence enough to escape on its own accord.

If the medieval animals usually fared badly when facing trial, the one brilliant exception is the faithful Dog of Montargis, appositely named Fidèle, who actually appeared in court as the plaintiff in a murder case, according to an old French legend. A certain Chevalier Macaire, an archer in the guards of King Charles V of France, was jealous of an old enemy, Aubry de Mondidier, who had risen highly in the King's favour. When Mondidier was travelling through the forest of Bondy, together with his dog, Macaire shot him dead from an ambush, and clandestinely buried the body. The faithful dog reached the Royal court, however, and led the soldiers and courtiers to Mondidier's grave. Every time Fidèle saw Chevalier Macaire, the dog growled, snapped and attempted to attack him. This was considered a highly suspicious circumstance; although Macaire vehemently denied having anything to do with the death of his colleague, many people accused him of the crime. The King decided that the dog was to be given the right of a plaintiff, and that God was to judge the case; that is, that the two were to fight to the death in an arena. The distribution of arms in this strange duel was distinctly unfair. Macaire was given a strong, wooden shield, with which to ward off the dog's attacks, and a long, heavy cudgel, with which to belabour it; the faithful dog was only given a huge barrel, in which it could take cover from the Chevalier's blows. Fidèle eschewed such defeatism, however; when unleashed, the dog went for Macaire's throat like a bullet. An old engraving of this judicial duel depicts the dog at a disadvantage: Chevalier Macaire keeps it at bay with the shield, and aims a heavy blow against its head with his cudgel, at the same time violently kicking the animal in an area distinctly 'below the belt'. A vast crowd of spectators, including many well-dressed gentlemen and elegantly gowned ladies, surround the arena to cheer the contestants on. It is recorded that the faithful dog finally gained the upper hand in this fight, and forced Macaire to cry out for mercy and admit his crime. The victorious Fidèle was honoured by the King, but Chevalier Macaire was executed and his body buried in unhallowed soil.

Dogs in Jail

Normally, the wretched animals that had killed or severely wounded a human being did not survive their brushes with the law. The most frequent methods of execution were hanging and beheading, but more imaginative manners of death, like drowning, burning at the stake, and burying alive, were occasionally used by brutal, sadistic individuals. In some rare instances, the accused sow, dog or bull actually managed to escape its trial alive and well. In 1379, in the French village Saint-Marcel-le-Jeussey, two herds of half-tamed, filthy pigs attacked the son of their swine-keeper and tore him to pieces. All the pigs were arrested and jailed. Although only the three large sows had actually been observed to bite the unfortunate boy, their piglets and the other swine in the herds had hastened to the scene of the murder, and, by their squealing and aggressive action, clearly demonstrated that they approved of this evil deed. They were regarded as accomplices, and held under penalty of death. While the pigs were awaiting trial, a clergyman, Father Humbert de Poutiers, wrote a petition to Duke Philip of Burgundy, demanding that the piglets and the other swine were to be spared. Although he could not deny that they had tried to attack the boy, he pleaded their youth and the fact that they were certain to have been badly brought up by their criminal mothers. The Duke lent a gracious ear to this petition, and the pigs were released, to the delight of Father Humbert, who was actually the owner of one of the herds; it is likely that this fact, rather than any humane feelings for the imprisoned pigs, had prompted his actions.

In 1712, a ceremonial procession in an Austrian garrison town was disturbed by the drummer's dog, which suddenly ran forth and bit one of the municipal councilmen in the leg. The drummer was sued for damages, but he denied being the owner of this snappish cur and delivered it into the hands of the court, to do what they pleased with. The dog's punishment was a year's imprisonment in the so-called *Narrenkötterlein*, a pillory or iron cage erected in the market-place. Drunkards, blasphemers and petty criminals were thrown into this cage for a few days, to be mocked and jeered by the populace. The dog was also accompanied by the village idiot, who was a permanent resident in this cage. An even stranger case comes from late seventeenth-century Russia. A child in a wealthy family had been butted down a flight of stairs by a billy-goat. The goat was sentenced to one year in a prison camp in Siberia; its legal owner had to pay the Crown one kopek a day for its upkeep there.

Some students of the history of animal trials have remarked that it was odd that animals, but not vegetables or dead objects, were put on trial, but the macabre truth is that dead objects have many times faced trial during the history of humankind. The old chronicler Pausanias tells that an enemy of the famous athlete Theagenes, who had once been mauled by him in a boxing match, decided to take out his revenge *post mortem*. Every year, on the day Theagenes had died, he travelled to the island of Thanos, where a statue of Theagenes had been erected, to flog the statue of his old enemy with a strong bull-whip. These outrages continued for several years, until the long-minded old Greek whipped the statue with such fury that it toppled over and crushed him to death. After the statue had been tried by the Thanos high court and found guilty of manslaughter, it was thrown into the sea from a ship. Some years later, Thanos was struck by a failure of the crops and a general famine. When the island council consulted the Delphic Oracle to determine the cause of these bad times, she advised them to recall all individuals who had been banished from the island, but still the famine continued. When the councilmen went back to the Oracle to complain, she replied that they had forgotten their great countryman Theagenes. The statue was pardoned, dragged out of the sea, and replaced on its pedestal; the famine ceased, miraculously, after this belated act of justice had been performed.

Pope Stephen VI, who had saved Rome from the locusts, became notorious for prosecuting the corpse of his predecessor. After the deceased Pope Formosus had been accused of having usurped his title, his corpse, which had been reposing in its sarcophagus for eight months, was hauled up from the tomb, dressed in ceremonial robes and placed in the papal chair of St Peter's Cathedral. As soon as Formosus had been found guilty, the corpse was pushed out of the chair, and three fingers from the right hand were cut off, before the corpse was dragged out from the Cathedral, feet first, to be thrown into the Tiber. Stephen VI did not get a long time to rejoice for having settled the account with his predecessor in such a definitive manner; within a couple of months, he was himself deposed, jailed and poisoned by powerful enemies. Whatever remained of poor Formosus was resurrected from the Tiber and reinstated into its proper resting-place.

When Prince Dimitri of Russia, a son of Tsar Ivan IV, had been murdered in 1591, the insurgents rang the great church bell in the town of Uglich to incite the populace against the authorities. When the rebellion had been quenched, the furious Tsar dealt summarily with the individuals accused of having started it; the church bell was also at the dock, charged with a serious political offence. It was exiled to Siberia, where it was hung in another church and performed its former office for many years. It was not until 1892 that it was pardoned and returned to its former home in Uglich.

In ancient China, it also sometimes occurred that corpses were facing trial for the crimes the individual had committed during life. As late as 1888, the corpse of a salt smuggler was brought before the municipal court of Shanghai; he was duly convicted, and the semi-putrid body was decapitated on the city scaffold. At about the same time, even more bizarre things were afoot in the city of Fouchow. A general belonging to one of China's most illustrious families had fallen in battle. His mourning relatives knew well that, just before he went off to war, he had spent a lengthy session consulting the wooden statues of his favourite gods in the city temple. After the general had failed to return alive, his relatives prosecuted the gods for having given him bad advice. The Viceroy's Court found them all guilty as charged, with no attenuating circumstances. All fifteen wooden deities were unceremoniously evicted from the temple, their heads chopped off, and the remains were thrown in a pond, amidst cheers and applause from the populace.

Excommunicated Sparrows and Law-Abiding Rats

Already in the Middle Ages, certain humane philosophers and theologians were objecting against the frequent animal trials in France and Switzerland. One of them was the French Judge Philippe de Beaumanoir, who considered the criminal prosecution of animals meaningless and barbaric. Since animals had no discrimination of good and evil, and no conception of what constitutes a crime and a penalty, the punishment of them is without purpose. He was supported by no less authority than Thomas Aquinas, who doubted, in his *Summa Theologiae*, that God would sanction the excommunication of animals. Not even he was able to convince his fellow clerics, however, and the ecclesiastical animal trials instead became increasingly frequent. The reasoning seems to have been that even if the criminal prosecution of animals before an ecclesiastical court was theologically doubtful, it would be a greater evil to allow the insects or rodents in question to ravage the fields unimpaired, thus causing the death of human beings from starvation.

As before, a considerable proportion of the animal trials took place in France and Switzerland, a few in Germany, Italy and the Netherlands, very few in the rest of the world. The annals of the Court of Stockholm provides evidence of a refreshingly down-to-earth attitude toward miscreant livestock. When a cow had gored out the eye of a child, the Judge made the solomonic decision that the child's mother was to be given the cow, as a fine to its careless owner. In Britain, a similar attitude seems to have prevailed, and very few instances of animal trials exist upon record. One of them, the execution of a Scottish dog in the seventeenth century, was one in a series of witch trials, and the dog was suspected to have been possessed by one of the witches.

After the Reformation, the old Catholic tradition of excommunicating animals was criticised by the strict Lutherans, who considered it to be superstitious nonsense to put field-mice and weevils on trial, and to curse them in the name of the Holy Trinity. There is at least one example, however, of a Protestant parson utilising these time-honoured methods to rid his church of undesirable animal pests. In 1559, the Saxon vicar Daniel Greysser put the sparrows that infested his church under the ban, on account of their ceaseless chattering, their unclean habit of depositing their droppings on the heads and frocks of the churchgoers underneath their perches, and their scandalous unchastity. Some disloyal parishioners reported on Parson Greysser for his unconventional methods of keeping down the sparrows, which was an apostasy, they claimed, into the old popish superstitions. Duke Augustus of Saxony, who personally judged this clerical feud, instead commended the ornithophobic Parson for his diligence. Daniel Greysser had not, like the Bishop of Trier several hundred years before, relied upon supernatural means to rid his church of these winged marauders. He had employed several hunters to decimate the sparrows with their bows and arrows, and had personally smeared the rafters of the church with a viscous glue that was strong enough to immobilise the wretched birds forever, as soon as they settled on these sticky perches.

Even among Catholic theologians, opinion about animal trials began to change in the early seventeenth century; many of them adhered to Thomas Aquinas's opinion that God was unlikely to sanction the expulsion from the Church of creatures belonging to the brute creation. Already in 1534, animal trials were prohibited in Portugal, and several French dioceses soon followed suit. In 1717, the Pope himself forbade the excommunication of animals, and very few ecclesiastical animal trials occurred after this year. An exception comes from Brazil, where the Franciscan friars in the cloister of St Anthony, in the province of Riedade no Maranhão had been greatly tormented by termites, which devoured their food and undermined their houses and furniture. In 1734, an application was made to the Bishop of these parts, who was apparently ignorant of the Papal bull issued seventeen years earlier, since he was able and willing to summon the termites before his ecclesiastical court to give an account of their conduct. Their defending council appears to have taken his bizarre task quite seriously, and he defended the insects with both pathos and eloquence. Not content with merely presenting the usual argument that the termites were God's creatures and thus entitled to reasonable sustenance, he praised the diligence and industry of his clients, claiming that the white ants were far more laudable in this respect than their opponents in the law-court, the Grey Friars. He also, quite reasonably, reminded the Court that termites had lived in Brazil long before these Monkish invaders had chosen to settle there. With such powerful arguments in favour of the termites, the monks stood no chance of winning their case. The trial ended in a compromise: the monks had to provide the termites with a reservation, where they could live in peace without interference from the Grey Friars. The Court solemnly ordered the termites to leave the monastery and to remain henceforth within their reservation. As the Judge read this proclamation, in front of the termite-hills, the Monkish chronicler reports that all the insects marched out, in strict columns, toward their new abode.

In the countries where ecclesiastical animal trials had played a prominent part, the people were naturally quite unwilling to forsake this time-honoured method of ridding their fields of gluttonous rodents and noxious insects. In Switzerland, the sceptre of St Magnus was considered to have remarkable vermifugal properties. Between 1685 and 1770, it was regularly carried in processions between various Swiss and German towns. In rural France, curses and processions were used to drive away rats and insects well into the nineteenth century. In difficult cases, the peasants still summoned the animals before the local magistrate. In 1826, a swarm of locusts were convicted of vandalism by the village court of Clermont-Ferrand. Strangely enough, these rural animal trials also occurred in protestant Denmark, which completely lacked a prior tradition of excommunication of animals. In 1711, the village of Als in Jutland was much tormented by a plague of rats, which ate the crops in the fields, and dug out the earth with their multiple holes. The village quack advised that the rats were to be put on trial, and the local council sentenced all 'rats, field-rats, water-rats and mice, none expected' to leave the village of Als within eight days. Although they were not observed to walk away in strict marching columns, like the law-abiding Brazilian termites were supposed to have done, the complacent Danish rats meekly obeyed this summons. After having been tormented by these ravenous rodents for three long years, the entire territory became free of rats. This success paved the way for further Danish trials against rats, held in Viborg in 1736, and in Lyø as late as 1805.

Thieving Dogs and Reactionary Parrots

In early seventeenth-century France, secular animal trials were still a reality: pigs, bulls and mules regularly appeared before the bar. In Jean Racine's comedy *Les Plaideurs*, a dog is on trial, accused of having stolen a capon. After the defending and prosecuting council have presented their verbose and eloquent arguments, the judge sentences the dog to lifetime hard labour on the galleys, presumably as a ship's dog. But the barrister brings in a litter of puppies, the 'children' of the accused, and sentimentally pleads with the judge not to make these tender, guiltless creatures into orphans. The judge, who is a father himself, is deeply touched by his arguments: the thieving dog is acquitted and reunited with its puppies. The joke about the dog on trial seems rather pointless today, but Racine and his intellectual contemporaries wanted to poke fun at the animal trials, which they thought a barbarous relic from the Middle Ages.

Toward the end of the seventeenth century, several other French lawyers and intellectuals objected to the animal trials, and the authorities had to relent: fewer and fewer animals faced trial. A contributing factor was that in most towns and cities, the fierce, scavenging street-pigs were kept at bay by the city magistrates in a much more efficient way. In some cities, like Naples and Grenoble, the city watchmen had the right to shoot them on sight.

In 1792, at the height of the Terror regime, an eccentric old invalid named Saint-Prix was arrested by the French police. He had been accused of having royalist sympathies by his neighbour, the revolutionary constable M. Jardy. Later the same evening, the latter individual wanted to search the house of Saint-Prix, under the pretence that he suspected that certain forbidden books and pamphlets were kept there. As he opened the door of one of the wardrobes, the prying constable received the shock of his life: a large mastiff, dressed in blue livery, leapt out and knocked him to the ground. After a furious fight, the mangled sans-culotte, whose trousers had been entirely torn off, was able to leap out through a window. M. Jardy ran to the city hall, in order to make a complaint against the dog. The mastiff was arrested by a troop of soldiers and jailed, accused of assault and contra-revolutionary activities. As Saint-Prix faced the revolutionary tribunal, one of the strongest points of evidence against him was that the dog's blue uniform had been made to resemble those of the Royal guards. The sentence was that both the dog and its master were to be guillotined; the order for this macabre execution carried the name of the notorious revolutionary magistrate Fouquier-Tinville, and was signed by his secretaries, Messieurs Lavillette and Chavet.

The same year, a parrot faced trial in Paris, also accused of counter-revolutionary activities. In a busy street, it had loudly called out, in front of a hostile crowd of sans-culottes, 'Vive le Roi, Vive nos prêtres! Vive les nobles!' The parrot and its owners, two noble ladies, were arrested and brought before the revolutionary tribunal. In the courtroom, the magistrates tried to persuade the bird to speak, but in spite of their dire threats, it merely whistled disdainfully. The owners of this tactless, indiscreet bird, Madame Louise de la Fiefville and Mademoiselle Françoise de Béthune, were probably most grateful that their parrot kept its beak shut for a change; they still had to face several difficult questions about who had taught it to repeat such treacherous utterances. They were threatened with the guillotine, but pardoned due to lack of evidence. The reactionary parrot was kept in custody, however, since it had been sentenced to political re-indoctrination in the hands of Citoyenne Le Bon, one of the vile *tricoteuses* who delighted to sit near the Paris scaffold and mock its hapless victims as they were led up to be guillotined. In her company, the parrot soon learnt to shout 'Vive la Nation', as well as a large repertoire of curses and bawdy songs, which is likely to have dismayed and shocked the two noble ladies when the bird was later returned into their care.

Murderous Pigs and Learned Philosophers

The criminal prosecution and capital punishment of animals is a dark chapter in the history of mankind. These macabre and sometimes well-nigh incredible trials have been almost completely forgotten: there is nothing written about them in the schoolbooks or in works on popular history. Most legal historians have considered them a puzzling but unfruitful sidetrack in the development of legal thought. In particular, they seem at a loss to explain why, at a time when most European philosophers considered animals as little more than automata, devoid of both sense and reason, these same animals were seemingly put on a level with human beings when facing justice.

The German legal historian Karl von Amira was the earliest scholar to publish a systematic study of animal trials. He pointed out the crucial difference between the complicated ecclesiastical animal trials, which went on for months, with much eloquent pleading from the defending and prosecuting council, and the summary punishment of murderous sows and bulls through the secular courts. It is true that these two types of trials were different in form and development, but conceptually they were quite similar. At some of the ecclesiastical animal trials, the priests had gathered some representatives of the prosecuted animals: a bowl of insects or a cage full of squeaking mice was put on the defendant's bench. After the animals had been convicted, these animals were ceremonially beaten to death, and it was lamented that their entire tribe had not appeared at the bar. These two types of animal trials also had a similar temporal and geographical distribution. Their centre was in France, from whence they spread to Switzerland, Italy, Germany and the Low Countries.

Some early students of the criminal prosecution of animals wanted to explain the old animal trials as the consequences of a primitive, superstitious popular culture; the execution of brute beasts was likened to a child breaking a flower-pot as a punishment for having tripped over it.

This explanation had justly been discredited by later historians. There were few instances of criminal prosecution of animals in the early middle ages, but in the fifteenth and sixteenth centuries, a time of both legal and cultural progress, the animal trials became increasingly frequent. Furthermore, the tribunals dealing with the erring beasts were hardly any primitive village assizes: dogs, pigs and mules were convicted by the *Parlement* of Paris, and in 1621, the Leipzig law faculty gave an opinion about the proper mode of execution of a cow. Similarly, the foremost ecclesiastical animal trials were led by senior clerics.

Another early hypothesis was that the prosecuted animals were anthropomorphised: that they were, in legal terms, treated as human beings. The arguments were that the methods of execution, the costs of the upkeep of the animals in jail, and the bills of the hangman did not differ much between animal and man; the rest of the reasoning does not fit the existing evidence. It is true that the infanticidal sow at Falaise had been dressed up in man's clothing before the execution, but it was unique in the annals of animal trials in being granted this dubious honour. Interestingly, the original description of the church painting made to commemorate the pig's execution mentions that not only had several hundred people gathered to witness its punishment, but *many herds of swine* had been driven together in the square before the scaffold. The Vicomte de Falaise probably wanted to demonstrate, in a didactic manner, what happened to murderers, whether they were two or four legged.

Yet another opinion was advocated by the eccentric American scholar Edward Payson Evans, who spent forty-four years of diligent labour in the Royal Library of Munich, where he studied animal trials and other arcane subjects. His magnum opus, *The Criminal Prosecution and Capital Punishment of Animals*, was published in 1906. Evans had started work on this book in the early 1880s, and published some abstracts from it as early as 1884; during the years, he had dug up many astonishing instances of animal trials from various French and German archives and periodicals. In his analysis of the reasons for animal trials, Evans pointed out the crucial role of the Catholic Church, and the widespread notion that animals could be possessed by demons. It was important for the Church to keep up the ecclesiastical animal trials: they united the parishioners and, if the excommunication of the animals was a success, inspired confidence in the omnipotence of the Church. The people were kept busy praying and walking round in processions in the fields. The clerics did not neglect this unsought-for opportunity to reclaim unpaid tithes, and to exhort promises of chastity and sobriety, and the banning of playing cards and gambling with dice. If the conjuration of the animals was a failure, the clergymen used to blame the sins of the people to avoid losing face.

In a lengthy study of animal trials, published in 1981, the American philosopher J.J. Finkelstein criticised Evans's book roundly, although he grudgingly had to admit that the vast majority of the raw material that his eccentric countryman had dug out of various dusty archives and forgotten periodicals was beyond reproach. Finkelstein proposed that the medieval interpretation of the passage in Exodus about the necessity of killing the ox that gores a man or woman to death, was the instrumental motive of the secular European animal trials. Such was the horror inspired by the animal killing a human being that the animal was considered unclean even after having been executed. The Bible not only prescribed the stoning of a goring ox – or, in medieval interpretation, the hanging of a pig that had killed a child – but also forbade the consumption of its meat. Finkelstein's theory is contradicted by some of the original evidence, however. Sometimes, the Dutch or French peasants wholly disregarded this old superstition, cut down the pig's body from the gallows and roasted the criminal whole. Another serious objection to Finkelstein's theory is that the ancient Greek and Roman legal systems had no tradition of excommunicating or punishing animals. The Romans viewed the animal as a senseless thing, which it was meaningless to punish. In cases of animals killing or injuring human beings, they advocated the principle of *noxae deditio*: the injured party was given the offending animal as damages. Finkelstein's theory cannot explain a series of animal trials, begun in the thirteenth century, and continued for more than 500 years, purely on the strength of this Biblical pretext.

According to the medieval, anthropocentric conception of the world, Man had been created as the image of God, and he was to rule the earth. This gave Man an extraordinary power over the animals, since his laws were not only valid for other human beings, but for all Creation. The animals had been created to provide the humans with labour, food and clothes; they were not expected to take any initiatives of their own; least of all, to injure any one. A bull goring its owner to death set aside God's ordinance just as a flock of locusts devouring the crops in the fields. Man was not allowed to abuse his immense power over nature, however, and every creature had to get a fair trial. Once, in 1576, when the hangman had summarily killed a pig at the gallows after it had bitten the ear off a child, the community viewed this as a disgrace, since the pig had been denied a fair trial.

In medieval society, rationality and fairness were very important. When a pig kills a small child or vermin destroy the crops in the fields, there was a sense of injustice and irrationality that society had to address. The comfort derived from the ritual magic of legal formalism, followed by a public execution, served to lull the sense of insecurity that was derived from poverty, epidemics, and social conflicts. Nor is it a coincidence that the heyday of the animal trials coincided with the establishment of Roman law and court procedure in late medieval Europe. The criminal prosecution of animals, which otherwise had no rational *raison d'être*, upheld the dogma of the Church's power over nature, and the illusion of a fair and just society.

Another argument to explain the remarkable longevity of the ecclesiastical animal trials is that they often seem to have achieved their purpose. In many instances, it is recorded that the animals that had been tried, sentenced and excommunicated gradually became fewer within a year or two. This is likely to have depended less on supernatural reasons than on the laws of population dynamics of insects or rodents. If the voles, for example, had been multiplying rapidly for two years, they were faced by an increased number of predators and a much harder competition for food; a cycle of abundance was followed by one of scarcity. The clerical exterminators of vermin thus had the odds set in their favour. Some of the more dramatic results of the excommunication of insects may also have been due to natural cases; for example, the mass death of flying insects might have been caused by a sudden frost.

The Legacy of the Animal Trials

In the late nineteenth century, the old ecclesiastical animal trials were gradually forgotten, although some French ethnologists have found traces of them in certain quaint rural ceremonies to 'conjure away' insects and vermin. The trials against individual animals have continued well into our own time. Although the murderous medieval pigs times no longer roam the streets, animals still regularly appear at the bar for having killed or seriously injured people. The last time a pig was put on trial was in Pleternica, Slavonia, in the year 1864. A sow that had torn both ears off a little girl was sentenced to death; the fine paid by the sow's owner was to be used as a dowry for the poor girl, so that the loss of her ears did not prevent her from getting married.

The vast majority of pigs, oxen and other traditional farm animals are today kept well apart from the human race, most of whom only make their acquaintance in the shape of tastefully packaged parcels of meat on the supermarket shelves. Since the goring bulls and murderous sows of old are today incarcerated before even having a chance of committing any crime, the dog has taken over the pig's role as man's worst enemy in the courtroom. In 1905, when a travelling salesman was attacked by robbers in Délémont, Switzerland, the two footpads had with them a large, fierce cur, which they set upon the wretched man. When the three criminals faced trial, the two men were sentenced to life in jail, whereas the dog, which had actually mangled the salesman to death, was executed.

The vast amounts of pet dogs kept, and the irresponsibility of some of their owners, has forced members of the canine tribe to appear in court at regular intervals. In most European countries, the owner of a dog is responsible for the beast's actions. If the dog bites people, it is muzzled and the owner fined; if the owner defies this decision, the dog is put down and the owner even more heavily fined. Jurisdiction in Africa and South America seems to leave much to the individual judges in cases of animals appearing before the bar. In 1974, a dog in Libya was tried and convicted of biting a human, and sentenced to a month in prison on bread and water. In 1991, an Argentine dog was sentenced to lifetime imprisonment for having killed a three-year-old child. Even more bizarre, a goat in Tanzania, which had grazed on a private lawn, was sentenced to four days in jail by an eccentric judge. Another criminal goat, which had stolen fruit from a street peddler, escaped with two days behind bars.

Some American states have prosecuted dangerous dogs well into the twentieth century. In 1926, a stray German Shepherd in Kentucky was charged with the attempted murder of a small child, sentenced to death and executed in the electric chair. In 1960, the five-year-old German Shepherd Duke was prosecuted for having attacked several citizens of New Canaan, Connecticut. For well-nigh a year, Duke had amused himself by chasing cyclists and biting them in the legs and buttocks. Duke's owner, a wealthy lady, employed a clever lawyer to defend her doggy. This gentleman seems to have been as smooth an operator as Barthélemy Chassenée in Autun 450 years earlier. Duke was not allowed to appear in court; instead, film slides of him as a cute little puppy were shown to the jurors, and Duke's mistress told sentimental tales about her doggy's great devotion to her. To the chagrin of the dog-bitten citizens of New Canaan, Duke's life was spared, although he was sentenced to be imprisoned at a dog's kennel. But the lawyer appealed even this relatively mild sentence, since he was able to demonstrate an affidavit from the animal psychologist Dr John Behan, the Principal of the West Redding Canine College, who had treated Duke for several weeks. Dr Behan certified that Duke had learnt to handle his aggressions, and that his personality and temperament had improved greatly during his stay at the canine academy. Judge John T. Dwyer then decided that Duke was to be released into the custody of his original owner.

Equally ludicrous is the tale of Taro, New Jersey's Death Row Dog. On Christmas Day 1990, this 110-pound Akita became Bergen County's prisoner no. 914095 after biting his owner's niece on the lip. The niece's family wanted Taro dead, but dog owner Mr Lonnie Lehrer was equally determined to free his dog. Trial followed trial, and appeal was followed by appeal; soon, the legal costs had risen to $100,000. By early 1993, things were looking bleak for Taro. The police and prosecutors debated whether he should be executed by a lethal injection, or face the electric chair. But the newspaper and TV publicity did the trick. Although Taro was far from an attractive dog, more than a thousand Americans offered to adopt him. Mr Lehrer turned them all down, even a millionaire who offered him $250,000 to buy the dog, and the service of a high-powered legal team to carry on the fight. The Death Row Dog was also becoming an embarrassment for the Governor of New Jersey, who had to admit that public money was not particularly well spent on keeping a large dog in prison for almost three years. In February 1994, a compromise was finally reached. Taro was adopted by anonymous new owners in Winchester County, who would assume full financial responsibility for the dog's future actions. Although Taro is reported to have wagged his tail merrily when walking out of jail, the prison warden was not pleased to see this vicious canine set at liberty, comparing the dog to John Dillinger. To pacify the niece's family, Taro was forever banned from entering New Jersey soil. The *New York Times* announced this verdict under the memorable headline 'Taro leaves Death Row, Jail, and New Jersey soil, for Good'.

8

The Riddle *OF THE* BASILISK

> Like as the Basiliske, of Serpents seede,
> From powerful eyes close venim doth convay
> Into the lookers hart, and killeth far away.
>
> Edmund Spenser, *The Faerie Queene*.

If any present-day scientist would aspire to write a review of the state-of-the-art knowledge in every branch of natural science – medicine, zoology, botany, geology and ethnography, among others – he would have been called a fool or an incurable enthusiast. Due to the extreme sub-specialisation of modern science, and the immense progress in molecular biology and experimental medicine, even a dedicated team of researchers, with a limitless supply of empty CD-ROMs to cram full of information, would have failed in the attempt. Science Citation Index, the major bibliographical update of each year's progress in medicine, technology and the natural sciences, is today presented online rather than in book form, due to the torrent of novel information flowing through the ever-growing number of scholarly journals.

It is a matter of debate who was the last person who managed to keep abreast of the advances in all branches of natural science. Many of the old cosmographers, like Ulysses Aldrovandi, Sebastian Münster and Athanasius Kircher, were men of immense learning, and their works were far-reaching and extensive, although much relying on earlier authorities.

Already the earliest modern biologists – Carl Linnaeus, John Hunter, Albrecht von Haller, George Louis de Buffon and Johann Blumenbach – did not write with such a large scope in mind.

It can be determined with some certainty, however, who was the first to produce such a monumental work. The Roman savant Gaius Plinius Secundus enjoyed a varied career, in turns being employed as an officer, a lawyer, and a district governor. He was also, throughout his life, a copious writer of history and biography. When attempting another project, an encyclopaedia of the whole of nature, he proudly announced that this design was a novel one: no Greek or Roman writer had previously produced a work of these extensive contents. In the thirty-seven books of his *Natural History*, Pliny collected the obtainable information from the existing works on all aspects of biology, medicine, geography and ethnology. A life of diligent study prepared him for this magnum opus. Pliny used to spend all day in his study, reading and taking notes; he slept as shortly as possible, and when he ate, bathed or travelled in a sedan chair, his secretary always read aloud.

Like many noble and erudite Romans, Pliny was also a man of action: he spent considerable time as an officer in the Roman cavalry, and later commanded the Roman fleet in the Mediterranean. At the eruption of Mount Vesuvius, in AD 79, Pliny led the mission to evacuate the inhabitants of Herculaneum by sea, with considerable success. But when Pliny himself went ashore, climbing a mountain to study the eruption of the volcano at close range, he was suffocated to death by the sulphurous fumes – a martyr to science if there ever was one. Much relying on earlier works, and abounding with imaginative stories and unsubstantiated theories, Pliny's *Natural History* is today an easy target for pedantic scholars. It should be kept in mind, however, that it was the first work of its kind, incorporating the information in many earlier books on natural history, more than 460 of which are mentioned in the text. The majority of these earlier works are now lost due to the ravages of time, whereas Pliny's *Natural History* is likely to live on forever.

In the eighth book of the *Natural History*, Pliny describes the strange beast called Catoplebas, a kind of largish gnu living in Ethiopia. Its head was so heavy that it constantly faced the ground; this was fortunate, since all living creatures that met its gaze expired instantaneously. Pliny then pointed out a fact well known to many of his readers, namely that the basilisk serpent had the same power. This venomous serpent was a native of northern Africa. It was not more than twelve inches long and was adorned with a bright white marking on the head, like a diadem. The basilisk does not grovel in the dust like other serpents, Pliny wrote, but advances lofty and upright. Its sibilant hiss puts all other snakes to flight, and it kills the desert bushes and shrubs by its mere presence. Such poison and evil is contained within this loathsome beast that it scorches the grass and bursts the rocks asunder. Its Greek name was Basiliscus, a diminutive form of *basileus*, meaning 'little king'; its Roman name, Regulus, was derived in the same fashion. The basilisk was considered the king of serpents (or reptiles) in the same fashion as the lion was the king of four-footed beasts.

The Basilisk in Antiquity

In the classical literature, Pliny's account of this snake-like, lethal basilisk was repeated by several other writers. In his *Theriaca*, Nicander described it with great eloquence. The warning hiss of the basilisk induced all other serpents and vermin to leave the offal they were consuming and to seek protection in their dens, leaving the basilisk to its hideous repast. When sated, the basilisk gave another sibilant hiss, but the other reptiles did not dare to eat the food that had been touched by their venomous king. In Heliodorus' famous novel *Aethiopica*, the reality of such phenomena as love at first sight and the evil eye is argued from the indisputable fact that the basilisk 'by its mere breath and glance will shrivel and cripple whatever comes its way'. In Lucan's *Pharsalia*, the habits of the basilisk are further described:

> Sibilaque effundens cunctasque tenentia pestes,
> Ante venena nocens, latè sibi submovet omne
> Vulgus, et in vacua regnat Basiliscus arena;

This can be translated by:

> The hissing of the basilisk all serpents terrify:
> knowing of its venom, away from it they fly;
> No living thing comes near it: like a hidden hand,
> the loathsome beast will rule the desert sand.

The basilisk contained such poison that it could kill both men and beasts merely by looking at them. If a valiant Moorish hunter, armed with a lance and seated on his swift Arab horse, was bold enough to attack the monster, he did not have long to triumph after having speared it, according to Lucan:

Quid prodest miseri, Basiliscus cuspide, mauri,
Transactus? Velox currit per tela venenum,
Invaditque manum;

This can be translated by:

What boots it, wretched Moor, that thou hast slain
the basilisk, transfix'd him on the sandy plain?
Up through the spear the subtle venom flies,
The hand absorbs it, and the victor dies.

The only way for the Moor to save his life was to cut off his hand before the basilisk's venom spread to the remainder of his body.

A safer and, according to Pliny, more effective way of basilisk hunting, was to put a weasel down the creature's lair, the location of which was apparent from the blackened, withered surroundings. The weasel and the basilisk had a natural antipathy for each other, and, by means of eating rue, the weasel could make itself impregnable to the poison of its formidable opponent. The basilisk was promptly 'ferreted out' of its lair and took to flight like a weakling, but the weasel mercilessly pursued and killed it. Aelian does not agree with Pliny that the frail weasel has the power to conquer the basilisk, instead suggesting that the crowing of a cock would keep the monster at a safe distance; travellers to Africa sometimes brought roosters with them as protection against the desert basilisks. Another old legend claimed that the lion was also frightened by the cock's crowing, but the African travellers who trusted the frail and timorous birds to protect them against a pack of hungry lions were unlikely to return to tell others about their mistake.

According to the *Codex Alexandrinus*, Alexander the Great once encountered a basilisk while on his way to India with the Macedonian army. By means of a clever ruse of war, he personally put this loathsome creature out of action. Alexander and his men were travelling through a mountain pass when suddenly the soldiers fell to the ground stone dead, one after the other, without being hit by enemy projectiles. When Alexander and his scouts climbed a rock to survey the surrounding area, they saw a foul basilisk standing outside its den, killing the Macedonian soldiers with its lethal stare. The situation was a precarious one, but Alexander had not studied the legend of Perseus and Medea without learning useful stratagems for use against such monsters. He ordered a large shield to be polished until bright as a mirror. Armed with this shield, he ran forth toward the basilisk's den, into which the loathsome beast had taken protection from the barrage of stones thrown by the soldiers. When the basilisk emerged from its lurking-hole, the first thing it saw was its own reflection; the foul beast received such a shock that it expired there and then.

The Basilisk of the Bestiaries

In early medieval time, Europe lost contact with Africa, and the snake-like basilisk living in the Cyrenaican desert joined the ranks of other mythical monsters of old. The highly limited zoological knowledge of these dark ages was summarised in the bestiaries, descriptive and illustrated works on the traits of various animals, often in the form of moralising fables. In these works, the taxonomy of the larger reptiles was simple and straightforward: the dragon had wings and four legs, the basilisk wings and two legs, and the snake entirely lacked extremities. The basilisk was further differed from the two-legged wyvern by this creature having the head of a serpent instead of that of a cock, and the feet of an eagle. The basilisk's supernatural gifts are further expounded upon in the bestiaries: the trees wither and their fruits rot when the loathsome beast passes them by, and every living thing dies in agony when struck by its death-darting glance. When the basilisk looked upwards, the birds fell from the skies, like ripe plums, into the gaping mouth of the loathsome beast.

Although Pliny and Aelian had described the basilisk as a smallish snake, the early bestiary writers disagreed. They advocated a novel theory of the generation of basilisks, which made the birth of this creature as anomalous as its habits of life. This theory was first mentioned in the twelfth-century bestiary of Alexander of Neckham, and is the subject of a lengthy discourse in the bestiary of Pierre de Beauvais. An aged cock, which had lost its virility, would sometimes lay a small, abnormal egg. If this egg is laid in a dunghill and hatched by a toad, a monstrous creature, with the upper body of a rooster, bat-like wings, and the tail of a snake, will come forth. Once hatched, the young basilisk creeps down a cellar or a deep well, to wait for some unsuspecting man or beast to be overcome by its noxious vapours. These medieval writers emphasised that the basilisks occurred not only in the African desert, but also in the heart of Europe: they were prevalent in Italy and France, and in the German forests. African travellers were still advised, however, to dress in leather outfits which protected them against the basilisk's venom, and to bring weasels and cocks with them, to set upon the loathsome beasts.

This medieval, cock-like version of the basilisk was also known as a cockatrice, a word originating as a misinterpretation of 'cocodrillos' (crocodile); it was first used at the end of the fourteenth century as a translation of the Latin 'basiliscus'. The basilisk had also become firmly established as a religious symbol, signifying the devil. Some theologians, among them the learned Eusebius, even speculated that the basilisk was the reptile that had tempted Eve, 'as he is most venomous, and king, as it were, of the serpents'. Other theologians objected that no human being could ever be tempted into accepting anything from such a deformed, pestiferous creature. The Holy Scripture has several references to cockatrices. In Isaiah (xi, 8), it is said that 'the weaned child shall put its hand in the cockatrice's den', while Jeremiah solemnly declares that 'I will send serpents, cockatrices, among you, which will not be charmed; and they shall bite you'. Many philologists are of the opinion, however, that the cockatrice of the Bible is a mistranslation of a Hebrew word signifying a particularly poisonous breed of snake. The basilisk is frequently found in medieval ecclesiastical art. In north European church frescos, a popular motif is a woman in Hell suckling two basilisks, as a punishment for adultery; these gruesome images were intended to remind the parishioners of the importance of a moral and decorous life. The basilisk is not uncommonly encountered among various grotesque church decorations, in France and Italy as well as in northern Europe. Carpaccio's painting of St Tryphonius subduing the Basilisk does not portray a real basilisk, however: the creature has four legs, a lion's body and the head of a mule. Either Carpaccio's knowledge in basilisk lore was highly defective, or the creature in the painting was merely meant to be some kind of grotesque monster; it is another possibility that the name of the painting was added at some later date. A remarkable early representation of the basilisk in church art is present on a granite portal tympanum from the old church of Källs Nöbbelöv in southern Sweden, made by the master sculptor Tove in 1180. It portrays a typical medieval basilisk, with a cock's head, wings, and the winding tail of a snake, being subdued by St Michael, who thrusts his spear into its gaping beak.

Basilisk Powder

Not the least curious part of medieval basilisk lore was the trade in basilisk powder. This substance, which was made from ground basilisk carcasses, had several uses. Firstly, it was widely used in alchemy. 'Spanish gold' could be made by treating copper with a mixture of human blood, vinegar and basilisk powder. In the confused and fantastic imagery of English alchemy, the term 'basilisk' was not infrequently used, signifying either plain evil or, through the basilisk's strange upright posture and power over life and death, eternal fame and immortality. In George Ripley's fifteenth-century *Compound of Alchymie*, a magical 'Oyle' is

> ...made by Crafte a Stone Celestyall
> Of Nature so fyrye that we yt call
> Our Baselysk, otherwyse our Cokatryce,
> Our great Elixir most of pryce.
>
> Which as the syght of a Basylysk hys object
> Kylyth, so sleuth it crude Mercury,
> When thereon itt ys project,
> In twynke of an Eye most sodenly.

Basilisk powder had several other uses. The salesmen advocated its use to exterminate vermin of all kinds, and to keep the house clean. They pointed out that the corpse of a basilisk, hung up in the Temple of Apollo, had kept this temple free from spiders and vermin in all times. If a house was rubbed with a pinch of basilisk powder, all swallows, spiders and serpents were driven away. Basilisk powder was also used in medicine, as an antidote for poisons, and in art: a dash of basilisk powder produced a bright red paint much favoured by artists. The Spanish

Moors were Europe's major dealers in this bizarre substance, supplying it to alchemists, artists and medical men. There was much speculation how the powder was produced. According to a thirteenth-century German manuscript, the clever Moors fabricated it in underground basilisk farms. Old cocks were kept in an underground stone cavern, and induced to lay eggs by being particularly well fed. The eggs were hatched by toads and put in large copper vessels, wherein the basilisks developed. The vessels containing these loathsome beasts were then roasted on a big fire for several days, and the remains of the basilisks inside was ground to ashes. To obtain the most precious kind of basilisk powder, one third of dried and mortared blood of a red-haired man was added.

The Basilisks of Rome, Basle And Vienna

In the early fifteenth century, under the pontificate of Leo IV, a basilisk was found under the arch near the Temple of Lucia in Rome. Its noxious vapours afflicted the Romans with a terrible plague, but the holy Pope slew the loathsome beast with his prayers. At about the same period of time, according to the chronicles of Laevinus Lemnius, two old cocks were discovered at Zierichzee in Zeeland, each sitting on an egg. A large mob assembled, fearing that the basilisks would be hatched, and later lay waste the entire province. The cocks were beaten away from their eggs with sticks, and the pious Dutchmen later solemnly strangled these abnormal birds, in the presence of several clerics, and smashed the basilisk eggs.

In 1474, another old cock was discovered laying an egg in Basle. This provoked another outburst of basilisk hysteria: the bird was captured, jailed, and tried for this outrage against nature. In a lengthy speech, the prosecutor pointed out that the criminal rooster had threatened the whole town by endeavouring to hatch forth a loathsome basilisk. Even if a basilisk was not seen to appear, an egg of this kind, laid by a cock, was invaluable as an ingredient in various magical concoctions used to conjure up evil spirits; the laying of such an egg thus assisted the powers of evil. The cock's barrister had a difficult case to argue, since the rooster had popular opinion against it to a marked degree; its every crowing was interpreted as the confession of novel vices. He stated that the bird admitted the act of laying the egg, but that it was an unpremeditated and involuntary action of its body; thus, the rooster had violated no law. The clever prosecutor secured a conviction in this courtroom drama by invoking the case of the Gadarene swine: animals could be entered into by a devil and should then be destroyed. The judge solemnly convicted the rooster to be burned alive at the mountain of Kohlenberg, a place of execution reserved for particularly hardened criminals and blasphemers. A mob consisting of several thousand people had gathered to see the cock and the basilisk egg being burned at the stake. The executioner was requested to cut the bird's abdomen open before the fire was lit; he did so, and it was apparent that it had three more eggs, in different states of development, within its oviduct. The people gave a great cry when aware of this miracle: the pyre was lit, and when, early the following morning, the cocks of Basle greeted the sun with their crowing, only a heap of ashes remained of their abnormal, egg-laying comrade.

In the year 1202, strange things were afoot in Vienna: people fainted or were seized with violent epileptic fits while passing an old well near the town centre. Men of observation concluded that a basilisk must be hidden in the well, poisoning it, and the air surrounding, with its pestiferous breath. After a long and dangerous hunt inside the dark well, the intrepid basilisk hunters were able to extract the loathsome beast from its lair; fortunately, it was already dead, and could no longer harm them. A statue in sandstone, depicting this zoological marvel, was erected near the well, and could be admired there for many years. At Halle, in Saxony, another ancient monument, erected to commemorate the fact that a basilisk had been seen there, was standing as late as the 1690s. In 1556, a party of workmen, who had been clearing an old well in the town of Meyland, fell dead from their ladder, one by one. It was suspected that a basilisk was responsible, but no specimen of the loathsome beast was found, although people were looking for it for several weeks. In a French town, exactly the same thing happened a few decades later, but the basilisk hunt was again unsuccessful.

The Basilisk of Warsaw

The critically minded reader might rightly object that all these observations of basilisks are of a particularly diffuse character: often, no one actually saw the loathsome beast that was supposed to be lurking down in the well or vault. But there is one detailed and apparently convincing sighting of a basilisk, the hideous beast observed in Warsaw, in the year 1587. The five-year-old daughter of a knifesmith named Machaeropaeus had disappeared in a mysterious way, together with another little girl. The wife of Machaeropaeus went looking for them, along with the nursemaid. When the nursemaid looked down into the underground cellar of a house which had fallen into ruins thirty years earlier, she observed the children lying motionless down there, without responding to the shouting of the two women. When the maid was too hoarse to shout any more, she courageously went down the stairs to find out what had happened to the children. Before the eyes of her mistress, she sank to the floor beside them, and did not move. The wife of Machaeropaeus wisely did not follow her into the cellar, but ran back to spread the word about this strange and mysterious business; the rumour spread like wildfire throughout Warsaw. Many people thought the air felt unusually thick to breathe, and suspected that a basilisk was hiding in the cellar. Confronted with this deadly threat to the city of Warsaw, the senate was called into an emergency meeting. An old man named Benedictus, a former chief physician to the King, was consulted, since he was known to possess much knowledge about various arcane subjects. The bodies of the children and the maid had been pulled out of the cellar with long hooked poles. When Benedictus examined them, they presented a horrid appearance, being swollen like drums, and with the skin much discoloured. Benedictus, who had seen many things during his fifty years of medical experience, at once pronounced the state of the corpses an infallible sign that they had been poisoned by a basilisk. When asked, by the desperate senators, how such a formidable beast could be destroyed, the knowledgeable old physician recommended that a man should descend into the cellar, to seize the basilisk with a rake and bring it out into the light. To protect his own life, this man had to wear a dress of leather, furnished with a covering of mirrors.

Benedictus did not feel quite prepared to try out this plan in person, he said, due to age and infirmity. The senate called upon the burghers and military, but found no man of sufficient courage to seek out and destroy the basilisk. A Silesian convict named Johann Faurer, who had been sentenced to death for robbery, was at length persuaded to make the attempt, on grounds that he was given a complete pardon if he survived his encounter with the loathsome beast. Faurer was dressed in creaking black leather covered with tinkling mirrors, and his eyes were protected with large eye-glasses. Armed with a sturdy rake in his right hand and a blazing torch in his left, he must have presented a singular aspect when venturing forth into the cellar. He was cheered on by at least two thousand people, who had gathered to see the basilisk being beaten to death. After searching the cellar for more than an hour, Faurer finally saw the basilisk, lurking in a niche of the wall. Old Benedictus shouted instructions to him: he was to seize it with the rake and carry it out into the broad daylight. The brave Johann Faurer accomplished this task, and the populace ran away like rabbits when he re-appeared in his strange outfit, gripping the neck of the writhing basilisk with the rake. Benedictus was the only one who dared to examine the strange animal further, since he believed that the sun's rays rendered its poison less effective. He declared that it really was a basilisk: it had the head of a cock, the eyes of a toad, a crest like a crown, a warty and scaly skin 'covered all over with the hue of venomous animals', and a curved tail, bent over behind its body. The strange and inexplicable tale of the basilisk of Warsaw ends here: none of the writers chronicling this strange occurrence detailed the ultimate fate of the deformed animal caught in the cellar. It would seem unlikely, however, that it was invited to the city hall for a meal of cakes and ale; the versatile Benedictus probably knew some infallible way of disposing of these monsters.

The Basilisk of Copenhagen

On Easter Sunday 1649, the German doctor Ludwig Kepler was enjoying his breakfast, together with his family. He was a son of the famous astronomer Johannes Kepler, and a practitioner of repute. When he thrust his spoon into a boiled Easter egg, he was aghast to find a small snake-like creature inside it! Ludwig Kepler's account of this strange happening neglects to mention if the basilisk had become hard boiled or soft boiled. He does point out, however, that this unexpected encounter with the King of Serpents at his own breakfast table did not diminish his appetite for eggs; indeed, he had eggs served at regular intervals, to be examined for the presence of young basilisks within. After eight years of futile study, Ludwig Kepler consulted the Danish anatomist Thomas Bartholin, a well-known authority on basilisks. In April 1651,

Bartholin's knowledge of basilisk physiology had been put to practical use in a crisis affecting the fate of the Danish monarchy. When one of the royal cupbearers was collecting eggs from the hen houses situated within the castle of Copenhagen, he was greatly frightened to see, right before his eyes, an old cock laying an egg! The startled ganymede ran back to the royal kitchen, where his fantastic tale soon spread like wildfire among cooks, servants and courtiers. King Frederick III of Denmark ordered that the basilisk egg should be closely watched for several days. It was smaller than an ordinary hen egg but larger than a pigeon egg. No basilisk appeared, however, and the egg was later put in the royal cabinet of curiosities, where it was to reside for many years. The royal chefs were frightened that the cock had laid more eggs than one. When cooking, they broke each egg with great caution; none of them had a good recipe for a basilisk omelette, and they feared that the King of Denmark would not appreciate being served the King of Reptiles on his breakfast tray.

The egg-laying cock had also been captured by the Danish courtiers. King Frederick ordered that it should be dissected by Thomas Bartholin in his own presence; to their surprise, they found that the cock had normal male genitals. Thomas Bartholin doubted that it could really have laid an egg by the natural route, but the kitchen servant stubbornly maintained that this cock, and no other bird, had laid the egg in question. While discussing the case in a scholarly treatise, Bartholin mentioned the possibilities that the abnormal egg either might have been developed from the old cock's rotting semen, or that it had been formed in the intestines. Ludwig Kepler suspected, however, that Thomas Bartholin was doubting the veracity of the individuals involved in the scandal, but that he did not want to disappoint his Royal master, whose museum had been graced with the presence of the King of Serpents, albeit in an undeveloped state. Frederick III also had the skeleton of the old cock prepared and mounted in his museum, where it was to reside for almost 200 years.

For many years, Thomas Bartholin pondered the riddle of the basilisk. In 1673, he encountered some other alleged cock's eggs. He was, by this time, quite unconvinced of the existence of basilisks, and determined to incubate both normal hen's eggs and an alleged cock's egg, by placing them in an alembic of heated sand. This experiment, which some of his contemporaries must have considered very hazardous indeed, did not have a fatal outcome; no basilisk leapt out of the alembic to poison the courageous Danish anatomist, but the cock's egg proved to be sterile, and filled only with a whitish, gelatinous jelly. Thomas Bartholin declared that these alleged cock's eggs had, in all probability, been laid by elderly hens, which were constitutionally unable to produce normal eggs. He had himself observed the laying of these small, sterile eggs from elderly birds of that kind.

What still puzzled Thomas Bartholin was the manifold sightings of young basilisks inside eggs. He had himself seen one in Denmark. His friend, the famous anatomist Nicolaus Steno, told him that he had recently witnessed a remarkable scandal during a stay in Florence. An egg broken to be cooked for the Grand Duchess of Tuscany was found to contain a living 'small serpent', which darted out with great alacrity as soon it was freed from its confinement. The cook succumbed to a nervous attack, as did the kitchen maids, and the court was buzzing with rumours. The Grand Duchess ordered that a body of anatomists and zoologists were to scrutinise the young basilisk, to determine how it had been engendered. The Danish visitor, who already held an acclaimed position in anatomical circles, was also consulted. The board of experts pronounced it likely that the basilisk had, indeed, been produced from the egg of a cock, hatched by a toad, but Thomas Bartholin doubted this explanation. Himself, he rather suspected that the root of the matter was that an amorous Italian serpent had coupled with a hen, and that the little snake within the egg was the result of this outrage against nature.

A couple of years after the basilisk of Copenhagen had joined the royal museum, Frederick III again consulted Thomas Bartholin. The King had purchased a dried basilisk from a dealer in natural curiosities, planning to exhibit it together with the cock and the egg, and thereby demonstrating all stages in the development of the loathsome beast. After closely examining this strange exhibit, Bartholin had to disappoint the proud royal collector: the 'basilisk' was a fake, constructed from the body of a ray. Nevertheless, this counterfeit basilisk was exhibited in the royal museum for many years, but in the catalogue, Bartholin's brother-in-law Holger Jacobsen confessed that it was a manufactured specimen.

Cock's Eggs and Faked Basilisks

The Italian Count Ulysses Aldrovandi was one of the foremost polymaths of the Renaissance: he was called the Pliny of his time, and planned a huge series of folio volumes to illustrate his immense collections from the animal, vegetable and mineral kingdoms. At the time of Count Aldrovandi's death in 1605, only four volumes, dealing with the birds and insects, had been published. His students worked for decades to compile eight more volumes from his immense collection of manuscripts. Like many of his contemporaries, Ulysses Aldrovandi was fascinated by the riddle of the basilisk. He described all aspects of this loathsome beast in a long manuscript, which his posthumous editors incorporated into his *Historiae Serpentum et Draconum libri duo*. A man of immense learning, Aldrovandi had compiled the opinions of many obscure Latin authorities: natural historians, poets, and writers of anecdotes. He also presented his own views on the riddle of the generation of this loathsome beast. Aldrovandi was himself the owner of a dried 'basilisk' that had once belonged to the private museum of the Emperor Maximilian of Austria. The learned Mercuralis had accepted it as a true basilisk, but Aldrovandi saw that it had been manufactured from a dried ray.

Ulysses Aldrovandi had spent much time observing the development of the egg and chicken; to this day, he remains one of the pioneers of embryology. Although he knew that birds resembling cocks could, on rare occasions, lay eggs, he believed these eggs to be small and sterile, without a yolk; they were reminiscent of the eggs laid by old, decrepit hens. This made him doubt that the basilisk was engendered from a cock's egg. Aldrovandi had never seen a basilisk, living or dead, nor had any of the hundreds of scholars within his acquaintance. After this piece of deductive reasoning, rare enough in early seventeenth-century basilisk studies, one would have expected Aldrovandi to have wholly denied the existence of this loathsome beast, but he was imaginative by nature, and reverent toward the many earlier writers who had described the basilisk in detail. Furthermore, his friend Fabricius ab Aquapendente had once given him a 'young basilisk', which this learned anatomist had found in an egg which he was eating. Another, even stranger egg in Aldrovandi's collection had the imprint of a small, winding snake on its shell! Aldrovandi was not sure that it had 'the mark of the basilisk', however. He also considered the possibility that the hen had been frightened by a snake, and that this experience had, by the strange workings of the maternal imagination, been imprinted on the shell of the egg.

Throughout the seventeenth century, eggs containing snake-like 'young basilisks' turned up at regular intervals; these macabre findings were discussed in the leading scholarly journals of the time, and did much to keep the basilisk lore alive. In 1673, a live 'little snake' was discovered in an egg broken by one of the ladies in waiting to the Duchess Dowager of Parma; once again, the King of Serpents was haunting royalty! The loathsome beast was described by Dr Jerome Santasofia, Professor at the Parma medical school, and Dr Jacques Grandi, anatomist of Venice: it was as long as a forefinger, with a flattened head, and as thick as a cherry-stalk. Six years later, Dr André Cleyerus described another egg with 'the mark of the basilisk': the relief of a winding little snake was encrusted into the shell.

In early March 1672, the Jew Isaac Lefkowitz, living in Thurn, Poland, was cooking a meal of egg soup for his large family. When broken, one of the eggs turned out to have a black, wriggling, snake-like creature inside it! Isaac Lefkowitz cried out in terror and threw the egg away from him. The odour from the egg was overwhelming, and his wife and small children fainted when struck by these noxious vapours. His eldest son managed, with his last remaining strength, to kick this stink-bomb of an egg out through the door. Out on the street, it was trodden underfoot by the playing little children, who did not have enough sense to fear the basilisk. The distraught Lefkowitz called the anatomist Dr Simon Schultz, who examined the flattened remains of the Polish basilisk. In his case report, Dr Schultz cautiously discussed the possible explanations of this *lusus naturae*. Either it had been a cock's egg, and thus a genuine basilisk, or else, the hen laying the egg must have eaten a snake's egg, whose molecules had, in some strange and disastrous manner, mixed with those of her own chicken.

In 1671, the Jena physician Friedrich Madewisius published his doctoral thesis on the basilisk. In the manner of the time, he quoted the opinions of a multitude of earlier writers on this subject. The conclusion is that, although no one had ever seen a basilisk and lived to describe it, it could not be doubted that this monstrous creature really existed. The question of its generation was more difficult: Madewisius quoted various theories, among which he supported the version that it was spontaneously generated from the putrid, infected effluvia inside the egg laid by a decrepit old cock. Another German thesis on basilisks was published in 1697, after a certain Dr Johannes Haenfler had had occasion to examine the egg of a peacock, laid in the yard of Judge Prentzlo, and widely exhibited as a prodigy.

When Thomas Bartholin exposed the faked basilisk of Copenhagen, one of his arguments was that he had seen several similar artificial specimens during his travels on the continent. Many seventeenth-century naturalists had a dried 'basilisk' in their collections, although some of them, like Ulysses Aldrovandi, were aware that it was a fake. Aldrovandi also had a dried dragon, which he figured in the *Historiae Serpentum et Draconum*, with the comment that 'showmen fashion diverse-shaped figures from dried rays and foist these on the ignorant either for dragons or for basilisks'. Not a few royal museums were among the buyers of faked basilisks: the wealthy and ignorant princes were pleased to pay huge sums to purchase a specimen of the King of Serpents for their collections. Although King Frederick's faked basilisk is no longer in existence, several other specimens are still preserved, many of them in Italy: there are basilisks in both Milan and Venice, and the Museo di Storia Naturale in Verona has not less than three. One of these was purchased in the early seventeenth century by Signor Francesco Calzolari, a wealthy Veronese apothecary who was a correspondent of Ulysses Aldrovandi. Already in the 1622 museum catalogue, this basilisk was exposed by two skilful naturalists who declared that 'this monstrous animal is not a Basilisk, nor a Dragon, but made from a fish called the Ray, by artificial means'.

In his 1716 catalogue of the cabinet of curiosities belonging to the brothers Besler, J.H. Lochner von Hummelstein described another dried basilisk: a winged, four-legged monster, which is also likely to have been fabricated from a ray. In his *Traité Générale des Pesches*, the French zoologist H.L. Duhamel du Monceau described another quite artistic basilisk, which had been constructed from a dried lizard and a ray. At least one faked basilisk was on show in London. According to a rare handbill kept at the British Library, entitled 'A Brief Description of the Basilisk, or Cockatrice', it was the property of James Salgado, a Spaniard and converted Priest. The basilisk had been purchased from a reputable Dutch physician. Mr Salgado may have been the author of the Latin doggerel:

Quos vivens vidi, nunc mortus.
Uni de vitam, dum me gens numerosa videt.

which was translated as

All men I kill'd that I did see
But now I am dead one lives by mee.

Poor Mr Salgado did not live well off his basilisk, however; according to the handbill, he brought it before his benefactors in London to implore them to 'help a distressed stranger who is reduced to very great straights'.

Shakespeare's Basilisks and Cockatrices

According to Edward Topsell's *History of Four-footed Beasts*, Britain was once considered a particular haunt of basilisks. An old tradition said that a brave (and inexhaustible) man once wandered through every road of the entire British Isles, covered with a multitude of mirrors; when these noxious animals saw themselves or each other, they all expired. This bold basilisk exterminator must have been remarkably successful, since apart from the pathetic Mr Salgado's dried specimen, there are few reports of basilisks invading Britain. The Diary of Samuel Pepys mentions some serpents in Lancashire which 'grow to a great bigness' and feed on larks which they kill by using their death-ray vision, making the birds fall down from the sky into the jaws of the waiting snake; this may well have been a remnant of an older basilisk tradition. Otherwise, the British basilisks and cockatrices were only encountered in contemporary literature and poetry, where they appear in many guises.

William Shakespeare's plays abound with basilisks, which are regularly used to symbolise the evil eye. In the second part of *Henry VI*, the King accuses Suffolk for Gloucester's murder in an impressive speech:

> Upon thy eyeballs murderous tyranny
> Sits in grim majesty to fright the world.
> Look not upon me, for thine eyes are wounding:
> Yet do not go away; come, basilisk,
> And kill the innocent gazer with thy sight;
> For in the shade of death I shall find joy,
> In life but double death, now Gloucester's gone.

In *Richard III*, the hunchbacked, evil future King courts the Princess Anne at her late husband's funeral: his insinuating compliment:

> Thine eyes, sweet lady, hath infected mine

has little success with the fair one, however, and she answers him:

> Would they were *basilisks*, to strike thee dead!

William Shakespeare was not the earliest writer to use the basilisk as a metaphor. Already in Geoffrey Chaucer's *Personne's Tale*, the sentence

> That sleeth right as the Basilicok
> sleeth folk by the venym of his sighte,

occurs, and in Caxton's *Jason*, it is said that

> Certes madame your eyen
> basilique have hurte me unto the death.

In Pope's *Messiah*, there are instead shades of the Biblical basilisk:

> The smiling infant in his hand shall take
> The crested basilisk and speckled snake.

Josiah Sylvester's translation of Guillaume de Salluste du Bartas's *La Semaine* revives the traditional image of the basilisk:

> What shield of Aiax could avoid their death
> By th' Basilisk, whose pestilentiall breath
> Doth pearce firm Marble, and whose banefull ey
> Wounds with a glance, so that the soundest dy.

The same poet, an early enemy of tobacco-smoking, also published a witty poem appositely named *Tobacco Battered, or the Pipes Shattered about their Eares that idely idolize so base a weed*, containing the lines:

> If then *Tobaccoing* bee good: How is't,
> That the levdest, loosest, basest, foolishest,
> The most unthrifty, most intemperate,
> Most vitious, most debaucht, most desperate,
> Pursue it most: The Wisest and the Best
> Abhor it, shun it, flee it, as the Pest,

Or pearcing Poison of a Dragons whisk
Or deadly Ey-shot of a Basilisk.

In Beaumont and Fletcher's *Philaster*, the basilisk is used as an invective against women:

Let me love lighting, let me be embraced
And kissed by scorpions, or adore the eyes
Of basilisks rather than trust the tongues
Of hellbred women.

Even stranger: the word 'cockatrice' was commonly used, throughout the seventeenth century, to mock a loose woman, particularly if she was the kept mistress of some military officer. In Ben Jonson's *Cynthia's Revels*, it is said that:

No courtier but has his mistress;
No captain but has his cockatrice,

and in John Taylor's works, a woman is described with the words:

And among souldiers this sweet piece of vice
Is counted for a captain's cockatrice.

John Dryden alluded to the later, garbled version of the basilisk legend, that the foul beast could only kill by looking at some object, and that it died when looked upon:

Mischiefs are like the cockatrice's eye;
If they see first, they kill; if seen, they die;

Sir Francis Bacon used the same metaphor in *Henry VII*:

This was the end of this little cockatrice of a King that was able to destroy those that did not espie him first.

In his *Robespierre*, Samuel Taylor Coleridge likened this French tyrant to

The crowned cockatrice whose foul venom
Infects all Europe.

The End of the Basilisk

In the massive zoological treatises of Conradus Gesner, Ulysses Aldrovandi and Edward Topsell, much material was fetched from Pliny and from the medieval bestiaries. Proper knowledge of domestic animals was intermixed with far-fetched tales of strange monsters; pigs, hens and horses appeared side by side with mantichoras, mermaids and unicorns. The majority of naturalists were still in favour of the existence of the basilisk. One of the few dissidents was the French naturalist Jean Bodin, who asked himself 'If the basilisk kills by being seen, then who has ever seen it'; his learned adversaries solemnly reminded him that since Pliny's time, it was common knowledge that the basilisk killed while seeing its foe, not merely by being seen. In the sturdy tomes of John Jonstone and Edward Topsell, basilisk lore was thoroughly reviewed. Jonstone made the telling remark that the descriptions of this loathsome beast by different authors through the ages were so dissimilar that they might reflect several different species of animals. Sir Thomas Brown discussed the riddle of the basilisk at length in his *Pseudodoxia Epidemica*. He was bold enough to doubt the old fable that the basilisk 'proceedeth from a Cock's egg hatched under a Toad or Serpent', considering it 'a conceit as monstrous as the brood it self'. Although he did not doubt that many strange and venomous reptiles could be engendered in this way, he doubted that this abnormal form of generation would always produce a basilisk. Nor was he quite disposed to accept the basilisk's death ray vision since like contemporary physicists, he correctly believed 'that sight is made by Reception, and not by Extramission; by receiving the raies of the object into the eye, and not by sending any out'. In spite of these objections, he was impressed by the testimony of many earlier authorities, including the Holy Scripture, and lamely had to admit 'that such an animal there is… we cannot safely deny'.

The shortage of actual observations of basilisk did not prevent imaginative naturalists from discussing the loathsome beast. The Jesuit Father Athanasius Kircher was one of the basilisk's staunchest defenders. In his *Mundus Subterraneus*, published in 1664, he declared that it would be considered very bold indeed for any individual to deny that basilisks existed, and that they were engendered from cock's eggs. His Jesuit brethren at Perugia had informed him that in February 1661, a cock had laid an egg from which a terrible basilisk had burst forth: it had wings, sharp teeth, and a long, curved horn on its forehead. It is left tantalisingly unclear how this formidable monster was disposed of. Father Kircher had himself never seen a basilisk, dead or alive. The nearest thing was a strange cock living in the garden of the Grand Duke of Tuscany. It had a snake-like tail, long legs and a large comb like a crest. Some people believed it to be a tame basilisk and ran away when the Grand Duke's servants took the bird for a walk around the park.

The German Eberhard Happel incorporated a long section on basilisks in his *Relationes Curiosae*, published in 1687. The loathsome beast was taken quite seriously, and the evidence for and against its existence discussed with Teutonic precision. Another German naturalist, Abraham Theodor Krafft, again discussed the basilisk at length in a manual about how to effect 'The complete Extermination of Animals Dangerous to Men and Cattle'. As judged from his advice of various cruel methods to eradicate household pests, Dr Krafft was no lover of animals, but he was full of respect before the basilisk, whose supernatural talents made it the nightmare of an exterminator of vermin. As late as 1736, a complete zoological treatise on the basilisk, written several years before by the prolific naturalist Georg Caspar Kirchmaier, was reprinted both in Latin and in German, and later translated into English. The early modern zoologists, like Linnaeus, Buffon and Blumenbach, were more difficult to convince about the basilisk's existence. Like many of the fabulous animals from the bestiaries, like the dragon, the mantichora and the griffin, the basilisk was an early casualty of the Age of Reason. By the mid-eighteenth century, no basilisk had been sighted for more than 150 years, and even traditionalist theologians had to accept that even if there had once been such animals, they were no longer walking the earth.

Long after the King of Serpents had been dethroned from its prominent position in zoological taxonomy, he still reigned supreme in folklore. Ethnologists have traced basilisk lore to all parts of Europe, and even to Arabia and China. In particular, the idea of the development of a basilisk from a cock's egg was extremely widespread. It was considered a bad omen if a hen crowed like a cock: the farmer must kill this unnatural bird and not suffer it to produce another egg. This old belief is the subject of an English proverb:

A whistling girl and a crowing hen
Are neither fit for gods nor men

as well as a German one:

Wenn die Henne kräht vor dem Hahn
Und das Weib redet vor der Mann
So soll man die Henne braten
Und das Weib mit Prügeln berathen.

There were also regular outbreaks of basilisk hysteria after a cock had been observed to lay an egg. This had been judged to be impossible by the naturalists, but neither the cocks nor the common people heeded this anathema. In 1730, a Swiss cock was executed for such a crime against nature, and as late as 1838, an Irish cock faced trial after having been observed to lay several eggs. After reliable farmers had testified as to its unnatural behaviour, the bird was sentenced to burn at the stake, along with one of its eggs. As the pyre was burning fiercely, the superstitious people believed that the egg burst asunder, and that a dreadful creature like a serpent came forth. The need to bring these wicked and scandalous birds to justice was further emphasised by the discovery, at regular intervals, of eggs containing snake-like creatures. These bizarre eggs kept turning up long after the rest of the basilisk lore had been laid to rest. When, in 1810, an egg laid by a duck belonging to Mr Clemenshaw, of Winmoor, near Leeds, was broken up to be cooked for dinner, a 'young snake', stated to be ten inches in length, fell out. According to the *Canadian Courant*, when a lady broke an egg to cook it in an omelette in November 1827, a small snake, two inches in length, burst out and crawled about the frying pan with much avidity.

The Riddle Solved

In antiquity, the North African desert made a profound impression on the early Greek and Roman travellers: they had never seen such a withered, barren landscape, and there was much speculation as to the cause behind the formation of these huge wastelands. One hypothesis was that the basilisks and other venomous reptiles inhabiting the Cyrenaican deserts had destroyed them by their noxious fumes. The 'basilisk' described by Pliny resembles a still existing desert serpent named *Lytorhynchus diadema*; just like in his description, it is about six inches in length, yellowish brown in colour, and with a white 'diadem' on its head. This harmless reptile was blamed for the vegetation becoming blackened and shrivelled in the sweltering heat, and the rocks bursting by the night frost in winter. Pliny's description of the basilisk serpent might also have been inspired by early accounts of the natural history of cobras. These snakes can raise their heads and bodies from the ground when teased or enraged, and they sometimes crawl with their heads upraised like the basilisk; their 'spectacle' sign on their neck shields may have inspired the tale of the basilisk's royal crest. Nor can it be excluded that tales of the spitting cobra and its propensity to hit the eyes of its adversary had influenced the basilisk's ability to kill from a distance. The great skill of the mongoose in fighting the cobra and other venomous serpents probably inspired Pliny's account of the enmity between the weasel and the basilisk. This tale also illustrated his own theories about the equilibrium of nature: every animal, even the most terrifying monster, must have a natural enemy capable of destroying it.

It is not unlikely that the lore of the snake-like basilisk of antiquity can also be linked to Egyptian mythology; it may thus have been established many centuries before Pliny's account. An important clue is given by the *Hieroglyphica* of Horapollon, which likens the Greek *basiliscus* to the Egyptian ouraion snake. He further writes that if the ouraion snake breathes upon any living being, it dies, and the snake does not have to bite it. The ouraion snake was a royal attribute among the Egyptians: indeed, the snake emblem adorning the brows of the Egyptian pharaohs is an ouraion snake, which is to protect the pharaoh with its fiery breath.

The legend of the basilisk hatched from a cock's egg can be traced back to the tenth century but no further. During antiquity, it was even thought that the crowing of the cock drew away the African basilisks. A possible source of both these versions was Herodotus' fanciful tale of the winged serpents of Araby, which every year invaded Egypt in great numbers. They were defeated by the ibis birds, which attacked the serpents and ate them whole. The Egyptian peasants were grateful to their native birds, but their heroic act had brought about lurid changes in their reproductive physiology: through eating the venomous serpents, the ibises themselves became completely saturated with poison, and laid eggs containing young serpents instead of chicks. This may well have been the origin of the medieval tale of the basilisk coming from the cock's egg. The observations of Ulysses Aldrovandi and Thomas Bartholin did much to discredit this old belief, but it remained until the early eighteenth century. In 1706, the French anatomist Lapeyronie was instructed by the French Academy of Sciences to examine an alleged egg-laying rooster. The eggs in question were plainly laid by an elderly hen. Lapeyronie concluded that cocks were constitutionally incapable of laying eggs, and that the small, abnormal 'cock's eggs' shown to him were instead produced by old, sickly hens. The majority of later writers have agreed with him: for example, when the French zoologist C. Davaine wrote a lengthy review about anomalous eggs in 1860, he considered all the old reports of basilisk embryos inside eggs to be wholly imaginary, and due to an overheated imagination.

In 1780, the great British surgeon and anatomist John Hunter described an 'extraordinary Pheasant': it was a pheasant hen that had, in old age, acquired the plumage of a cock. Several other anatomists made similar observations: Buffon, Blumenbach and Geoffroy St Hilaire among them. The phenomenon itself had been described already by Aristotle, and Livy wrote that among the portents observed just before Hannibal's invasion of Italy in 217 BC were 'the changing of a hen into a cock and a cock into a hen'. Modern ornithologists agree that spontaneous intersexuality among birds really does exist, but that it is only possible for hens to acquire male sexual characteristics: several modern cases have been described, in chicken as well as in wild fowl. The physiological background for this is that just like human beings, birds possess latent male and female secondary characteristics, the expression of which is controlled by the production of male or female sex hormone. Just like a woman with an adrenal or ovarian disorder leading to the production of an excess of male sex hormone may undergo virilisation, a hen bird can develop a similar disease of the ovary, disturbing the balance of female and male sex hormone, and acquire the coat of feathers of a rooster. This phenomenon is sometimes observed in a decrepit old hen, whose ovary atrophies in old age; the production of male sex hormone from the rudimentary right gonad takes over and the bird undergoes partial or total virilisation, even usurping the male prerogative of crowing. The oviduct and ovary of these aged 'cocks' are quite atrophied, and they are incapable of laying eggs. It has occasionally been observed, however, that hens in the prime of life may change their sex due to some disease reducing the production of female sex hormone from the ovary. This might be caused by a tumour or cyst in the ovary, or by some kind of granulomatous inflammation. These remarkable 'roosters' may have fully developed secondary male characteristics, but are still capable of laying eggs. It has even been recorded that one unique hen, which was previously the mother of several chicks, became fully masculine in behaviour, fertilising the eggs of a normal hen and becoming the father of chicks also!

Another remarkable observation was made by the Canadian zoologist L.J. Cole in 1927. A brown leghorn rooster had laid several eggs, which were of normal size and structure. The rooster's comb and wattles were rather like those of a hen, however, although the plumage was typically male in character. The sex change is likely to have occurred swiftly: some feathers from its former coat were remaining and they were those of a hen. The bird was mated with a white Leghorn rooster, which must have felt rather confounded when viewing his prospective bride; this did not prevent nature taking its course and a number of normal chicks being raised. Remarkably, the egg-laying rooster regained its female coat of feathers half a year later, and returned to its eventless life at the Wisconsin egg central, without any apparent ill effects of its brief masquerade in male plumage. The bird was never autopsied, and one can only speculate that it must have had some self-limiting inflammatory or granulomatous disease of the ovary. The famous egg-laying rooster of Basle, which suffered a hotter death than in the stew as a punishment for its crimes against nature, is likely to have suffered from a similar disorder.

The fact that these legendary oviparous roosters really do exist explains one of the most puzzling parts of the riddle of the basilisk. Another mysterious feature of the generation of that loathsome beast was the occurrence of eggs containing 'young basilisks'. These abnormal eggs were described at regular intervals during the seventeenth and eighteenth centuries: in all, more than fifteen observations exist, many of which were published in the scholarly journals of the time. In the nineteenth century, these bizarre findings were doubted by ornithologists and natural historians; they have even been used by modern writers to exemplify the ignorance and credulity of the old writers on natural history. Some zoologists have suggested that the old 'basilisk eggs' were in fact eggs of the grass snake, but it is a gross insult against competent natural historians like Ulysses Aldrovandi and Thomas Bartholin to suggest that they could not tell the egg of a grass snake from that of a hen. Another, slightly more reasonable hypothesis is that the 'basilisk embryos' were in fact the so-called chalaza-parts of the egg, string-like structures that connect the yolk of the egg to the poles of the shell. In an abnormal egg, which lacks the normal yolk, the chalaza structures may be fused, and resemble a writhing little snake. The zoologists who have followed Lapeyronie in advocating this hypothesis would have difficulties to explain, however, why the 'young basilisks' were often found in eggs with normal yolks, in which the chalaza structures are divided. Furthermore, the seventeenth-century observers often reported that the basilisks were alive, and sometimes that they moved about with great vigour.

The answer to this riddle may seem even more bizarre than the two theories reviewed earlier, but unlike them, it is supported by several reliable modern observations of the phenomenon in question. Hens, like humans, occasionally harbour intestinal worms within them. The largest of these are roundworms like the *Ascaris lineata*. These ascaride worms, which may become one, or even two, inches long, live their natural lives within the hen's small intestine, but they may also crawl out into the so-called cloacum, where the gut and the oviduct join. Usually, they later follow the hen's droppings out into the open, but some worm, inspired either by a desire to explore its surroundings, or by a defective sense of direction, might actually take a wrong turning, and instead travel up the oviduct, to be included into the fowl's egg. If it reached the isthmus part of the oviduct, it would be incorporated into the white of the egg, and would constitute a very unpleasant surprise for the individual trying to eat it. If it had not reached as far as that, it would instead be incorporated into the eggshell; this explains the eggs with 'the mark of the basilisk' observed by Aldrovandi and Cleyer. A close study of the old and new literature thus vindicates the veracity of the old naturalists: the 'basilisk embryos' observed inside hen eggs were no mere figments of the imagination, but roundworms incorporated into the white of the egg. Several instances of this unsavoury phenomenon have been described by modern ornithologists. A review of worm parasites in chicken eggs by Dr W.M. Read and colleagues, published in 1973, details nineteen recent instances and recommends 'candling' of the eggs before a strong light to detect worm-infested eggs. According to a story published in many American newspapers, Ms Ursula Beckey, of Long Island, cracked some eggs to make an omelette in October 1979. Out of the third egg crawled a three-inch 'snake'! Four months later, she filed 3.6 million dollar damages against the shop that had sold her the eggs, claiming that the shock might well have killed her, and that she now felt nausea just looking at an egg. Her barrister had got hold of the wrong end of the stick, to put it mildly: his expert comment on this strange case was that 'I have been told that a snake of this size in an egg must have come from a mother snake at least six feet long'!

Many historians of zoology have marvelled that the basilisk, this protean monster, depicted in many different shapes and forms, could remain within the texture of seventeenth- and eighteenth-century zoological taxonomy. With its many fantastic attributes, the basilisk did not inspire confidence even to the most imaginative writers. Scientific biology had caught up with it long ago, its appearance was preposterous, no person had seen a live specimen for hundreds of years, and even its fabled generation from a cock's egg was doubted by many writers. The reason for the basilisk's puzzling longevity is likely to be that two veritable mainstays of its legendary attributes had a foundation in fact: birds resembling cocks can, in rare cases, lay eggs, and intestinal ascarides have been found inside eggs, masquerading as young basilisks. Hopefully, today's leading biologists will be more favourably judged in 300 years' time than the savants who pondered the riddle of the basilisk: superstition, exaggerated confidence in earlier authorities, and misinterpretation of factual observations in practical ornithology led them for an unavailing chase after an imaginary monster.

While the classical basilisk is today only to be encountered in heraldry, its name – although not its distinguished position as King of Serpents – has been usurped by a family of large iguana lizards living in the rain forests of central America; their generic name is *Basiliscus*. The males of these modern basilisks have a high crest on their heads. They are beautiful, slender lizards that climb trees with great agility; the largest among them, the *Basiliscus americanus*, can become more than three feet long. Although they cannot poison wells, break stones asunder with their eyesight, or peck holes in iron doors, the basilisk lizards have another remarkable accomplishment, although one definitely not associated with the devil. They can walk, or rather run, on water, using their powerful hind legs and balancing their long tails. Some time ago, I had occasion to examine a young basilisk lizard: it demonstrated a remarkable quickness and a voracious appetite, but lacked the sufficient run to make an attempt to walk on water. The basilisk studied its visitor with great interest, and under the penetrating stare of these reptilian eyes, one was reminded of Shelley's *Ode to Naples*:

> Be thou like the imperial basilisk,
> Killing thy foes by unapparent wounds!

Right: 48 Jumbo, the Children's Giant Pet: another advertisement poster from Barnum & Bailey's circus. There was $100,000 on offer for any person producing a larger and heavier elephant.

Below: 49 Jumbo advertising Kerr's Spool Cotton.

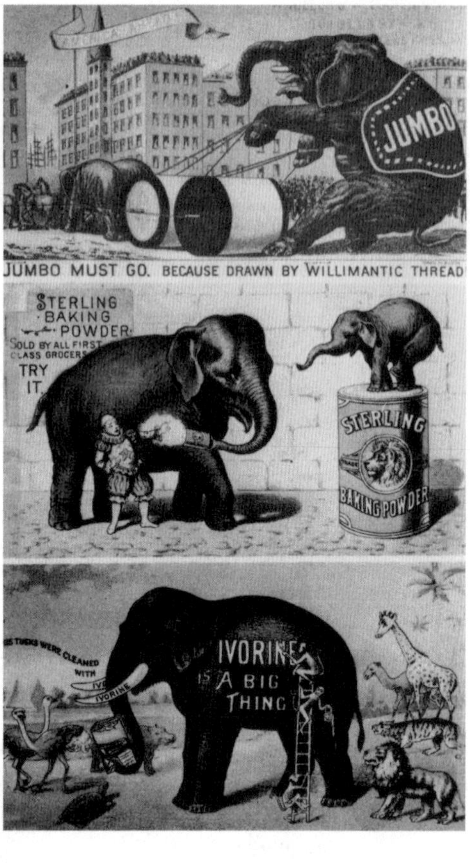

Right: 50 Three contemporary advertisements, using the famous Jumbo to puff some popular American brands of thread, baking powder and toothpaste.

Below: 51 Three contemporary drawings, giving a dramatic, although hardly accurate, version of Jumbo's demise.

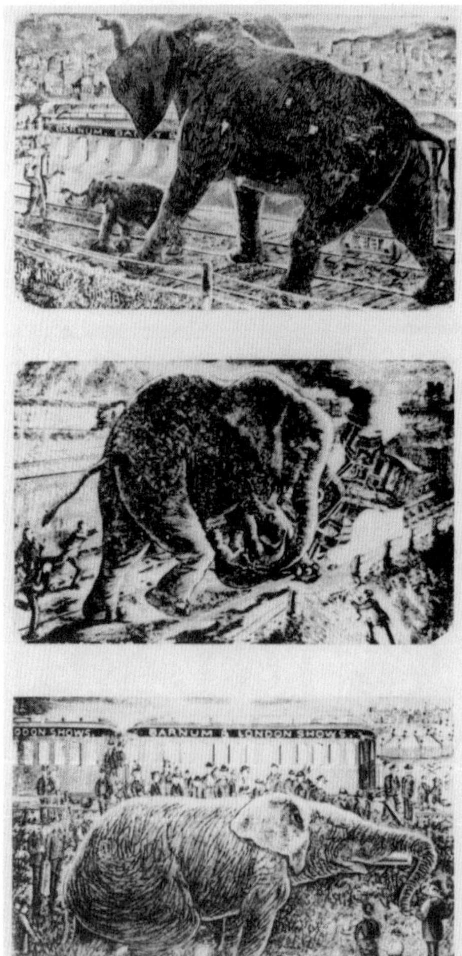

Opposite above: 52 A rare photograph of Jumbo with Matthew Scott, showing the impressive size of the animal.

Opposite below: 53 Jumbo's corpse, from an original photograph.

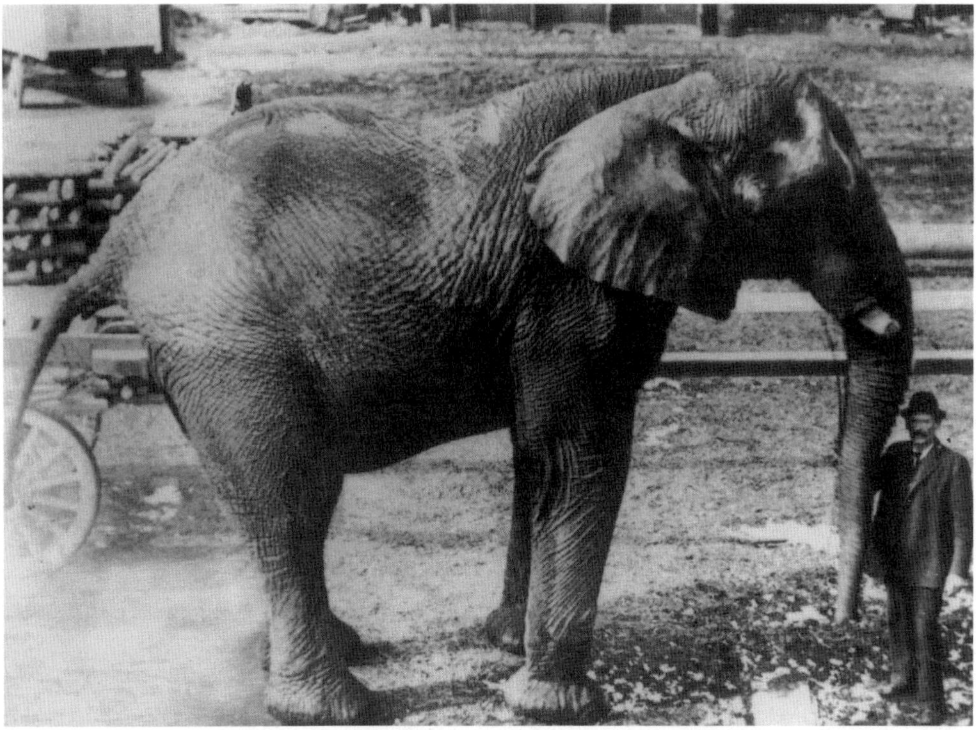

Above: 54 The stuffed Jumbo.

Left: 55 Jumbo's mounted skeleton.

56 The Bishop of Lausanne cursing the inger, from a nineteenth-century Swiss print.

57 A drawing of various criminal animals, including a pig having a meal of child's trotters; from the sixteenth-century legal treatise *Praxis Rerum Criminalium*, by Jodocus Damhouder.

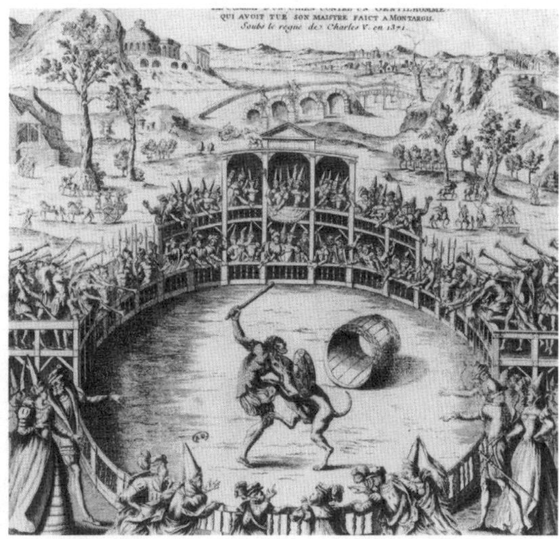

58 The fight between Chevalier Macaire and the faithful dog, from an old print.

Left: 59 *Supplice d'une Truie*, an engraving by Lhermitte after the original fourteenth-century fresco in Falaise.

Below: 60 The trial of a sow and her six piglets in Lavegny in 1457, for having killed and partly eaten a child, from Chambers' *Book of Days*.

61 A snake-like basilisk; from Edward Topsell's *Historie of Four-Footed Beasts*, published in 1607.

Right: 62 A cock-like basilisk; from the *De Labyryntho* of Johann Stabius.

Below: 63 A grim-looking basilisk, from John Jonstone's *Historia Naturalis*, published in 1657.

64 The basilisk at the portal of the church of Källs-Nöbbelöv, Sweden.

Right: 65 The basilisk kills a man with its death-ray vision, but is attacked by a fierce-looking little weasel. A drawing from the famous Salisbury Bestiary.

Below: 66 The frontispiece of Pierre Borel's *Historiarum et Observationum Medicorum*, published in 1676, depicting its author together with a tame basilisk.

Above: 67 The basilisk and the mirror; a drawing from the 1661 edition of Joachim Camerarius' *Symbolorum et Emblematum*.

Above left: 68 A drawing of a basilisk, published by Georg Wedel in the *Ephemerides* of 1672.

Above right: 69 A faked basilisk kept in a private museum in Italy in the late 1800s.

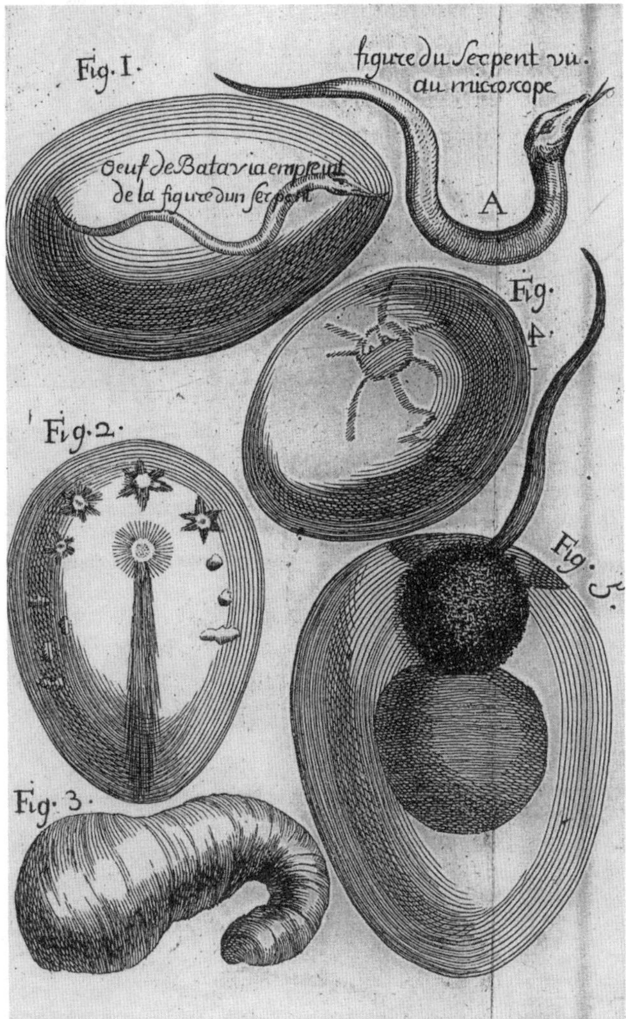

Right: 70 An egg with the mark of the basilisk (top of image), from an article by Cleyerus in the *Ephemerides* of 1673. The other eggs are presumed to have marks of the sun and stars.

71 A miniature illustration from a German manuscript of Sir John Mandeville's *Travels*, depicting the goose-tree and the lamb-tree growing side by side.

72 Another early illustration of the vegetable lamb, from Mandeville's *Travels*.

73 A remarkable drawing of the Tartar lamb, from Claude Duret's *Histoire Admirable des Plantes*.

Above left: 74 A vegetable lamb looking like a rather pot-bellied German Shepherd impaled on a beanstalk; from the works of Joannes Zahn.

Above right: 75 The frontispiece of John Parkinson's *Paradisus Terrestris*, showing Adam and Eve wandering around in the Garden of Eden, admiring its multitude of plants; note the vegetable lamb in the background.

Below: 76 Sir Hans Sloane's vegetable lamb.

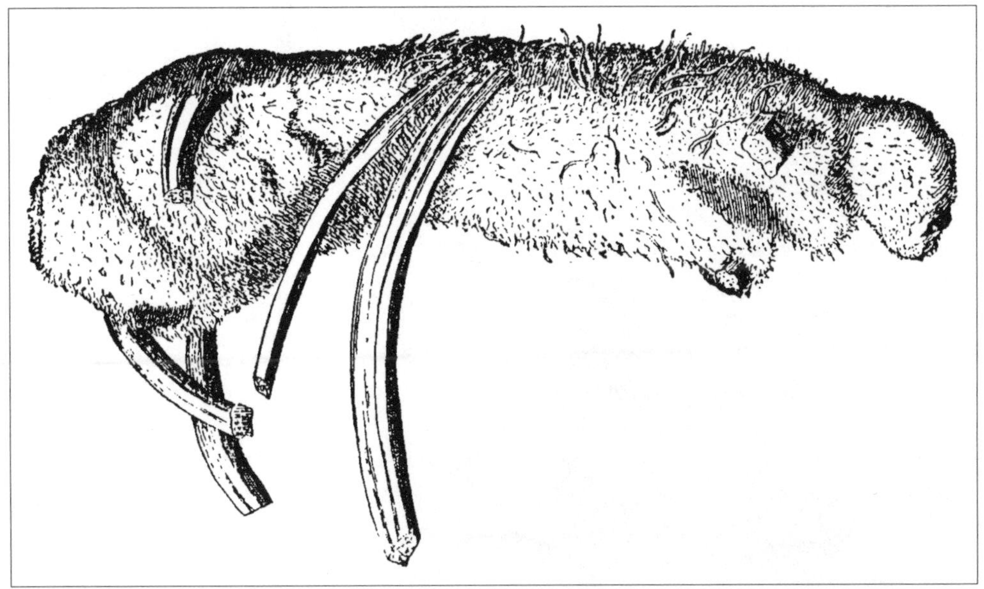

77 Dr Breyn's elegant vegetable lamb, as depicted in the *Philosophical Transactions* of 1725.

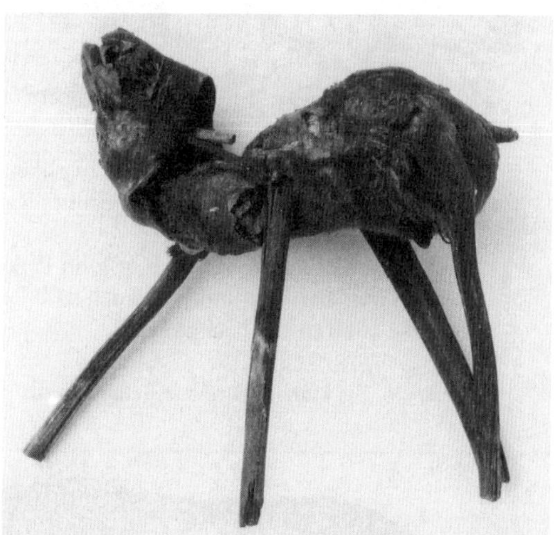

78 The old vegetable lamb at the Natural History Museum.

79 The vegetable lamb at the Museum of Garden History.

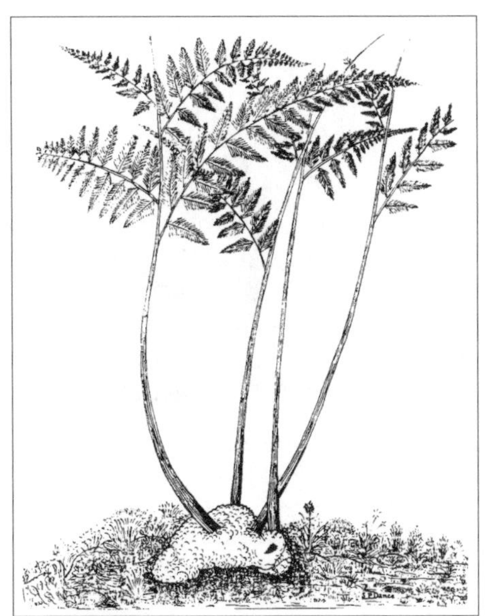

80 The wooly rootstock and straight stems of an arborescent fern.

Left: 81 A vegetable lamb and some tree-growing geese in a beautiful miniature from the manuscript *Livre des Merveilles*, written in 1453.

Below: 82 Tree-growing geese; a drawing from the Salisbury Bestiary.

Above: 83 The goose-tree as drawn in the *Dendrographia* of John Jonstone.

Right: 84 A remarkable drawing of the goose-tree, from the *Ornithologia* of Ulysses Aldrovandi.

Left: 85 A tree whose fruits turn into fishes if they fall into the water, and into birds if they fall on shore. From Claude Duret's *Histoire Admirable des Plantes*.

Opposite top: 86 Another drawing by Ulysses Aldrovandi, this time from his dissertation *De Mollibus Crustaceis et Zoophytis*, depicting all stages in the transformation of barnacles into geese.

Opposite middle: 87 Lemmings fall from the sky in Sweden; they march forth in a column, but are attacked by ermines, one of which is caught in a trap. An illustration from the *Historia Gentibus Septentrionalibus* of Archbishop Olaus Magnus.

Opposite bottom: 88 A Scandinavian shower of fish, from the *Historia Gentibus Septentrionalibus* of Olaus Magnus.

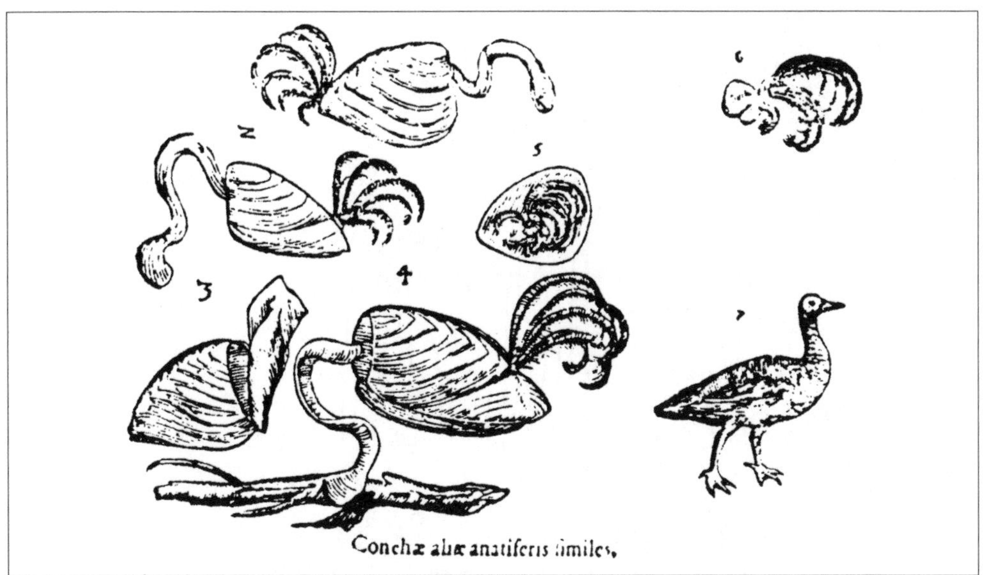

Conchæ aliæ anatiferis similes.

89 A shower of frogs occurring in the year 1345, as figured in the *Prodigorum ac Ostentorum Chronicon* of Conradus Lycosthenes.

90 A British shower of small frogs, depicted in Frank Buckland's *Curiosities of Natural History*, with the caption 'Suddenly to descend, to the astonishment of rustics'.

Above left: 91 Showers of wheat, fish, frogs and worms; from the *Der wunder-reiche Überzug unserer Nider-welt* by Erasmus Francisi.

Above right: 92 A shower of rats; another quaint illustration from Francisi's book.

Below: 93 A British shower of wheat, accompanied by a strange apparition in the sky, looking not unlike an UFO.

94 A shower of cats, dogs and pitchforks, an amusing caricature drawing by George Cruikshank.

95 A fanciful drawing of a Chinese shower of fish, said to have occurred in the 1930s.

96 A newspaper photograph of an American policeman surveying what was presumed to have been a shower of fish.

97 A drawing of Mr Gråberg's frog and a cross-section of the quarry in which it was found, from the *Kungliga Vetenskapsakademins Handlingar* of 1733.

Left: 98 The toad-in-the-hole is discovered, a rather fanciful illustration to Philip Henry Gosse's *Romance of Natural History*.

Below: 99 A drawing of the Blois toad, as reproduced in *La Nature* of 1885.

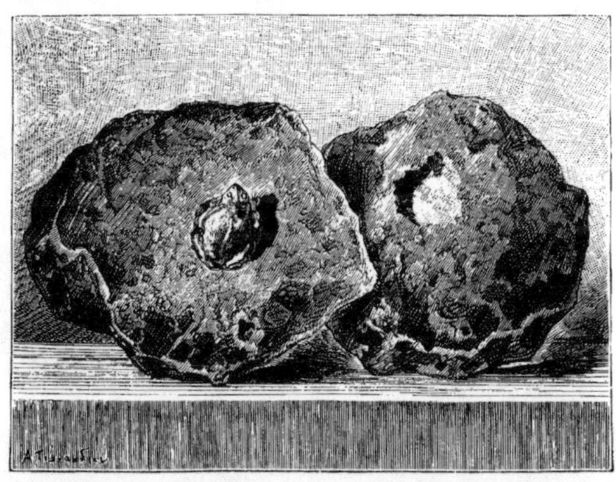

100 The block of coal with the Cwmtillery frog (or toad) being admired at the International Exhibition, from the *Penny Illustrated Paper* of August 23, 1862.

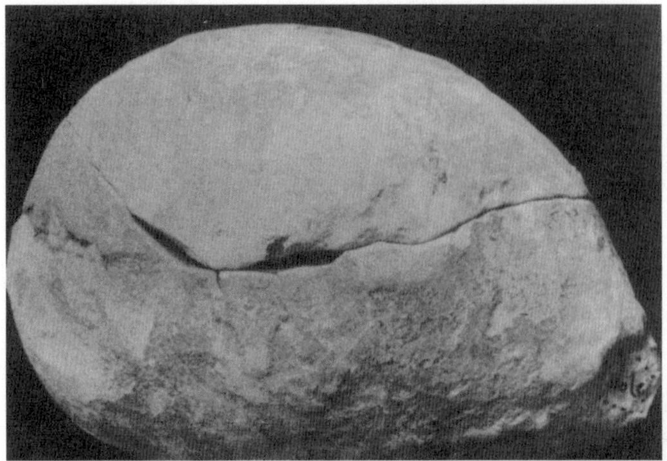

Above and right: 101 and 102: Two contemporary photographs, published in the *Illustrated London News*, of the flintstone nodule containing a dead toad discovered by Charles Dawson.

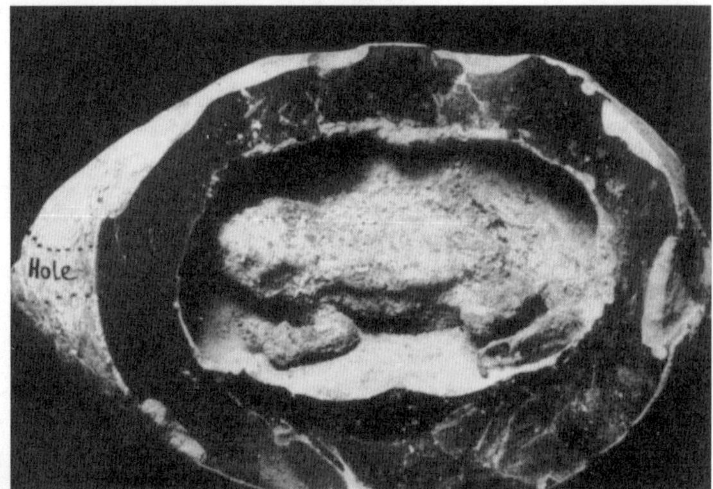

103 The Brighton toad-in-the-hole today.

9

The Vegetable Lamb *AND THE* BARNACLE GEESE

They say 'At first to living things the Earth,
At her formation, gave spontaneous birth;
When youthful heat was through the glebe diffus'd,
Mankind, as well as insects, she produc'd;
That genial wombs by parent Chance were form'd,
Adapted to the soil, which, after warm'd
And cherish'd by the Sun's enlivening beam,
With human offsprings did in embryo teem.'

Richard Blackmore, *The Creation: A Philosophical Poem in Seven Books* (1712).

Aristotle spent much time pondering the question how all animals, plants and other objects in nature were constructed, and how they had been engendered in the first place. He established an elaborate philosophical system, considering both the origins of life and the everyday formation of new individuals. Everything in nature, whether it belonged to the animal, plant or mineral kingdoms, was made up partly of matter and partly of a form, or soul. Matter is the empty substrate, itself without capacity to exist; the form is what raises matter to a bodily shape or changes its characteristics. A block of stone thus has a form that makes it just that; when it is sculpted into a statue, it begets a new and higher form that incorporates the artist's intention. The form of a living creature, which could also be called a soul, was of course much more complicated than that of a block of stone, but their fundamental prerequisites were the same.

A key question for Aristotle and his adherents was how all the newly generated animals and plants were supplied with forms. It was well known that that humans and higher animals were bred by normal reproduction; their souls were thus engendered from those of their parents. According to Aristotle's *History of Animals*, certain lower animals 'are not produced from animals at all, but arise spontaneously: some are produced out of the dew which falls on foliage... others are produced in putrefying mud and dung, others in wood, green or dry, others in residues, whether voided residues or residues still within the living animal'. Eels and little fishes were spontaneously generated from the foam of the sea, insects from specks of sand whirled into the air by hot gusts of wind, and wasps from the putrid cadavers of dead horses. The ancient Egyptians believed that many different creatures could be generated in the fertile humus left by the flooding of the Nile, as described by Edmund Spenser in his *Fairie Queene*:

> As when old father *Nilus* begins to swell,
> With timely pride aboue the *Aegyptian* vale,
> His fattie waues do fertile slime outwell
> And ouerflow each plaine and lowly dale:
> But when his later ebbe gins to auale,
> Huge heaps of mudd he leaues, wherein there breed
> Ten thousand kindes of creatures, partly male,
> And partly female of his fruitful seed;
> Such vgly monstrous shapes elsewhere may no man reed.

Aristotle's theory of spontaneous generation was accepted, with reverence, not only among his contemporaries, but well into modern times. Virgil and Pliny added some embellishments of their own: they attached to each insect a corresponding type of putrefied flesh, from which this breed of insect could be generated. Thus, bees were formed from the flesh of oxen, as eloquently explained in Virgil's *Georgica*, on the authority of 'an Arcadian Bee-master'. A freshly slaughtered calf is put among fresh cassia and thyme and broken branches. The Bee-master then bides his time:

Meanwhile, within the marrowy bones of the calf, the humours
Grow warm, ferment, till appear creatures miraculous –
Limbless at first, but soon they fidget, their wings vibrate,
And more, more they sip, they drink the delicate air:
At last they come pouring out, like a shower from summer clouds,
Or thick and fast as arrows.

Wasps and hornets developed from the carcasses of horses, and beetles from those of asses. Plutarch added that small rats could be formed from earth, and serpents from human corpses. That oysters were spontaneously generated no one doubted, least of all Opianus, the author of a poem on fishes:

They couple not nor bring forth any young
But of themselves they breed the Mud among
As Oisters do, Glib Oisters that no Male
Nor Female have.

Ovid's *Metamorphoses* contains a beautiful section extolling the wonders of spontaneous generation, here presented, like many of the other classical poems quoted, as 'Englished' by the seventeenth-century translator of Daniel Sennert's work on spontaneous generation:

So, when the seven channeld Nile forsakes the Plain,
When ancient Bounds retiring Streams contain,
And late-left Slime aethereal Fervors burn
Then various Creatures with the Gleab up turn:
Of those some in their very time of Birth;
Some Lame, and others half alive, half Earth.

The traditional concept of spontaneous generation reigned supreme throughout the Middle Ages. Several early Arab naturalists of eminence, Averroes and Avicenna among them, accepted Aristotle's teachings about parentless generation of lower animals. Other medieval writers added their own touches. The twelfth-century abbess Hildegard of Bingen maintained that reptiles had been generated from the ground stained with Abel's blood, and certain influential astrologers, Henry of Hesse and Michael Savonarola among them, emphasised the power of the stars in controlling the spontaneous generation of frogs, bats, mice and fish. Leonardo da Vinci was yet another prominent supporter of this latter theory. Paracelsus merged the dogma of spontaneous generation with his own system of alchemy. Under the influence of the sun and the stars, the four elements could merge together and form most kinds of animals. Snakes, tortoises and insects could be generated from putrid matter, and basilisks from the blood of menstruating women. Paracelsus even suggested experiments to artificially generate a small human being, a *homunculus*, from putrid excrements and semen that was incubated in a glass flask and supplied with nutritious fluids.

Another reckless adherent of Aristotle's theory of spontaneous (or equivocal) generation was the Italian mathematician, naturalist and physician Girolamo Cardano. Cardano was a universal genius in the manner of his time: he has achieved everlasting fame by being the first to publish a solution to the general third-degree equation. His extensive biological writings are not always characterised by the same stringency as his early mathematical flashes of genius, however. His opponent Herman van Booerhave was not far wrong when he claimed that when Cardano was right, he surpassed all contemporary scholars in wisdom and farsightedness, but when he advocated various adventurous theories, he surpassed them all in folly. A large section of his treatise *De Subtilitate* is devoted to various aspects of spontaneous generation. According to Cardano, not only lower animals, like ants, flies, fishes and crayfish, were generated from putrid matter; many vertebrates, like lizards, mice, hares, birds and gazelles could be equivocally engendered in this way.

In the early seventeenth century, the existence of a spontaneously generating force in nature was generally accepted. When the theologian Wolfgang Franzius published his *Historia Animalium Sacra* in 1612, claiming that no animal could be generated without parents, he was ridiculed by his contemporaries. A new era in the annals of spontaneous generation began in 1636, when the Wittenberg physician and philosopher Daniel Sennert published his *Hypomnemata Physica*, a section of which was devoted to formulating a novel hypothesis of spontaneous generation, which differed from those of Aristotle and Cardano in several respects. Daniel Sennert was an early atomist, who refused to accept that the atoms of matter could independently rearrange themselves into a living creature with a soul. Since God was no longer capable of creating any new souls, the spontaneously generated animals had to be derived from matter that had once been living. The soul of a horse was capacious enough to suffice for all the thousands of bees that were generated from its putrid cadaver. Everywhere in nature were the souls of insects and spontaneously generated small animals, awaiting the opportunity to generate a living organism from putrid meat and offal. The novelty of Daniel Sennert's teachings, which later philosophers have called seminalism, is that he was the first to clearly deny the equivocal generation of living creatures from non-living inorganic substances; new life could only develop from once living matter.

Réné Descartes wholly disagreed with Daniel Sennert: he denied that animals or vegetables possessed any kind of form or soul: they were just automata, without any higher qualities. A St Bernard dog was of course a more accomplished creature than a tulip, but only in the same sense that a church organ had a more complicated mechanism than a beer-barrel. According to Descartes, it took so little to make an animal that it was by no means surprising that worms and insects could be spontaneously generated from putrefying matter. Just as cheese could be made from milk, worms and larvae could be made from decaying cheese; matter was just transubstantiated from one condition to another.

Another remarkable theory of equivocal generation, a mixture between the alchemy of Paracelsus and the seminalism of Daniel Sennert, was advocated by the German Jesuit Athanasius Kircher. In his monumental *Mundus Subterraneus*, published in 1665, he praised God as the great originator of equivocal generation. In the chaotic protomass, God had deposited a universal life force, consisting of salt, sulphur and mercury. When the fumes of this vital force came into contact with putrefying animals or vegetables, a large variety of beings could be spontaneously generated. Father Kircher described a number of simple experiments, which he recommended the reader to try out himself, if he was unwise enough to doubt the existence of this vital force in all nature. If one wanted to create frogs, for example, one could collect some clay from a ditch where frogs were known to have been living and incubate it in a large vessel, with continuous addition of rainwater. Another popular experiment was to incubate a putrid lump of meat in an open vessel, to see the crawling maggots being spontaneously generated within it.

The vast majority of seventeenth-century British naturalists, including Robert Hooke, Robert Lovell and John Jonstone, were adherents of spontaneous generation. Sir Francis Bacon accepted the equivocal generation of insects, snails, eels, frogs and toads. William Harvey claimed, in his *De Generatione Animalium*, that everything living must have been developed from an egg. But his concept of an 'egg' was very much different from that of modern biologists: it was an imperfect, often indeterminate object, the 'first Rudiment from which an Animal doth spring'. For example, Harvey considered a caterpillar as the 'egg' from which the perfect imago developed by metamorphosis. Nor did he rule out that this 'egg' could be spontaneously generated. He basically agreed with the current division of animals into viviparous, oviparous and spontaneously generated, writing that 'some Animals are born of their own Accord, or (as they commonly say) of Putrefaction'. When Sir Thomas Browne, who was otherwise another supporter of equivocal generation, dared to doubt whether mice could really be formed in this way, he was taken to task by the conservative Aristotelian Alexander Ross in no uncertain terms:

> He doubts *whether mice can be procreated of putrefication*! So he may doubt whether in cheese and timber worms are generated; or if butterflies, locusts, grass hoppers, sel-fish, snails, eels, and such are procreated of putrefied matter... To doubt this is to question Reason, Sense, and Experience...

This widespread seventeenth-century belief in spontaneous generation is also reflected in literature. William Shakespeare several times alludes to the spontaneous generation of animals, most particularly in *Antony and Cleopatra*, where he speaks of serpents and crocodiles generated from the mud of the Nile. Similarly, Ben Jonson, in *The Alchemist*, speaks of bees, hornets, beetles and wasps generated from the carcasses and dung of creatures. In a discourse written in 1592, Thomas Nashe compares the money-grubbing upstarts, adventurers made courtiers, and dishonest businessmen of the Elizabethan era with the imperfect, spontaneously generated animals. 'Brewers that, by retailing filthy *Thames* water, come in a few years to bee worth fortie or fiftie thousand pounds' are compared with foul creatures bred from corrupted water, and 'Mother *Bunches* slimie ale, that hath made her and her fil-pot facultie so wealthy', to frogs bred from slime. Butchers getting rich by selling diseased and fly-blown beef are aptly likened to crawling maggots bred from putrid meat. Jonathan Swift made an interesting allusion to spontaneous generation in *Gulliver's Travels*. When the tribe of noble horses, the Hoyhnhnms, debate whether or not to exterminate the sub-human Yahoos, one of them suggests that the first two of this abominable tribe suddenly appeared together on a mountain 'whether produced by the Heat of the Sun upon corrupted Mud and Slime, or from the Ooze and Froth of the Sea, was never known'. Dean Swift was well aware of the musings of Paracelsus that human beings could also be spontaneously generated, since he used the abominable descent of the Yahoo race from mud and slime as an example of the brutish, uncivilised state of human beings without the Christian religion.

One of the most remarkable fallacies in the annals of spontaneous generation was the widespread credence that a class of so-called zoophytes, spontaneously generated hybrids between animals and plants, existed. For several centuries, it was vigorously debated whether a lamb could really develop from a plant, and if young geese grew on trees, hanging from the branches like ripe pears. These monstrosities were described in many zoological and botanical treatises of the time, and traces of the vegetable lamb of Tartary and the barnacle geese of Scotland still exist in the zoological terminology.

The Vegetable Lamb of Tartary

When, in the year 1356, Sir John Mandeville, a valiant and honourable knight residing in St Albans, had become incapacitated by age and rheumatism, he decided to write his memoirs. He had a good deal of interest to relate, since his life had been filled to the brim with travel and adventure. Sir John had set out for Palestine in 1322; in later years, his long and perilous journeys had taken him to Turkey, Great and Little Armenia, Tartary, Persia, Syria, Arabia, Upper and Lower Egypt, Libya, Ethiopia, Chaldaea, Amazonia, and India. His journeys combined the best of several worlds: like a time-traveller, he was conversant with the hoary myths of antiquity, the marvels of the East, and the manifold wonders of medieval natural history. Sir John had seen centaurs, hermaphrodites, cynocephalics, cyclops, pygmies, tailed men, men without heads, and 'many other divers folks of divers natures'. A certain Oriental tribe had enormous ears hanging down to their knees; another had upper lips of a prodigious size, which they used as parasols. He had seen the Dead Sea, in whose waters iron floated and feathers sank to the bottom, and the

Mountain of Ararat, on the top of which the wreck of the Ark of Noah could still be distinguished in clear weather conditions. He had visited the King of Calonak, who had more than 1000 wives, 200 children and 14,000 tame elephants; the latter were, in case of war, equipped with manned castles of wood to carry on their backs, to frighten the enemy host. At Polumbrium, Sir John had drunk from the Fountain of Youth; in Ceylon, he had seen a lake filled with the bitter tears shed by Adam and Eve after they had been banished from the Garden of Eden. He had seen the gold-mining ants of Taprobane, but did not dare to investigate the treasures of these ferocious insects any further, since 'deise Pissemyres ben grete as Houndes'. Only one of the marvels of the East had eluded the Knight: about the Earthly Paradise he had nothing truthful to tell, since he had never been there.

During his stay in Tartary, Sir John Mandeville was much impressed with the gluttony of the people: both the Grand Khan and his loyal subjects ate lion, dog, leopard, rat and donkey meat with a voracious appetite, without caring whether their beef-steaks had been dressed or cooked in any way. An even more singular local speciality was a large fruit, like a watermelon, which grew on a long stalk; when opened, it proved to contain a living little lamb. The Tartars greedily ate this strange being when fruits of this kind fell into their hands. Sir John was audacious enough to eat a piece of the lamb himself, probably served raw according to local custom. He does not describe what this vegetable lamb tasted like, but with the decorous piety manifested even in his tallest stories, he writes that 'of that Frute I have eaten; alle thought it were wondirfulle, but that I knowe wel that God is marveyllous in all his Werkes'.

Another version of the legend of the vegetable lamb of Tartary was given by Baron Sigismund von Heberstein, who had served as the German Emperor's Ambassador at the Court of Muscovy, in 1517 and 1526. After returning to Germany, he published his *Rerum Muscovitarum Commentarii*, a valuable collection of historical anecdotes about Russia and its people. A courtier named Daniel Danielovich had told him that his father had once been sent to the Tartar King as an emissary from the Duke of Muscovy. Near the Caspian Sea, Danielovich the elder had seen a plant called the 'Borametz' or 'little lamb': it grew from a large seed the size of a melon, and attained the height of about two and a half feet. Strangely to tell, it resembled a little lamb, with eyes, ears, head and wool, although it grew from a stem. It had hoofs, but they were not horny, and rather resembled hairs brought together into the form of a cloven hoof of a lamb. The living plant had blood, but its flesh rather resembled crab-meat, and was of so excellent a flavour that the defenceless plant was the favourite food of wolves and other rapacious animals. Another acquaintance of Heberstein's, an interpreter named Michel, had also heard of this plant. He claimed that its very soft and delicate wool was often used by the Tartars as padding for the caps worn on their shaven heads.

Baron von Heberstein's description of the vegetable lamb was eagerly read by naturalists all over Europe. The living plant was considered one of the most remarkable examples of spontaneous generation: if a creature of this size could grow from a seed, it was not difficult to understand how simpler animals could be generated in this way. Girolamo Cardano was inspired by Heberstein's account to include a passage on the existence of living plants in his *De Rerum Natura*. He argued that if a being had blood it must have a heart, and that the soil in which a plant grows is not fitted to supply a heart with movement and vital heat. Nevertheless, he did not deny the vegetable lamb's existence, since if there were sponges in the sea, why should there not be similar plant-animals on land? Nor did he consider it impossible that, if the atmosphere was particularly thick and dense, a plant could have sensation and 'imperfect flesh, such as that of molluscs and fishes'. He also knew for a fact that wolves ate the Boramez with avidity, although no other carnivorous animals were wont to touch it.

Cardano's enemy Julius Caesar Scaliger was always ready to attack him with cutting satire and insulting invectives. His *Exotericarum exercitationum*, a solid tome of 1,200 pages, was wholly devoted to a heavy-handed criticism of Cardano. Scaliger had already become notorious through his fierce and scurrilous campaign against Erasmus of Rotterdam, which had disgusted many of his contemporaries. Scaliger was something of a sceptic, and Cardano's more imaginative musings in natural history, like that swan sings at the time of its death, that the bear forms its cub by licking, and that the peacock is deeply ashamed of its ugly legs, gave him ample scope for his vituperative talents. The section about the living plant was no exception. Scaliger chose to pretend that he was wholly convinced by Cardano's account of the Boramez lamb; he repeating all the ludicrous arguments to make them seem even more absurd. He ended his diatribe with the words 'this is merely a little sauce and seasoning to your fable of the Lamb; but I would like to know from you how four distinct legs and their feet can be produced from one stem?' The later commentators on the Boramez question missed the point of this heavy-handed irony altogether; they misinterpreted Scaliger's intention to ridicule Cardano and proposed that Scaliger was just another believer in the vegetable lamb. After Erasmus had died, and an unfounded rumour of Cardano's death had begun to circulate, Scaliger wrote a hypocritical eulogy of these two men, cantingly bewailing that his incisive criticism of their works had led to the premature death of these two notable philosophers. But it was Cardano who was given the satisfaction that Scaliger, who was the elder of these two quarrelsome Italian savants, predeceased him in 1558, mercifully oblivious that posterity would claim that he had wholeheartedly agreed with Cardano on the subject of the Tartar lamb.

The early botanist Claude Duret was even more enthusiastic about the Boramez plant, which he described and figured in his *Histoire Admirable des Plantes*. Of all the trees, bushes and herbs in the world, the vegetable lamb was the one that filled him with most pride and wonder before the creative power of God. It would have been more apposite to question why the Lord had created such a monster in the first place, since the lamb's life was by no means a pleasant one. The Boramez greedily devoured all bushes and herbs near its own stem, but when the crops within its limited reach had been consumed, the wretched creature succumbed to starvation. More often, the lamb died a bloody and violent death. According to legend, God had tried to place the defenceless plant under protection by forbidding all predators to attack it. The wolves did not honour this ancient agreement, however, happily becoming vegetarians to get the opportunity to taste the tender flesh of the Boramez; the earth-bound lamb could do nothing except utter a terrified bleat when surrounded by a pack of wolves coming in for the kill.

According to another obscure old legend about the Boramez, it was one of the first plants created by God: one of them grew in the Garden of Eden. It is unknown whether the figure of the vegetable lamb had a strange, religious significance, or any connection with the early myths of Christianity. There is no direct evidence that this was the case, but the lamb is, after all, the symbol of Christ, whose body could, according to the traditional account of the Transubstantiation, be miraculously resurrected from vegetable products: bread and wine. When the botanist John Parkinson published his *Paradisus Terrestris* in 1629, its beautiful frontispiece depicted Adam and Eve wandering in the Garden, admiring the multitude of plants; in the background, a vegetable lamb is growing in one of the borders. Parkinson had probably been inspired by Guillaume de Saluste du Bartas's poem *La Semaine*, which describes how Adam takes a stroll among the newly created trees and plants in the Garden of Eden, when he is startled to see a Boramez in one of the hedges:

Feeding on grass, and th'airy moisture licking
Such as those Borametz of Schythia bred
Of slender seeds, and with green fodder fed;
Although their bodies, noses, mouths and eyes,
Of new-yeaned lambs have full the form and guise,
And should be very lambs, save that for foot
Within the ground they fix a living root
Which at their navel grows; and dies that day
That they have browzed the neighbouring grass away.

This section of the poem is concluded with a eulogy to the marvellous lamb:

Oh! wondrous nature of God only good,
The beast hath root, the plant hath flesh and blood.
The nimble plant can turn it to and fro,
The nummed beast can neither stir nor goe,
The plant is leafless, branchless, void of fruit,
The beast is lustless, sexless, fireless, mute:
The plant with plants his hungry paunch doth feede,
Th' admired beast is sowen a slender seed.

Throughout the mid-seventeenth century, the Boramez legend was still accepted by the scholars; in their weighty tomes, men like Fortunio Liceti and Athanasius Kircher declared themselves convinced that the vegetable lamb existed, and that it was one of the most remarkable pieces of evidence that spontaneous generation was a reality. Among the few to object were Sir Francis Bacon, who was quite unconvinced that a plant could possess the power of thought and movement, and the German scholar Antonius Deusing, who pointed out that no living person had seen this marvellous lamb-plant. He was answered by the Dutch merchant captain Jan de Struys, who claimed that the Boramez was by no means an uncommon sight in the meadows on the western bank of the Volga. The Tartars harvested some of them, to make their soft, white fleeces into caps. Jan de Struys had several times purchased these skins, and had always been able to sell them for twice the money he had paid when back in Holland. One of these vegetable lamb-skins was kept in the museum of the entomologist Jan Swammerdam.

When, in 1570, Sir Richard Lea had been appointed Queen Elizabeth's ambassador to the court of the Tsar of Russia, he was determined to procure a Boramez skin. He wanted to bring it back to England as evidence that the vegetable lamb really existed, and also because he considered these skins as powerful antidotes against the plague 'and other Noysome diseases'. Several noble Russians assured him that there did 'grow out of the ground certain living creatures in the shape of Lambs, bearing Wooll upon them, very like to the Lambs of England'. A stalk like that of an artichoke grew out of the earth; it had a bud upon it, which grew into the shape of a lamb. The Boramez ate the grass surrounding it, but 'when it had eaten up the grass within its reach it would dye'. The Russians assured Sir Richard that the Tartars were wont to flay the skins off these monstrous lambs and sell them, although these vegetable lambskins were very rare and valuable. But after Sir Richard had ordered a mortar to be sculpted from a large, beautiful agate, which he had brought with him for use as trade goods, the Tsar declared himself willing to trade a coat lined with Boramez skins for this mortar.

On his way back to London, Sir Richard Lea visited the court of the King of Sweden. According to a document kept in the Archives of the Royal Society of London, King Johan III's first question to the English Ambassador was whether he had seen the skin of a vegetable lamb. When Sir Richard replied that he had not only seen, but was actually in possession of several of them, the King envied him greatly, since he had himself for several years been wanting to purchase such a skin. But in spite of the persuasive powers of the Royal money-coffers, Sir Richard was unwilling to sell him the lambskin coat, which he valued far above the 'divers other rich Furrs, and other Rarities of great price' in his baggage.

Sir Richard Lea was very proud of his Tartar lambskin coat. A kinsman of his wife, Mr Edward Smith, several times saw it in his house, and heard the remarkable story of how it was procured. In 1609, Sir Thomas Bodley wanted to purchase the lambskin coat, and even had hopes of exhibiting it before King James, who had expressed an interest to see it. But Sir Richard was unwilling to part with it, and it was not until 1615 that the Tartar lambskin coat was taken to Oxford, probably after the demise of its original owner. But if Sir Richard had expected the Oxford dons to appreciate the rarity of this unique garment, his hopes were in vain. When Edward Smith was visiting the Bodleian Library in 1624, he was shocked to find that the Tartar lambskin coat was hanging in Sir Thomas Bodley's own closet, and that it showed evident signs of wear and tear. Neither the dons nor the librarians knew its rarity and value, and Mr Smith took them to task in no uncertain terms, in a letter to Mr Rouse, the Keeper of the Library. According to the books of account of the Bodleian Library, a glover was paid five shillings to mend the lambskin coat in 1634, and ten years later, further expenditure was incurred for 'sewing, mending and ayring the Tartar lambes coat'. It is not unlikely that it later passed into the Oxford cabinet of curiosities collected by John Tradescant, since the catalogue of the first contents of his museum, published in 1656, mentions a 'coat lyned with *Agnus Scythicus*'. In 1666, the Tartar lambskin coat was discussed at the Royal Society of London. Christopher Wren was asked to inform himself about this curious garment upon his return to Oxford, but still, its later whereabouts remain uncertain. Since the Tartar lambskin coat is stated to be increasingly moth-eaten for each stock-taking of the library, it is likely to have been devoured by insects near the end of the seventeenth century. Interestingly, the books of account of the Bodleian Library mention that a copy of the famous Boramez illustration in Claude Duret's book was painted and framed in 1643, probably for exhibition alongside the lambskin coat. This painting was kept in the Ashmolean Museum as late as 1890, but it cannot be traced today.

Another Scandinavian coveting a Boramez skin was Professor Olaus Wormius, of Copenhagen. When his friend, the Rev. Christian Stougaard, accompanied Prince Valdemar Christian on a journey to Russia, he brought back a fleece of the vegetable lamb as a present for Professor Wormius. It was kept at his famous *Museum Wormianum*, along with an elaborate painting of a Boramez lamb. This museum was later purchased by the King of Denmark, but both fleece and painting were lost in the late eighteenth century. Quite a few vegetable lambskins were kept at various museums in the mid-seventeenth century, but none of them appear to remain today. The trade in Boramez skins to Western travellers was impeded by a report from the German surgeon Engelbert

Kaempfer, who had accompanied a research expedition to Persia and Russia. For many months, he had been looking in vain for a Boramez. The inhabitants of these parts always told him that the vegetable lambs were growing just beyond the next forest, or that the fields where they grew were infested with dangerous brigands with a dislike to Westerners. The persistent German did not let himself be fobbed off, however, until he had scoured most of Tartary in his vain hunt for the elusive lamb. The Tartars wanted to sell Boramez fleeces to him, but it was apparent to Dr Kaempfer that these were skins from unborn (Astrakhan) lambs, which had been dried and prepared. He strongly suspected that the Boramez specimens kept at various museums had the same origin, and that there was no such thing as a vegetable lamb.

It was to take until 1698 before any complete specimen of the vegetable lamb was brought before European naturalists. This year, Sir Hans Sloane, the secretary of the Royal Society of London, demonstrated a strange object, which most resembles a woolly branch of wood with four legs, slightly more than a foot in length. It had arrived in a Chinese cabinet of instruments and curiosities, and had originally belonged to a certain Mr Buckley; this gentleman had purchased it from an Indian merchant who had assured him that he was buying a genuine Boramez. It was apparent to Sir Hans Sloane, however, that the specimen was made from the large root-stock of a fern, which rather resembled the body of an animal, being covered with 'a Down of a dark yellowish Snuff-Colour, shining like Silk, some of it a quarter of an Inch long'. The individual who had manufactured it had cut off the roots from the root-stock, and fashioned four of the stems of the fern's leaves to resemble the lamb's legs.

Much later, in 1725, Sir Hans was able to demonstrate another vegetable lamb before the Royal Society. It belonged to the German physician Johann Philip Breyn, who had been given it by a friend who had purchased it in Russia as a genuine Boramez. Dr Breyn was highly impressed with its animal-like appearance. Indeed, it is likely to be the most skilfully faked Boramez ever constructed, although it has the air of a dapper little fox terrier rather than that of a stolid lamb. Dr Breyn cherished his vegetable lamb, although he realised that it was a manufactured specimen, made from the rootstock of a fern. In the *Philosophical Transactions* of the Royal Society, he ridiculed the credulous scholars and unreliable travellers who were responsible for the wide dissemination of the Boramez lore. None of them had seen the marvellous plant, but had been tricked by the skins and the faked lambs. The commerce with these odd tourist souvenirs seems to have been quite extensive. They were sold by the Russians, Indians and Chinese; the latter being particularly skilful in fabricating the rootstocks into little lambs or dogs. Sir Hans Sloane and Dr Breyn were proven to have been right when the first of these large arborescent ferns were taken to Europe. From its woolly rootstock, the long, straight stems arise; these ferns can be more than twelve feet high, the large leaves included. Carl Linnaeus, who himself had seen a faked vegetable lamb taken from China to Sweden by a traveller, named this species of fern *Polypodium barometz*. In the mid-nineteenth century, some of these ferns were taken to England, where they were successfully cultivated in the Botanic Gardens at Kew by Sir William Hooker; he gave them their present name: *Cibotium barometz*.

Unfortunately, both Sir Hans Sloane's original specimen and Dr Breyn's elegant vegetable lamb seem to have been lost; at least, there is no record of either of them after the mid-eighteenth century. When Britain's foremost connoisseur of vegetable lambs, Mr Henry Lee, searched for Sir Hans Sloane's lamb in the 1880s, he was disappointed to find out that both the vegetable lamb and the Chinese cabinet of surgical instruments and appliances in which it had arrived had been lost or mislaid long ago. Henry Lee claimed that another lamb was kept at the museum of the Royal College of Surgeons at the time of his investigation. Although this statement has been doubted by some historians of this museum, it is hard to completely disprove it, since the vegetable lamb might well have been yet another casualty of the horrific German bombing raid in May 1941, along with Chunee's bones and many other specimens.

But although the number of old Boramez specimens has been sadly diminished through the ravages of time, the vegetable lambs are not yet a completely extinct species. A Boramez lamb, made from the rootstock and stems of a large fern, is kept at the Natural History Museum, South Kensington. It resides in a large old chest of drawers, which has been its home for more than 200 years. This lamb was figured by John and Andrew Rymsdyk in their *Museum Britannicum*, published in 1778, as one of the most curious objects in the British Museum. I have had the opportunity to examine this lamb closely; it is not very well constructed, compared to Dr Breyn's lamb, but evidently very old. It is not, as judged by the contemporary illustration and description, the lamb that was shown to the Royal Society by Sir Hans Sloane in 1697; its legs are straight, while Sir Hans's Chinese specimen was severely bandy-legged, and not even able to stand up without assistance. Mr Henry Lee, who examined this lamb in the 1880s, had no idea of its origins, but a study of Sir Hans Sloane's museum catalogues has convinced me that this great collector in fact had *two* vegetable lambs; it is the second of these, which he had procured in the 1710s or early 1720s, that has been kept for posterity.

Another, much more handsome vegetable lamb has also withstood the ravages of time. Instead of being stored in a chest of drawers like its cousin at the Natural History Museum, it is one of the most curious exhibits of the Museum of Garden History in Lambeth. This specimen is really quite lamb-like, and makes a strange impression on the museum visitors, gazing at them from under its glass cupola; the style of arrangement of its showcase is suggestive of the mid-nineteenth century. It was formerly in the possession of a Cambridgeshire doctor, whose family had owned it for more than 150 years. Perhaps it was once examined by Charles Darwin's grandfather, Dr Erasmus Darwin, who was inspired to incorporate some stanza about the Boramez legend in his *Botanic Garden*, published in 1781. The 'golden hair' of the lamb is clearly an attempt to assimilate the legend to the specimens constructed from fern roots. Strangely enough, Darwin removed its supposed place of growth from Tartary to the Arctic, where the soil would hardly be rich enough to nurture a plant of this kind:

> Cradled in snow, and fanned by Arctic air,
> Shines, gentle Borametz, thy golden hair;
> Rooted in earth, each cloven foot descends,
> And round and round her flexile neck she bends,
> Crops the grey coral moss, and hoary thyme,
> Or laps with rosy tongue the melting rime;
> Eyes with mute tenderness her distant dam,
> And seems to bleat – 'a vegetable lamb.'

In 1887, the former naturalist to the Brighton Aquarium, Mr Henry Lee, published a slender volume, today quite rare, about the vegetable lamb of Tartary. He disregarded Dr Breyn's notions that the faked lambs were the heart of the matter, since the vegetable lamb legend had existed for several hundred years before these specimens were exhibited. Instead, he proposed that the earliest versions of the legend, in which it was emphasised that the lamb was visible only when the fruit of the plant had opened, spoke in favour that the 'vegetable lamb' was, in fact, an early misconception of the cotton plant. Although this theory has been supported by several later writers, there is good reason to doubt Lee's attempt at explanation. After the campaigns of Alexander the Great, the cotton plant had become well known throughout the classical world, but the Greek and Roman annals do not support the hypothesis of any strange myths linking it with vegetable lambs; this plant was also well-known to the old Chinese. It is hard to understand how such a strange misinterpretation of the cotton-plant could possibly have arisen, long after this plant, and its practical usefulness, had become common knowledge.

Instead, there is reason to consider an old Chinese myth, first described by Dr Gustav Schlegel in 1889. A manuscript from the Tang dynasty, written in the middle of the tenth century, described some quite extraordinary methods in Chinese sheep farming. The shepherds waited until the lamb-plants started to grow, and when they were about to sprout, they built a high wall to protect them from the wild beasts coming to devour them. When the lambs were fully grown, the shepherds pulled down the wall, donned cuirasses and colourful robes, and galloped toward the wretched lambs on horseback, beating on drums and clashing cymbals in order to frighten them. The vegetable lambs, whose stems were connected with the earth, were terrified by this attacking horde and tore loose from their moorings, rending their navels with a shriek and running before the shepherds' horses to the water-pasturages. It was particularly emphasised that the lambs must be scared out of their wits to tear lose from their stems; if an attempt was made to cut it off, the vegetable lamb died from the haemorrhage. Dr Schlegel encountered a similar account of 'lambs which grow simultaneously out of the ground' in a manuscript compiled prior to AD 429, speaking in favour of the vegetable lamb legend being very old indeed. Vegetable lambs were also referred to in an eleventh-century manuscript and in the undated statement of a certain Chang Ye about his voyage to the West.

Interestingly, a similar legend was extant among the old Jews. An old Hebrew book entitled the *Talmud Ierosolimitanum*, written by a certain Rabbi Jochanan in the year 436, tells of a strange plant-animal called the

Jeduah. Its form was like that of a lamb, but it grew from a stem. When the hunters fired arrows through this stem, the creature fell to the earth and died. Its bones, put into the mouth of a soothsayer, endowed him with the gift of prophecy. According to another version, the Jeduah had a human shape, and it was most ferocious, attacking any creature unwise enough to venture into its limited boundary. When it had devoured all the foliage within the tether of its stem, this strange being died from starvation; more often, it was killed by hunters who cut or shot off its stem.

It can thus be proven that Chinese and Jewish traditions about vegetable lambs, similar to the classical European version as told to Sigismund von Heberstein in 1526, existed already in the fifth century AD. These traditions particularly pointed out that the lamb grew from a powerful stem connected with its navel and did not develop in large fruits – a claim that makes Henry Lee's hypothesis extremely unlikely. Similarly, Gustav Schlegel's own theory, that the vegetable lamb was really the camel, can be disregarded as absurd and in complete disagreement with the known facts about the Boramez legend. A later hypothesis, published by Dr Berthold Laufer in 1915, that the vegetable lamb was a misconception of the thready excrescences of certain seashells, seems equally unconvincing. Instead, the vegetable lamb legend seems to have been taken over from a pre-existing Chinese tradition, which existed already in the fifth century, and probably even earlier. It is impossible to state its definite origin, but it is unlikely to have been either the cotton-plant, the camel, or the pinna sea-shells. The legend is likely to have been spread from China to other parts of the Orient, like India and Tartary; it was first encountered by Western explorers in the fourteenth century.

It is more difficult to explain why the vegetable lamb myth became even more widespread in the seventeenth century, when the non-existence of the vegetable 'water-sheep' should have become evident to the Chinese and the Tartars. Some sources indicate that the Tartars enjoyed making fools of the Western explorers who came to search for the Boramez plant, deliberately feeding them tall stories about the vegetable lamb and its strange habits; the incorporation of the Boramez into scientific zoology made them succeed beyond their wildest hopes. For years to come, scientific expeditions venturing into Tartary kept a regular lookout for the vegetable lamb, but without finding any other trace of them than the skins and faked lamb specimens sold to them by the inscrutable Orientals.

As late as 1791, the French botanist Dr de la Croix followed Guillaume du Bartas and Erasmus Darwin in extolling the strange lamb-plant in a poem translated by that erudite biographer of the vegetable lamb, Mr Henry Lee. An explorer is on his way to Asia, when:

In his way he sees a monstrous birth,
The Borametz arises from the earth:
Upon a stalk is fixed a living brute,
A rooted plant bears quadruped for fruit,
It has a fleece, nor does it want for eyes,
And from its brows two woolly horns arise.
The rude and simple country people say
It is an animal that sleeps by day
And wakes by night, though rooted to the ground,
To feed on grass within its reach around.
The flavour of Ambrosia its flesh
Pervades; and the red nectar, rich and fresh,
Which vineyards of fair Burgundy produce
Is less delicious than its ruddy juice.

The Barnacle Geese

Sir John Mandeville's *Travels* were immensely popular among his contemporaries. Numerous medieval manuscripts of this early best seller still exist, many of them beautifully written, with illuminated and hand-coloured miniature illustrations. After the advent of book printing, the gouty old Knight's adventures were translated into English, Latin, Spanish, German, Italian, Czech, Irish and Danish, and became one of the most commonly read books of the time. But in the late eighteenth century, suspicious historians began to examine Sir John's masterpiece closer: they found that it almost entirely consisted of unacknowledged extracts from other, earlier travellers, with some imaginative additions from Mandeville's own pen. As a result, Mandeville's *Travels* were considered a worthless fraud and plagiarism. Some historians even suspected that there had never been any Sir John Mandeville: his alleged reminiscences were instead the work of a Liège physician named Jean de Bourgogne, also known as Jean à la Barbe, or Bearded John. In our own time, Mandeville has achieved a well-deserved renaissance, however: although his memoirs are definitely a forgery, literary historians agree that they have been compiled in a particularly skilful manner, and presented in a forceful and stylish prose.

We today know that the part of Mandeville's *Travels* that dealt with the vegetable lamb was plagiarised from the reminiscences of the much-travelled Italian monk Odorico of Pordenone. That he had eaten a piece of the lamb was Mandeville's own invention, however; the strict Franciscan monk would not have dared to eat of such a monstrous being without the sanction of the Pope. After the Tartars had described the vegetable lamb, Friar Odorico told them about a similar wonder of nature that occurred in certain Scottish Isles: a particular kind of geese grew on trees, and hung by their beaks from the branches of the goose-trees until mature and ready to fly away. In the *Livre des Merveilles*, a medieval manuscript kept at the Bibliothèque Nationale in Paris, this scene is symbolised by a beautiful miniature illustration. The Orientals solemnly hand a vegetable lamb over to Friar Odorico and his companions, who give them, in return, a branch of the Scottish goose-tree; the East and the West meet here, for one of the first times, and exchange their greatest marvels.

The earliest origin of the barnacle goose myth is, like that of the vegetable lamb of Tartary, unclear. The earliest authoritative account of these marvellous birds is that of Giraldus Cambrensis in 1187, but certain obscure earlier sources may well be alluding to them. Nor is it known exactly where the barnacle geese myth originated. Arab and Chinese versions are known, but several sources point to Britain. The majority of early writers place the breeding-place of the barnacle geese in Ireland or Scotland. A famous riddle in the eighth-century *Book of Exeter* asks:

In a narrow was my web, and beneath the wave I lived;
Underflowen by the flood; in the mountain-billows
Low was I besunken; in the sea I waxed
Over-covered with the waves, clinging with my body
To a wandering wood – .
Quick the life I had, when I from the clasping came
Of the billows, of the beam-wood, in my black array;
White in part were my pranked garments fair,
When the Lift upheaved me, me a living creature,

Wind from wave upblowing; and as wide as far
Bore me o'er the baths of seals – Say what's my name?

According to some philologists, the correct answer is – a barnacle goose.

The learned Giraldus Cambrensis, who had visited Ireland during the reign of Henry II, wrote in his *Topographia Hiberniae* that this country harboured a kind of geese called *Bernacae*, which were formed in the most extraordinary way. They were produced from logs of fir timber tossed along by the sea, hanging by their beaks like seaweed and deriving their nourishment from the sap of the wood and the froth of the sea. When very young, their bodies were surrounded with shells, but later they grew a strong coat of feathers and were able to tear loose from the log and fly away. These barnacle geese were never seen to breed, nor to hatch eggs or build their nests, since new individuals were constantly spontaneously generated out at sea. Bishops and religious men in Ireland ate these geese with relish, even during Lent, arguing that they could not be counted as meat, since they were neither flesh nor born of flesh, but creatures bred from tree and water. A roast goose, served with a bottle of Burgundy from the cellars, must have been a welcome respite from the tiresome fasting period. The strict Giraldus doubted whether this practice was really pleasing to God, however, and he made a most astute analogy. He compared the Bishops eating these geese to a gluttonous savage devouring one leg of Adam, our first parent; although the First Man was not born of flesh, the cannibal in question could not be adjudged innocent of having eaten meat. Pope Innocent III agreed with him: at the Fourth General Lateran Council in 1215, he issued a Bull forbidding the eating of barnacle geese during Lent; this must have led to much bitter murmuring and gnashing of teeth among less ascetic monks.

According to another version of the barnacle goose myth, certain trees near the Scottish coast bore fruits from which the geese were developed, hanging from the tree's branches by their beaks. The goose-tree was always growing near the beach, its crown leaning out over the water to enable the geese to plunge into the waves when mature. In his thirteenth-century bestiary, the Frenchman Pierre le Picard told another story: the birds dropped from the tree's branches like pears when it was shaken by a storm. The birds that fell onto the shore were crushed to death, but those falling into the water were saved. In the usual moralising tone of the bestiaries, this wonder is given a parallel in human life: the people who are not washed in water (baptised) when young are as utterly lost as the crushed and broken birds on the stony shore, when they face God after the Last Judgement.

The majority of medieval writers placed the goose-tree somewhere in the British Isles: England, Scotland, Ireland or the Orkneys. Gervase of Tilbury, writing in 1211, stated that great numbers of geese grew upon the young willow trees that abounded near the Abbey of Faversham in Kent; these birds were eaten as 'fish' during Lent. One of the earliest opponents to the barnacle goose myth was King Frederick II, who kept a large menagerie at his court in Sicily, and wrote one of the earliest treatises on hawking. He considered this myth to be absurd, and presumed it to have arisen from ignorance about the actual nesting-places of these birds. He was seconded by the learned Dominican Albertus Magnus, who was otherwise a firm supporter of spontaneous generation. In his *De Animalibus Historia*, written about 1250, he declared that he and his friends had several times seen the so-called barnacle geese lay eggs and hatch them out in the ordinary way. When another learned cleric, Aeneas Sylvius Piccolomini, was sent on a secret mission to the Court of King James II of Scotland in 1435, he made inquiries about the true whereabouts of the celebrated Scottish goose-trees, perhaps hoping to bring a branch from one of them with him to Rome. Although the King and his entourage had little to tell him, the undaunted Piccolomini travelled to the northern parts of Scotland, but without finding any barnacle geese. Even then, the natives assured him that the goose-trees were growing in the Orkneys. Piccolomini, who was to become Pope under the name Pius II, later wisely commented on his wild goose chase in Scotland with the words that wonders always recede further away, when diligently sought after.

A new era in the annals of the barnacle geese began in 1527, when the Scottish historian Hector Boethius, who was a Professor at the University of Paris, published his *Historia Scotorum*, which contained a section on the barnacle geese, or *Claiks*, as he called them. He was well aware of the legend that these birds were generated from fruits from trees near the ocean, but was inclined to disbelieve it; he had sailed through the seas where these wonders were said to occur, but without finding a single specimen of this remarkable tree. Instead, he had once seen a huge tree trunk that was bored through with worms and had a quantity of barnacles hanging from it. When opened and examined, these barnacles seemed to have heads, feet and feathers like perfectly shaped little birds. People came from miles away to see this wonderful bird-tree, and it was finally deposited in the church of Saint Andrew, beside the town of Tyre. Boethius believed that the worms inside the log had been generated by 'the nature of the Ocean sea', and that they later developed into barnacles, which in their turn became fully-fledged birds.

All the sixteenth-century writers of cosmographies and encyclopaedias on natural history reviewed the barnacle goose myth in detail. One of the most erudite accounts, illustrated with a beautiful woodcut of the goose-tree, was in Ulysses Aldrovandi's *Ornithologia*. At this time, three versions of the old myth existed in parallel, causing some confusion among the naturalists. The early botanical writer Claude Duret, who had shown such enthusiasm before the vegetable lamb, dedicated an entire chapter in his *Histoire Admirable des Plantes* to the trees that were capable of breeding living creatures. Firstly, he reviewed the myth of the Scottish goose-tree, with the birds hanging from their beaks from the branches, before plunging fully-fledged into a small pond that providence had placed just under this marvellous tree, like in Du Bartas's *La Semaine*:

> So slowe Boötes underneath him sees
> In th'icy isles, those goslings hatched of trees,
> Whose fruitful leaves, falling into the water,
> Are turned (they say) to living fowls soon after;

Himself, Duret preferred another version of the myth, in which the fruits of the tree could develop into birds first when they had fallen into the water. He also reviewed, and illustrated, an even taller tale: namely that certain trees in Ireland had fruits which developed into fowls if they fell on dry land, and into fishes if they fell into the sea. This marvellous tree was also praised by the eloquent Du Bartas:

> ...that Tree from off whose trembling top
> Both swimming shoals, and flying troops do drop:
> I mean the Tree now in *Juterna* growing,
> Whose leaves disperst by *Zephyr's* wanton-blowing,
> Are methamorphos'd both in form and matter;
> On Land to Fowles, to Fishes in the Water.

Other seventeenth-century writers doubted the existence of an actual goose-tree, preferring the version of Boethius that worms generated from rotting timber could develop into barnacles and later into geese:

So, rotten sides of broken ships do change
To barnacles, O transformation strange!
'Twas first a green tree; then a gallant hull;
Lastly a mushroom; then a flying gull.

In 1596, a party of Dutch explorers, who were searching for the Northwest Passage to China, had nearly been shipwrecked in a violent storm. Their vessel was beached on an uninhabited, snowy island belonging to the desolate Novaja Zemilja archipelago. Here, they unexpectedly encountered a large colony of barnacle geese, which did not, however, act as described in the books of natural history. Instead of hanging by their beaks from the branches of the goose-tree, or growing from waterlogged logs of wood, they were peacefully resting on their eggs, and their nests were scattered among the snowy ridges of the island. The geese were rudely awakened when the starving Dutchmen charged forth to seize them, and flew up cackling 'Rot! Rot!' The Dutchmen only managed to tackle one of them, which they cooked and devoured, served with a huge omelette made from sixty of the birds' eggs. The German naturalist Antonius Deusing, who had been active in the campaign against the vegetable lamb, published another thesis about the barnacle geese in 1659, in which he doubted the traditional account of their origin. He referred to the Dutch travellers' tale, which had been published by Gerrit van Veer in 1609: since it had now been proven that the birds in question nested and lay eggs, the old tradition about their miraculous generation from barnacles adherent to rotting timber seemed more ludicrous than ever. Deusing also queried why no one had ever been able to cultivate the goose-tree in a botanical garden, or even to bring a branch or log of it to be examined by men of observation. In Sir Joseph Banks's collection of theses on birds, kept at the British Library, can be found two other seventeenth-century works devoted to elucidating the riddle of the tree-born geese. In his 1665 thesis *Ex Physicis de Ortu Avis Britannicae*, Dr Johannes Ernestus Hering likewise refuted the opinion that these geese were developed from the sea, from trees, from putrefaction, or from other matter, according to the marvellous ideas abounding at the time. In a later thesis, the *Discursus Historico-Physicus de Avis Britannicae*, Dr Georgius Funccius agreed with his colleagues that the legend of the barnacle geese seemed wholly exaggerated.

These sceptical German savants were answered by their countryman Athanasius Kircher, whose great appetite for curiosities had got the better of whatever sound judgement he possessed. The imaginative Jesuit proposed that even though the geese laid their eggs on the icy ridges of Novaja Zemilja, these eggs fell into the water when the ice melted, and floated, like a row of miniature buoys, down to the Orkneys. Their contents stuck to rotten timber and later metamorphosed into complete birds. Another distinctly odd interpretation of the barnacle goose myth was proposed by Father Philip Buonanni, in 1681. This clerical gentleman believed that immense quantities of eggs of these birds were laid on the ice, and later fell into the cold sea; enough eggs to nourish all Europe, if they could only be collected! When the ice melted, the eggs broke and their contents were mixed with the water. After floating to the Orkneys and Hebrides, these 'scrambled eggs' developed into perfect birds after adhering to old logs.

The learned Dane, Professor Olaus Wormius, had several barnacles at his museum, where he classified them as young geese. A French colleague had told him that many barnacle geese, some driven on foot, others 'salted' and brought in barrels, were taken from Normandy to Paris during Lent, to be eaten as shellfish by religious men. Some worldly Parisians, fearing that their partiality to roast goose might endanger their immortal souls, had consulted theologians from Sorbonne University; the learned clerics replied that their souls were in no danger whatsoever, since these geese could well be considered as fish. Thomas Bartholin, the foremost pupil of Olaus Wormius, shared his interest in barnacle geese. From his friend Otto Sperling, he had received a couple of barnacles, the innards of which he had examined closely with a microscope. It was soon clear to him that this creature was 'an insect or a worm' rather than a bird embryo; Thomas Bartholin was thus the first to refute the barnacle goose myth through his own experimental observations. His accurate drawings of the opened barnacle were the earliest of their kind. In his catalogue of the Royal Museum in Copenhagen, Thomas Bartholin's nephew Holger Jacobsen described the barnacles and recounted the barnacle goose legend at length, although he ended his discourse with the guarded comment: 'but whether real geese are produced is a matter of comment among the more sagacious'.

The legend of the barnacle geese was the longest-lived part of the traditional belief in the spontaneous generation of vertebrates. Both in Scandinavia, Germany and France, these wonderful birds found new friends well into the eighteenth century. In 1735, the historian Jonas Ramus declared himself convinced that geese were every day spontaneously generated from wrecks and waterlogged trunks of trees near the Norwegian coast. Another Norwegian, Bishop Hans Egede, the author of a book on the geography and natural history of Greenland, considered the 'treeborn ducks' as one of the foremost natural curiosities of these parts. They were developed from a viscous substance that adhered to waterlogged trunks of wood. A little worm was first engendered and later developed further into a barnacle, which was transubstantiated into a fully-fledged goose, which pecked a hole in the barnacle's shell and flew out. A similarly absurd hypothesis was advocated by the Frenchman Dezallier d'Argenville: the goose forced open the shells of the barnacle, pulled the animal out, and deposited its egg in there like some bizarre marine cuckoo, leaving the wretched crustacean in charge of the care and nurture of its offspring.

The French debate about the barnacle geese was finally ended in the 1780s, by the zoologists Guéttard and De la Faille. M. Guéttard published a critical review of the many different descriptions of the tree-growing birds, to lay the ghost of the barnacle geese once and for all. He was amazed that there were still people believing that barnacles could develop into young geese. De la Faille had cultivated barnacles on rotten logs of wood in an aquarium, without observing any signs that they would metamorphose into young birds. Like the majority of ornithologists, he was aware that there existed a particular kind of black geese that occurred in considerable flocks in autumn and winter, although they were never seen to breed or hatch their young. De la Faille was well aware, however, that the birds had normal genital organs; he presumed that they were hatching their goslings in some desolate Arctic territory. From the scholarly journals, this final debunking of the barnacle goose myth spread to the newspapers. The journalists were amazed that such a ludicrous old fallacy could have remained within scientific zoology for more than 800 years. Since this time, the expression 'l'histoire d'un canard' has been used to deride implausible tall tales; the present-day expression *canard* is thus a direct descendant of the tree-borne Scottish geese. M. Guéttard recorded that, at his time of writing, the habit of eating barnacle geese during Lent still remained among the common people. In the British Isles, this ancient custom remained even longer. In 1913, an Ulster clergyman wrote to inform the Zoological Society of London that his parishioners freely ate barnacle geese during the fasting period.

Carl Linnaeus was well aware of the barnacle goose legend, although as a rigid opponent of spontaneous generation, he was of course wholly unconvinced of the marvellous origins of these birds. In his system of zoology, he gave the tribe of small, dark sea geese the name *Branta bernicla*, as a memorial of their supposed origin from the barnacles. Today, ornithologists differ between two species of black geese: the Brent Goose (*Branta bernicla* of Linnaeus) and the Barnacle Goose (*Branta leucopsis* of Becht). Neither of them breeds anywhere in the British Isles or the European continent, but are winter visitors to these parts. The Barnacle Goose breeds in Spitzbergen and east Greenland; the Brent Goose in the Arctic, including Spitzbergen and the Novaja Zemilja. The reason why these geese were accused of growing from trees or from old logs was that huge flocks of these birds came to Germany, Holland and Britain every year. Since no person had ever seen them nest or hatch their young, it was widely presumed that they were spontaneously generated at sea. The statement of Albertus Magnus that he had seen barnacle geese nest in Germany cannot be uncritically accepted, since these birds nowadays do not nest or breed anywhere near these parts. It cannot, of course, be excluded that the black geese had been natives of Germany during this early period, but if this had really been the case, it is inexplicable why other writers had not used this fact as an argument against their generation from trees or barnacles.

Linnaeus was also inspired by the barnacle goose legend when he named the barnacles in his system of zoology. He called these remarkable creatures *Lepas anatiferae* (anatiferae=duck-breeding). As larvae, they lead an active and free-swimming life, developing through three stages, and considerably changing its appearance. In its third stage, it has developed its bivalve shells but still moves around vigorously, paddling with its six pairs of forked legs. The barnacle then selects the spot where it desires to spend the remainder of its existence, and presses its head against the surface; some kind of cement pours from its antennae, hardening at once in the water, and the barnacle is settled for life. It then grows rapidly; its shells are replaced with hard, calcified plates, and its legs become featherlike tentacles. The zoologist Sir Ray Lankester likened the strange life cycle of the barnacle to an active, healthy schoolboy suddenly having his head glued to the pavement, thus being forced to spend his entire adult life upside down, kicking food into his mouth with his feet!

The End of Spontaneous Generation?

During the second half of the seventeenth century, the spontaneous generation controversy became increasingly heated. On one side were an unholy alliance of atomists, Paracelsists, Cartesians and Aristotelians; from vastly different standpoints, they all supported spontaneous generation. On the other side was a steadily growing number of experimental biologists, who attempted to disprove spontaneous generation through their own observations. These biologists had support, however, from the religious traditionalists, who believed that God had once, at the beginning of time, created all animals and plants that were intended to inhabit the Earth. Since it was His intention that they were to be fruitful and propagate their species, He did not need any help in populating the Earth, least of all through spontaneous generation of various foul creatures from putrid matter.

One of the scientists who began to doubt the concept of spontaneous generation was the Florentine court physician Francesco Redi. In the 1660s, he planned an ambitious series of experiments to prove or disprove the equivocal generation of insects. He procured a large number of animal carcasses, from as many species as possible: snakes, lions, tigers, buffaloes, frogs, oxen, pigs, and many kinds of birds. He incubated putrid chunks of meat from these carcasses in large glass flasks, while a number of large fishes were allowed to decompose in bottles filled with unclean, stinking water. The same kinds of maggots were seen to develop in the dead tissues of many different species, from lion to swordfish. Furthermore, several different kinds of maggots and larvae could be collected from the putrid body of a snake. This disproved the old dogma that the nature of the putrid matter determined what kinds of creatures could be spontaneously generated from it. Redi also noticed that many large bluebottle flies were buzzing about over his experimental material, attracted by its odours. He made another experiment, incubating some lumps of meat in open vessels, and others in vessels covered by a net;

the result was that no larvae developed in the flasks covered by a fine-meshed net that kept the flies out. Similarly, dead fishes could be put in sealed vessels without any formation of maggots. Redi at once realised the importance of this observation: the adult flies laid their eggs on the putrid pieces of meat, and their larvae developed inside them.

In 1668, Francesco Redi published the book *Esperienze intorno alla generazione degli insetti*, which was published in a Latin translation three years later, and established his reputation as one of the great naturalists of his time. His experiment with the bluebottle flies and the pieces of putrid meat was simple and straightforward enough to be repeated at many universities around Europe; one after the other, the biologists had to agree that he was right. Further experimental support came from the physiologist Marcello Malpighi, who had proven that the supposed 'equivocal generation' of insects from the leaves of plants could be explained from the fact that they were developed from the extremely small eggs deposited there by adult insects. The spontaneous generation dogma was also severely undermined by the growth of microscopy. Already in Jan Swammerdam's *Historia insectorum generalis*, published in 1669, it was pointed out that even the most minute insect, which had previously been considered as little more than a speck of sand with wings, proved to be quite complicated when seen through the lens of a microscope.

The great Antonie van Leeuwenhoek systematically studied the development of various insects, using his powerful microscopes. He kept several fleas enclosed until he clearly observed them lay eggs, and then carried these eggs in his pocket until they hatched. To his surprise, an intermediate stage was observed: the flea larvae, which later spun cocoons and pupated. Inside these pupas, the adult fleas could be observed. Leeuwenhoek carried several families of lice in his stockings, allowing them to feed from his own flesh while he studied their development, and his wife was recruited to carry insect eggs in her bosom to keep them warm. The discovery of the life cycles of these insects was not only of great service to entomology, but also undermined the concept that these beings could be spontaneously generated from sweat and filth. Leeuwenhoek described the genitals and spermatozoa of many species of insects, and was well aware of their function. A particularly difficult matter for Leeuwenhoek was the alleged spontaneous generation of eels. Already Aristotle had observed that eels had no apparent sign of spawn, milt or sex, and it was not until 1691 that Leeuwenhoek discovered the uterus of the eel, and demonstrated the unborn little eels therein. When the imaginative Father Philip Buonanni, whose theories about oceans of floating 'scrambled eggs' developing into barnacle geese we already have encountered, tried to challenge Redi's experiments, Leeuwenhoek answered him in no uncertain terms. He was particularly outraged by the fact that many naturalists still differed between 'complete' and 'incomplete' animals. In his description of the fly's facet eye, he declared himself amazed that there were still people believing that such a beautiful, complex little animal as a fly could ever be spontaneously generated from putrefying matter, however small it might appear from the arbitrary scale of Man. The British physician and poet Richard Blackmore, an enemy of spontaneous generation, was much impressed by the recent advances in microscopic science:

> But the late inquirers in their glasses find
> That every insect, of each different kind,
> In its own egg, cheered by the solar rays,
> Organs involv'd and latent life displays;
> This truth, discover'd by sagacious art,
> Does all Lucretian arrogance subvert.
> Proud wits, your frenzy own, and, overcome
> By Reason's force, be now for ever dumb.

Even Francesco Redi and his adherents had to accept certain exceptions from their anathema against spontaneous generation. Redi himself readily admitted the spontaneous generation of gall-flies. Other biologists were deeply puzzled by the fact that Leeuwenhoek had, with the same microscopes he had used to disprove the spontaneous generation of parasitic insects, discovered the existence of protozoa and bacteria. Many of them considered that these minute beings, which could not be observed to possess any genital parts, could only be spontaneously generated. Many physicians were also of the opinion that lice could be spontaneously generated from human sweat and filth, nor was there much opposition to the concept that intestinal worms were spontaneously generated from the contents of the gut. The followers of Redi eagerly sought a way to disprove this concept, but without success due to the complex life cycles of these worms. Instead, some philosophers speculated that God had intended all species of parasitic insects and worms to serve as the constant companions of humankind. Already old Adam had harboured all known species of lice, fleas, mites and parasitic worms, although in the Garden of Eden they had all been benign, friendly and inoffensive companions, who had lived together with Adam in perfect harmony. After the fall of Man, this strange truce was ended, and all the parasites were instructed by God to torment him, and his descendants in perpetuity, in the most cruel fashion.

In the late eighteenth century, several naturalists tried to develop tapeworms by feeding animals worm eggs, but without success. In *Lebende Würmer im lebenden Menschen*, a standard work on parasitic worms, published in 1819, the German helminthologist Dr Bremser considered the development of tapeworms as the strongest evidence that spontaneous generation was a reality. It would take until the 1850s before this long-lived error in parasitology, which had done much to impede the scientific investigation of these parasitic worms, was finally disproved. By this time, several parasitologists suspected that the tapeworms were developed from a species of cystic worms called *Cysticercus cellulosae*. After the pig had consumed the tapeworm eggs occurring in human excrements, these cystic worms, which can be considered the larvae of the tapeworm, developed in porcine muscular tissue. When the pig is slaughtered and its pork eaten, the larvae develop into adult tapeworms inside the human alimentary canal. The German parasitologist Friedrich Küchenmeister planned a clever experiment to test this hypothesis. Unwilling try it himself, he had obtained the consent of the Government to use a convicted murderer as a 'guinea-pig'. The unsuspecting murderer was given a meal of worm-infested bacon, and after he had been executed, an autopsy was performed and the intestines were carefully examined. To his delight, Dr Küchenmeister found several young tapeworms. The German government commended Küchenmeister for his important work in solving a major health problem, although several British and French periodicals considered it characteristic of the barbaric mentality of the Teutonic race that unsuspecting prisoners were used as 'guinea-pigs' in dangerous experiments.

At about the same time as Dr Küchenmeister was active in the German prison kitchen, another stronghold of spontaneous generation fell in France. In the 1850s, the biologists were still unable to explain the appearance of bacteria and infusoria in sterile broths; many of them still inclined toward the hypothesis that these minute beings, which had no discernible genitals, could develop only through spontaneous generation. Moreover, in France, the spontaneous generation debate was becoming increasingly heated at this time. The French translation of Charles Darwin's *Origin of Species*, by Madame Royer, had been prefaced by a violent, anti-Catholic diatribe of her own concoction, and many religious people considered both Darwinism and the belief in spontaneous generation as a serious threat against religion. In 1860, the French Academy of Sciences offered a prize for experiments that could prove or disprove the spontaneous generation of bacteria and infusoria. Four years later, this prize was claimed by the great Louis Pasteur, who had incubated his media in flasks with long, curving necks that protected their contents from contamination with bacteria, fungal spores and other microbes. If the contents of the flask were boiled, and the neck kept intact, no microbial life appeared, but as soon as the neck was broken off, permitting contamination from the outside, micro-organisms appeared. Pasteur was widely applauded by his contemporaries, particularly by his religious countrymen. At a brilliant scientific soirée at the Sorbonne, held before the social elite of Paris, Pasteur solemnly proclaimed that 'Life is a germ, and a germ is life' and boasted that 'Never will the doctrine of spontaneous generation recover from the mortal blow of this simple experiment'. Although some conservative biologists declared themselves unconvinced by his reasoning, and defended spontaneous generation well into the end of the century, the vast majority of scientists and educated laymen supported Pasteur in the controversy.

In the sixteenth and seventeenth centuries, the philosophers and zoologists had no difficulty at all in classifying the living things on earth into two kingdoms. Those that moved, ate things, and grew to a certain predetermined size were animals, whereas those that did not move or eat, and grew indefinitely, were plants. The vegetable lamb and the barnacle geese were a conundrum to the early biologists, since these monstrous beings were part animals, part plants. They were fitted into a separate kingdom called zoophytes, together with certain submarine sponges. At the time of Carl Linnaeus and the other great taxonomists of the eighteenth century, the vegetable lamb and the barnacle geese had already been ousted from scientific zoology, and the border between animals and plants seemed more impenetrable than ever. Throughout the nineteenth century, the various newly discovered micro-organisms were distributed between the animal and the vegetable kingdoms according to the same time-honoured criteria: the protozoa, that could be observed to eat and move about, were considered as animals, while the fungi, algae, and bacteria were considered as plants. The immense progress in modern biology has made this old-fashioned taxonomy increasingly out-of-date. The discovery of the fundamental differences between procaryotic and eucaryotic cells has given the procaryotes: bacteria and blue-green algae, a kingdom of their own called Monera. Between the higher animals on one side, and the plants and fungi on the other, is also the kingdom Protista, containing protozoa and protophytes; within modern taxonomy, the bacteria and the unicellular eucaryotes have thus usurped the position once held by the vegetable lamb and the barnacle geese. Another interesting fact is that the old criterion that plants must be immobile is not always upheld in modern biology. Certain forms of plants actually have mobile gametes, but unlike the barnacle geese, they have to rely on their feeble cilia and flagella for a short and jerky ride, rather than to fly underneath the firmament on powerful wings.

The boundary between 'living' and 'non-living' has also become increasingly blurred, due to the immense advances in molecular genetics and microbiology. The existence of viruses was first proposed in the latter half of the nineteenth century, but it was not until the advent of electron microscopy that these subcellular agents could be studied more closely. A virus can be defined as a core of nucleic acid (either RNA or DNA) surrounded by a protein coat. It must use the metabolic machinery of a living host organism in order to replicate and produce more viral particles. The French virologist and Nobel Laureate André Lwoff proclaimed that 'whether or not viruses should be regarded as organisms is a matter of taste'. But if they are not living, what are they? Clearly not just pieces of DNA or RNA with lumps of protein hanging about them. It is amazing to contemplate that when a virus infects a cell, its nucleocapsid is taken into the cytoplasm and the DNA or RNA is finally incorporated into the genetic material of the still living cell, which is thus tricked into producing a multitude of viral proteins. Some of these shut off the normal activity of the cell, others are the components of the viral capsid and structure. At one stage, the 'virus' is thus a stretch of genetic material, a set of proteins and an 'intention' to form a complete virion. It would be incorrect to claim that the virus particle is spontaneously generated, however, since its assembly is non-random and highly specific; viruses have millennia of biological experience.

One step further down the line are the viroids, a group of plant pathogens that consist of circular strands of RNA, 250–575 bases long. They have no structural components, do not code for any proteins, and are dependent on the machinery of a living cell for replication. Their primitive design does not prevent these viroids from being significant pathogens: they cause the so-called 'Cadang-Cadang' disease of coconut palms and the 'planta macho' disease of tomatoes. The newly discovered prions at present represent the lowest form of self-replicating, parasitic 'life'. The prion diseases are a group of neurodegenerative maladies that are transmissible through inoculation and through dietary exposure to infected tissues. An abnormal isoform of a host glycoprotein seems to be the central, and probably the sole, infectious agent. The classical example of prion diseases is Kuru, a syndrome of slow degeneration of the brain transmitted by the practice, in parts of New Guinea, of eating the brains of deceased relatives in certain rituals. Today, the best-known prion disease is bovine spongiform encephalopathy (BSE), or mad cow disease, caused by the feeding of cattle with dietary protein supplements that had been 'enriched' with offal from sheep afflicted with scrapie, another prion disease.

Spontaneous Generation and the Origins of Life

During the French debate about spontaneous generation, one of the strongest argument proposed by Louis Pasteur's adversaries was that if living beings could not be generated from nonliving matter, how had life on earth then originated in the first place? This question is still valid for those who do not accept the dogma of divine creation. In the original 1859 edition of the *Origin of Species*, Charles Darwin avoided discussing spontaneous generation and the origin of life, apart from suggesting that all life on Earth evolved from a common ancestor. Cautious not to offend mainstream religious opinion more than he already had, he wrote that 'the Creator' had originally breathed life 'into a few forms or into one'. His supporter, the German physiologist and philosopher Ernst

Haeckel, suggested that the first living organism on Earth had formed through spontaneous generation: the gradual synthesis of more and more complex molecules, to achieve a primitive protocell. Some inspired speculations by Charles Darwin, about the origin of life, may well have been influenced by Ernst Haeckel's writings. In 1871, Darwin wrote in a private letter that if 'some warm little pond, with all sorts of ammonia and phosphoric salts, light, heat, electricity, &c., present' existed, any protein compound formed would be likely to undergo further metabolism rather than to be degraded, since there was at this time no other living matter. His eloquent grandfather, Dr Erasmus Darwin, had prophetically expressed a similar opinion in his *Temple of Nature*:

Then, whilst the sea at their coeval birth,
Surge over surge, involved the shoreless earth;
Nursed by warm sun-beams in primeval caves
Organic life began beneath the waves,
Hence without parent by spontaneous birth
Rise the first speck of animated earth.

In 1924, the Russian biochemist Aleksandr Ivanovich Oparin proposed that life had evolved through spontaneous generation of colloidal gels with the basic properties of life. Life on earth had appeared suddenly, by chance, but in a way completely explicable in terms of physics and chemistry. Even a communist firebrand like Oparin had a certain grudging respect for Louis Pasteur, and he had to concede that the experiments of this great Frenchman had conclusively proven that spontaneous generation was no longer a reality. Instead, Oparin cleverly proposed that once life had appeared on earth, further spontaneous generation was precluded since the colloid precursors in question would be consumed by the life that already existed. In 1936, Oparin revised his theory somewhat; now, he attacked the concept of spontaneous generation and saw life on earth as a natural stage in the evolution of matter. The first living thing on Earth that could itself procreate its species had developed as the result of a long, time-consuming series of chemical reactions, resulting in the formation of increasingly complex molecules, finally resulting in the formation of primitive cellular organisms.

Experimental studies of molecular evolution have established that the amino acid sequences of macromolecules in various organisms are much closer related than could be expected merely from chance: the same protein can be found in a corn plant, a microbe, a bullfrog and a human being. This provides strong evidence for the unity of life: that all living organisms on Earth evolve from one common ancestor. It is not known exactly when this earliest living being on Earth came into existence. The planet itself was condensed from a huge cloud of gas about 4.5 billion years ago. The earliest known microfossils, from Warrawoona in Western Australia, are 3.5 billion years old. These fossils contain bacterium-like bodies and laminated sedimentary structures resembling algal mats. Some of them resemble still extant chemoautotrophic and photoautotrophic procaryotic morphotypes. Studies of carbon isotype rations of kerogen in the Warrawoona sediments have indicated that photosynthesising, or even cyanobacterium-like, organisms existed as early as 3.5 billion years ago. These bacteria are quite highly advanced, and capable of oxygen producing photoautotrophy. This would imply that life on earth had, at this stage, already existed for quite a prolonged period of time, as would the striking morphological diversity of the species identified in the Warrawoona sediments. Furthermore, a recent physical analysis of certain west Greenland fossil carbon deposits older than 3.85 billion years provide evidence that life on earth existed already at this time, since there is a predominance of the lighter over the heavier carbon isotype, a characteristic feature of biological carbon assimilation. Since the young planet has been assumed to be quite uninhabitable during the first 500 million years of its existence, due to continuous bombardment of asteroid showers and violent volcanic eruptions, it is likely that the common ancestor of life on Earth appeared between 4.0 and 3.85 billion years ago.

The mechanisms of the emergence of life on earth still remain obscure. The earliest common ancestor of life had to possess genetic information instructing it how to function and reproduce, and the means to replicate and to carry out these instructions. Importantly, its system of replicating its genetic material had to allow for some random variation, allowing the evolution of new traits, and, with time, the development of more accomplished forms of life. This ancestor of life had to be non-parasitic, since there was nothing else living, which rules out viruses and viroids playing any role, at least in the forms they have today. Both Aleksandr Oparin and his early supporter J.B.S. Haldane were well aware that, if the prebiotic atmosphere had been as oxygen-rich as today, there was no possibility for the organic compounds needed for life being formed on earth. Instead, they proposed that the atmosphere on the young earth had been reducing, like that of the outer planets, containing very little oxygen, but instead being rich in hydrogen, methane gas, and ammonia. The earliest attempt to test Oparin's hypothesis was made in 1953 by Stanley L. Miller and Harold C. Urey. Miller constructed an artificial 'atmosphere' of methane gas, ammonia, water vapour and hydrogen gas above an 'ocean' of water. He then subjected the gases to repeated electrical discharges to simulate lightning. The result was that not less than ten per cent of the carbon in the system had become a constituent of various organic compounds; even more remarkably, many of the twenty standard amino acids had been formed.

This experiment has since been reproduced many times, with varying compositions of gases. Although there has been some opposition as to the true nature of the prebiotic atmosphere, mainly that it probably contained less hydrogen than presumed by Miller and Urey, the validity of their findings has not been seriously challenged. Indeed, another analysis of the Murchison meteorite has shown a spectrum of amino acids that is remarkably similar to that analysed by Miller, both in nature and in relative quantity. Thus, amino acids are among the most conspicuous products of abiotic chemistry, both on earth and in space. It has also been shown that these amino acids link together upon heating of the primeval so-called 'hot dilute soup', although generally not in a way reminiscent of today's proteins or oligopeptides. In the experiments of Professor Sidney Fox, the heating of a solution of amino acids to 170°C resulted in the formation of so-called proteinoid, micellar structures with a certain catalytic ability. Short peptides have also been shown to form through thioester bonds, under conditions less extreme than in the Fox experiments.

These primitive proteins are nothing like the highly specialised, present-day enzymes and catalysts, however. It is extremely difficult to envision a system in which proteins could replicate in the absence of nucleic acids. Indeed, there is much to be said for the concept that proteins must have been preceded by ribonucleic acid (RNA). In biochemistry as it is today, proteins are always coded for by RNA. An RNA molecule can be described as a string of ribose (sugar) and phosphate groups, to which are linked four different kinds of purine or pyrimidine bases: adenine, guanine, cytosine and uracil. These four bases constitute the alphabet of the genetic information, and triplets of them form the words: for example, the triplet cytosine-uracil-uracil instructs the protein-forming ribosome in the cell to add the amino acid leucine to the growing strand of protein. Several distinguished biologists have proposed that an 'RNA world' of gradually more and more accomplished, self-replicating RNA molecules preceded the first nucleic acid-encoded protein synthesis. Synthesis of increasingly complex protein enzymes then gradually evolved, until the age of the protocell, in which a functional system of RNA and protein were enveloped by a (probably lipid) membrane, was reached.

One major difficulty of this concept of an 'RNA world' as the earliest self-replicating form of life is that today, protein enzymes are needed for the synthesis of RNA molecules. According to Crick's central dogma, information always flows from nucleic acid to protein, never in the reverse direction; hence, RNA came before protein. The concept of an 'RNA world' received important support in 1983, when the American scientists Thomas Cech and Sidney Altman discovered that certain RNA molecules, so-called ribozymes, were endowed with catalytic ability. RNA enzymes such as these could thus carry out tasks in RNA processing that are today performed by proteins. Further experiments have demonstrated that certain modified ribozymes can carry out important steps in RNA processing, such as the splicing together of strings of oligonucleotides. Although no RNA-catalysed reproduction of RNA has yet been demonstrated, it does not take much imagination, given these important results in ribozyme biochemistry, to envision a self-sufficient RNA world, in which catalytic proteins played a subordinate part.

A second, more serious argument against the concept of the RNA world is that the biosynthesis of oligonucleotides is a quite complex process. It is true that several of the purines and pyrimidines can be produced from an aqueous solution of hydrogen cyanide and ammonia, but these reactions have low yields, however, particularly in prebiotic conditions. Nor has there been any wholly convincing model for the assembly of nucleotides from ribose, phosphate and adenine or other bases, least of all of the formation of long (fifty to sixty residues) polymers of these nucleotides. A formation of such a complex molecule could not occur through mere chance, or spontaneous generation, since it would not be enough to have just one or two residues formed: the same, very unlikely combination of molecules would have to occur time after time in an orderly manner. In his book *Vital Dust*, Professor Christian de Duve instead proposed that the conditions described by Miller could well allow the formation of catalytic multimers of hydroxy acids and amino acids. These multimers might, under certain conditions, perform many of the tasks of present-day enzymes, and catalyse the interactions between different varieties of RNA and protein. Another theory has been put forth by Professor Leslie E. Orgel and co-workers. Certain minerals and clays can function as catalysts and facilitate the polymerisation of amino acids and nucleotides, by binding and supporting oligomers. While, in an aqueous solution, at most decamers are formed, the presence of mineral (hydroxylapatite or illite) in the case of amino acids, or clay (montmorillonite) in the case of nucleotides, allows the formation of polymers of fifty to fifty-five residues. A polynucleotide of this size can function as a small ribozyme, and these ingenious experiments have considerably strengthened the concept of a self-sufficient RNA world.

The hypotheses of these distinguished scientists all assume that spontaneous generation, in the sense that the first living being, the ancestor of all life, was formed from nonliving matter, occurred about 3.85–4.0 billion years ago. It was not a strictly *spontaneous* or random combination of molecules, however, but a slow, painstaking, gradual formation of increasingly complex molecules. In his recent book *Gen-e-sis*, Professor Robert M. Hazen leaves it open whether genetics preceded metabolism, like in the RNA world, or if metabolism preceded genetics, with life arising in some obscure chemical cycle, with minerals providing energy. Another possibility would of course be that life began as a cooperative chemical phenomenon, with a crude self-replicating mechanism for genetic matter becoming linked with another crude system for providing energy.

An alternative hypothesis, first proposed by the Swedish chemist Svante Arrhenius, is that of panspermia. Life had originated elsewhere in the galaxy, and microbes or their spores had been transmitted to Earth either by meteorites, by stellar radiation, or through the deliberate seeding of life on Earth by a spacecraft manned by highly developed extraterrestrials. All these variants see life on Earth as one small part of an ubiquitous 'galactic life'. The acceptance of the panspermia hypothesis would depend upon the discovery of live organisms in interstellar space, something that has not yet been achieved.

Still, the supporters of lithopanspermia received a major boost in 1996, when a NASA team announced that a Martian meteorite in the

Antarctic contained fossil remains of bacteria. Although contested by some experts, this discovery would at least raise the possibility that Mars had once contained live bacteria, and that these microbes may well have travelled to Earth as passengers on a meteorite. Whether they would have arrived alive and well is another question, however, but in his book *The Origin of Life*, Professor Paul Davies recounts numerous observations of bacteria with remarkable ability to withstand heat, pressure and radiation. He raises the question whether life started on Mars, possibly many miles underground, and that the first living creatures on Earth were in fact Martian bacteria, blasted off the Red Planet on a meteorite after an asteroid impact.

Another intriguing observation concerns the asymmetry of the extraterrestrial amino acid enantiomers on the so-called Murchison meteorite, which fell in Australia in 1969. They show an enrichment of left-rotational isoforms, just like the amino acids that are components of life on Earth. This suggests that some process favouring left-rotational isoforms was in operation elsewhere in the Universe, providing further support for the believers in the panspermia hypothesis. Still, this hypothesis still does not answer the question of how life originated in the first place, only how it arrived at Earth.

10

ODD SHOWERS

'The land frogs are some of them observed... to breed by laying eggs, and others to breed of the slime and dust of the earth, and that in winter they turn to slime again, and that the next Summer that very slime returns to be a living creature; this is the opinion of *Pliny*; and *Cardanas* undertakes to give reason for the raining of *Frogs*; but if it were in my power, it should rain none but water *Frogs*, for those I think are not venemous...'

Izaak Walton, *The Compleat Angler* (1653)

It is told in the Holy Scripture that after the Children of Israel had made their escape from the pursuing host of the Pharaoh, they reached the desert of Sur. After wandering in this desert for three days, they wanted to drink water from a stream, but the water proved to be bitter and unfit for human consumption. The people murmured against Moses, complaining of their thirst. Moses called to the Lord, who showed him a certain kind of wood. Moses threw the wood into the water to make it sweet, and the people were finally able to quench their thirst. Later, when they had reached the desert of Sin, the Children of Israel were tormented by hunger. The people once again murmured against their saviours, Moses and Aaron, with the bitter words

'Would to God we had died by the hand of the Lord in the land of Egypt, when we sat by the flesh pots, and when we did eat bread to the full; for

> ye have brought us forth into this wilderness, to kill all this assembly with hunger!'

Moses again saved the day: the Lord let a rain of manna fall on the camp of the Children of Israel, and fallen quail could be collected in its vicinity.

Many generations of schoolchildren have been taught to believe in these marvellous happenings, imagining, no doubt, a shower of nourishing cereal and tender roast quail slowly descending toward the startled Children of Israel, who ran excitedly about and collected the food in their tunics and head-cloths, praising the Lord for this great miracle. The children would have been even more impressed if their schoolmaster had pointed out that fish, frogs, toads and worms could also fall from the sky. In fact, such anomalous showers of living animals or other unexpected substances from the skies have fascinated humankind since the beginning of time. They were long considered as portents: a shower of blood foreboded war and bloodshed throughout the land, while a shower of worms was a sure sign of divine displeasure. Throughout the sixteenth and seventeenth centuries, there was a vigorous debate among some of the foremost scholars of the time about the cause for these rains of living animals. Many ingenious hypotheses were put forth, and showers of fish, frogs and toads were described in the some of the most prestigious scholarly journals of the time. As late as the mid-nineteenth century, the existence, or non-existence, of these odd showers was vigorously debated in various periodicals. At the end of that century, however, the vast majority of scientists had declared these occurrences manifestly impossible, deploring that the vast majority of the ignorant populace still supported this vulgar error. The sceptics won the debate and as a result, news of a shower of fish or toads was relegated to the 'funny pages' of the tabloid newspapers. Today, we have come full circle with regard to this kind of anomalous precipitation, since modern science has not only allowed for its existence, but explained the mechanisms involved.

Strange Rains in Antiquity

In 1555, Olaus Magnus, the last Catholic primate of Sweden, published his *Historia Gentibus Septentrionalibus*, a monumental chronicle of the ethnology, geography and cultural history of Scandinavia. His chronicle was thorough and well written, with many quaint details; it deservedly became quite popular and gave rise to a considerable interest in Scandinavia among European scholars, who had previously cared little for the state of these cold, desolate isles of the north. An entire chapter of the *Historia* is devoted to the rains of fish, frogs, rats and worms that were of frequent occurrence in the Nordic countries. Olaus Magnus believed these odd showers to be caused by the inner warmth and stickiness of the Scandinavian clouds, which led to the spontaneous generation of living animals.

According to an old Swedish chronicle, blood rained down at Ringstadholm in 1316, a prodigy considered by some to portent the civil war between King Birger and his brothers. In 1473, a huge amount of worms rained down from the sky in Westgothia. Since these worms devoured the crops in the fields, the people considered them as a punishment sent by God. A peasant named Tord Jeppson advised that solemn prayers should be said to St Catherine of Wadstena, a local patron saint. After a cow had been sacrificed as a votive gift, the peasant succeeded in exterminating the worms; this odd happening was considered one of St Catherine's foremost miracles. According to the Swedish chronicle of Joen Petri Klint, blood rained down in the town of Söderköping in 1562, 1565 and 1567; in the latter year, this town was raided by the Danes and its castle burnt to the ground.

In his *Natural History*, Pliny detailed the Roman chronicles of odd showers. When Manius Acilius and Gaius Porcius were consuls, milk and blood once rained from the sky; on several later occasions, showers of meat, wool and bricks had been observed. In the year 53 BC, iron had rained from the sky near Lucania; the year after, the General Marcus Crassus and his entire army, containing a large contingent of Lucanian soldiers, was annihilated in the war against the Parthians. Shortly before the death of the Emperor Nero in AD 68, a rain of blood fell with such force that streams of blood and gore flooded the streets of Rome.

Pliny quoted several older sources on odd showers in ancient times, few of which are available today. It seems as if the existence of showers of live animals was a subject of debate already in the fourth century BC. In a note 'On animals that suddenly become visible', Theophrastus of Eresus, the pupil and successor of Aristotle, wrote that little frogs and snails could not, as many people thought, fall with the rain. Instead, their holes in the ground were flooded with water, forcing the animals out from their lairs in large numbers, and giving the illusion that they had been falling with the rain. The philosopher Claudius Aelianus is unlikely to have been convinced by these arguments, since he had himself once witnessed a brisk shower of living small frogs while travelling from Naples to Puteoli. He wrote that the foreparts of these supernatural animals crawled, supported by two feet, while the hind part ended in a tail; they are thus likely to have been half-developed tadpoles.

The Greek polymath Athanaeus of Naucratis, who flourished around AD 200, wrote a chronicle called the *Deipnosophists*, or the Banquet of the Learned, in which he quoted the works of more than eight hundred earlier authors whose works he had consulted at the then still extant Alexandrian Library. One of his subjects of interest was the strange rains of olden times. According to a certain Phoenias, it had once rained fish continuously for three days, in the environs of Chersonesus. Another old writer, Phylarchus, knew of several prodigious rains of fish, frogs and wheat. The strangest rain of all struck the inhabitants of the cities Peonia and Dardania: frogs rained down from heaven for several weeks. So great was their number that the streets and houses were full of them, and the inhabitants had to shut up their doors and windows. Even this measure was to no avail, however, since the frogs gained an entry into all the houses and even crept into the kitchen utensils. The people were not able to use any water, since it was poisoned by the rotting corpses of the frogs that had fallen into their tanks, and they could hardly put their feet on the ground, due to the profusion of frogs. In the end, they had to leave their native lands and move to another part of the country, because of the nauseating smell of the multitudes of dead frogs.

Prodigious downfalls of a similar kind often occurred in the British Isles in ancient times, at least if Thomas Short's odd *History of the Air* is to be trusted. In the year AD 4, 'it rained blood above five hours in London'. Short also tells us that in 766, it 'rained blood three Days, then venemous flies, then Mortality', and that in 1014, a heap of clouds fell, and smothered thousands. A famous old Irish chronicle, the *Annals of the Four Masters*, reports that in AD 690, 'it rained a shower of Blood in Leinster this year. Butter was there also turned into lumps of gore and blood, so that it was manifest to all in general. The wolf was heard speaking with a human voice, which was horrific to all.' Twenty-six years later, in 716,

Leinster was struck by another shower of blood; in the same year, silver rained in Othain-Mor and honey in Othain-Beag.

Olaus Wormius, Carl Linnaeus, and the Lemmings

In his *Historia*, Archbishop Olaus Magnus described another Scandinavian natural curiosity: the mice, or rather lemmings, that rained down from the skies in Lapland. They fell in huge showers, like the Egyptian locusts, and devoured all vegetation to be found in these barren mountains. The lemmings were feared by the Lapps and their dogs, since these supernatural rodents had a punishing bite: every creature touched by their poisonous, sharp teeth expired in agony soon after. These armies of airborne lemmings ruled Lapland like an enemy host: they marched about at will, laying waste the countryside and driving the wretched Laplanders before them. At a given time, the rodents all died, or were eaten by ermines and foxes. The Laplanders exulted, happy to be free of these murine invaders from the clouds – but not for long: the noxious decaying bodies of the lemmings spread a dreadful contagion, afflicting the Lapps with vertigo and jaundice. It has been demonstrated that Olaus Magnus fetched the major part of his chapter on these terrifying airborne killer lemmings from another contemporary source, the German Jacob Ziegler's *Scondia*. Some historians have suspected that Olaus Magnus plagiarised the whole section, without acknowledgement, from this work, and that the Archbishop had not even seen a lemming. This would not have been an isolated instance, since Olaus Magnus freely incorporated large chunks of other geographical works into his *Historia*. It has also been pointed out that the drawing of the lemmings in the *Historia* erroneously depicts them as black and with a long tail; it is likely, however, that the drawing was not made by Olaus Magnus personally, but by some individual with little zoological knowledge. In his text, the Archbishop quite correctly describes the lemmings as speckled in colour, and the size of a vole. In the years 1518 and 1519, Olaus Magnus had travelled widely in Lapland, while employed as the secretary of the notorious Arcimboldus, a reckless Roman seller of indulgences, whose excessive trade in absolution is said to have precipitated the Swedish Reformation. Olaus Magnus was a man of observation, and the sale of indulgences to the sinful Swedes of the northern outback is unlikely to have entirely prevented him from studying the Laplandish fauna.

Professor Olaus Wormius, of Copenhagen, the noted anatomist and zoologist, was one of the many naturalists who had read Olaus Magnus's description of the lemmings. His Norwegian friends had supplied him with further fanciful accounts of lemmings falling from above. In 1578, a great number of large, yellow mice were said to have fallen near the town of Bergen. In 1651, the parish clerk of Ravnefjord was travelling in a small boat with some friends, when two lemmings fell from the sky into the boat. Soon after, a powerful thunderstorm burst upon them. Another remarkable observation was made by an invalid old lady, who had received the shock of her life when a lemming fell from a clear sky into her apron. From the Bishop of Bergen, Olaus Wormius had received a 'pickled' lemming, which he dissected with great care, together with his friend, the celebrated anatomist Thomas Bartholin. To their surprise, they found that the animal's organs of generation were quite normal, arguing against that the lemmings were spontaneously generated in the skies.

In his 1653 treatise on 'The Norwegian Mouse', Wormius still accepted the rains of lemmings as a fact; in the manner of his time, he valued the testimony of older authorities higher than his own observations. He was undecided whether the lemmings were created *de novo* from decaying substances in the clouds, or if they were transported from faraway places by the wind. He rather leaned towards the latter theory, quoting earlier observations of fish and frog rains, but was at a loss to explain why only lemmings, and no other Laplandish animals, were falling from the clouds. In a section on supernatural aspects of lemmings, Wormius quoted the belief that the lemmings were sent as a divine punishment to make the sinful people repent their wicked ways. The Norwegian clergy were not without means to combat the strange, alien mice, however: Wormius quoted several curses and exorcisms to be used in the churches to drive the supernatural rodents away. Sometimes, the entire congregation knelt, trembling, before the local vicar, as he pronounced a solemn malediction on the invading lemmings.

When travelling in Holland, England and France in the 1720s, Carl Linnaeus was often asked by other naturalists whether it was really true that mice fell from the clouds in Lapland. His answer was non-committal: in spite of his respect for Olaus Wormius, Linnaeus was unwilling to accept these wonders without having witnessed them himself. In 1733, Linnaeus made an extended tour of Lapland, one of the objectives of which was to study the behaviour of the lemmings at close range. He was surprised to see that the lemmings occurred quite commonly in large parts of Lapland: their burrows could frequently be observed near grassy hillocks. The lemmings were not easily frightened: when Linnaeus teased one of them, it barked like a puppy and bit his stick. Carl Linnaeus observed that the female lemmings often had five or six young in their dens, and that they had eight teats, just like other mice. Linnaeus dissected several pregnant lemmings to observe the development of their young: he could thus definitely disprove the tale of their spontaneous generation in the skies.

Linnaeus was thoroughly unimpressed by the Laplanders, who were a mine of misinformation on various aspects of natural history. They maintained, as they had probably done to Olaus Magnus 215 years earlier, that the lemmings had a poisonous bite, and that they could not be eaten. Linnaeus observed, however, that dogs and foxes ate them with alacrity, and that humans could probably do so too. He did not try the experiment himself, but merely observed that 'no four-footed beast is too poisonous to be eaten, as is proven by the Chinese, who eat all kinds of animals'. The Laplanders also claimed that, in spite of the venomous nature of these rodents, the reindeer liked to gobble up the lemmings as a welcome variation to their herbivorous diet, but Linnaeus remained incredulous. The Laplanders finally tried to make the famous doctor from Stockholm believe another tall tale: that both men and reindeer could be sucked up by the thick clouds surrounding the mountain peaks, and transported widely before being put down on another mountain far away. This time, Linnaeus tried the experiment, wandering off on a tall mountain. He wrote that the sensation of being wholly enveloped by the cloud far up on the mountain was an eerie one: he could hardly see his hands before him. His hopes of an early return to Stockholm as a passenger on a cloud were thwarted, however, and he was fortunate to escape this adventure alive, without falling down a deep precipice or into some abyss covered by the light snow. After this experience, it was no wonder to him why the Lapps and their animals tended to disappear while walking these winding, perilous mountain pathways, in almost zero visibility.

Carl Linnaeus was well aware of the reason for the fable of the aeronautic 'Norwegian mice': the strange phenomenon of lemming migration, which occurred about once every ten or twenty years. Thousands of lemmings migrated down the mountains in strict marching order, eating every green thing in their path. Linnaeus wrote that 'if they encounter a lake, they do not make a detour around it, but swim it, even if they have to cross at its widest diameter; if they find a boat in their way, they do not escape, but endeavour to climb onto it, but only to leap into the sea on the opposite side'. In Sweden as well as in Norway, lemming migration had been considered a portent: the Dean of Lima told Linnaeus that he could recall that, a long time ago, the entire parish had gathered to say prayers against the invading, supernatural rodents.

Frogs from the Sky

In Thomas Short's *History of the Air*, it is briefly stated that in 1346, 'it rained Toads and Rain mix'd'. This was probably the same anomalous downfall described by the German chronicler Conradus Lycosthenes in his *Prodigorum ac Ostentorum Chronicon*. A quaint illustration depicts the amphibians being formed in the clouds, and diving down towards the earth when fully formed, to land safely on some grassy meadows. The Renaissance scholars no longer considered the rains of live animals as portents of divine displeasure; they instead endeavoured to find a rational explanation for these extraordinary phenomena. The doctrine of spontaneous generation provided one: it was easy to imagine that the toads and frogs were generated from putrid matter in thick clouds. They were hovering up there, adhering to the cloud, until being fit to fend for themselves in their natural habitat; the frog-clouds then released their numerous brood, which fell down with the rain. Although this theory may seem as hazardous as the wingless flight of the frogs towards the tempting ponds and marshlands down on earth, it was accepted by many early adherents of the spontaneous generation doctrine. Along with the vegetable lamb and the barnacle geese, the falling frogs and fish were considered among the foremost evidence that animals could be formed from vegetable or putrefying matter. For example, the Jesuit polymath Gaspar Schottus wrote in his *Physica Curiosa* that 'little frogs are not only formed through the action of rain on dust, but these animals also often fall to the ground with rain, having been generated in the clouds. I know of respectable witnesses to these occurrences; indeed, I have seen it happen myself.'

As the years went by, knowledge in amphibian physiology increased. It did not require a brilliant mind or a great knowledge in natural history to sit down by a pond to watch frogspawn develop into tadpoles, and then into adult frogs. These observations proved that amphibians usually developed in a normal fashion, and thus spoke against their regular descent from the sky fully formed. The Italian mathematician and naturalist Girolamo Cardano put forth a novel hypothesis: frogspawn could be carried up to the clouds by strong gusts of wind, and develop into complete frogs up there; when fully formed, they rained down in showers. This hypothesis was supported by the aforementioned Robert Plot, who had investigated some reports of frog rains in Staffordshire. In one of these, a man walking across a marshland on a foggy morning had his hat covered with small frogs that had fallen on him with the rain. Robert Plot had a spontaneous generation theory of his own: a particular kind of dust could be spread by the wind, and fermented by the actions of the sun and the rain, finally developing into frogs. His contemporary Samuel Pepys recorded an interesting conversation with Mr Elias Ashmole, a founding member of the Royal Society, at a dinner given by the Mayor of London. Mr Ashmole, a firm supporter of spontaneous generation, assured him that 'frogs and many other insects' really fell from the sky ready formed.

Even Francesco Redi, who had disproved the dogma of spontaneous generation of larger animals, had to find an alternative explanation for the rains of frogs and toads. He proposed that they were just a misinterpretation of the fact that, after a heavy rain, a multitude of young frogs left their waterlogged holes and crevices, giving the illusion that they had fallen with the rain. Many eighteenth-century naturalists agreed with him, and doubted the phenomenon of amphibian showers. The German herpetologist Dr Roesel and the British naturalist Gilbert White both denied the occurrence of frogs and toads falling with the rain, as did Carl Linnaeus.

In 1834, a certain Colonel Marmier reported to the French Academy of Sciences that during a ride on a country estate, he had seen the entire road being covered with small frogs after a heavy fall of rain. The old military man did not hesitate to declare that the animals must have fallen with the rain. The leading French herpetologist, Professor André Duméril, criticised this premature conclusion, however, and quoted the observations of Dr Roesel, who had himself observed the ground being covered with small frogs that emerged from their hiding-places among the vegetation after a heavy rainfall. The debate arisen by Colonel Marmier's letter was widely reported in the daily newspapers, and the surprising aftermath was that many Frenchmen sent their own experiences of showers of frogs or toads to the Academy. In not less than nine of these, the animals had clearly been seen to fall down with the rain.

In 1804, two gentlemen travelling to Toulouse in a charabanc observed a very black cloud, which burst upon them. They were showered with an immense number of frogs, which fell on their hats and cloaks, and covered the road and surrounding fields. When their charabanc started moving again, the travellers having recovered their senses after this unexpected amphibian deluge, its wheels ran over and killed a large number of these animals. M. Mauduy, curator of natural history at Poitiers, had himself witnessed two falls of frogs during heavy rain, in 1809 and 1822. What is probably the most remarkable shower of amphibians in modern times was reported by the civil servant M. Gayet. Forty years earlier, in 1794, when he was an army recruit, he had bivouacked near Lalain, along with 150 other soldiers of the grand guard. Nearby, the Austrian army had flooded a large territory with water from the river Scarpe. It was an oppressively hot, sultry summer day. Suddenly, at three o'clock in the afternoon, a heavy rainfall began. The soldiers had to leave the valley in which they had made camp to avoid being submerged by the floods. Suddenly, an immense multitude of toads the size of hazelnuts fell with the rain, and began to jump about among the startled guardsmen. M. Gayet spread out his handkerchief and caught a considerable number of toads in it. Some of them had their posterior portion elongated like tails, signifying that they were still in the tadpole state. This heavy shower of toads lasted half an hour, during which time the soldiers could feel the falling animals striking their hats and clothing. After the storm, many of them found toads lodged in the folds of their three-cornered hats; of all the bombardments these soldiers were to suffer during the endless revolutionary and Napoleonic wars, this is likely to have been the one that impressed them most.

In the middle of the nineteenth century, there was a vigorous debate about the reality, and cause, of these bizarre showers of amphibians. Many cases were reported, particularly in France and Britain. In the village of Selby, in Yorkshire, frogs about the size of a horsebean fell with the rain in 1844. The villagers caught several of them by holding out their hats, and noted that the animals seemed remarkably lively after their long wingless flight. This case was published in *Zoologist*, a reputable scientific magazine, but the editor, Mr William Newman, added a postscript that he, personally, was not among the supporters of this vulgar error that had gained such widespread credence among his countrymen. There were fewer reports of frog or toad showers from the United States. The earliest of them occurred in 1873, in Kansas City, Missouri. A shower of frogs darkened the air and covered the ground for a long distance; this case was published in *Scientific American* magazine.

High Flying Fish

A medieval shower of fish is said to have occurred in Saxony in AD 689, during the reign of King Otto III; it was described by Conradus Lycosthenes, and is the subject of another of his quaint illustrations. According to the *Annals of the Four Masters*, there was an Irish shower of fish at Tirconnel in 1506. Another early shower of fish was described in the *Philosophical Transactions* of the Royal Society of London. On the Wednesday before Easter 1666, a two-acre field near Wrotham in Kent was found to be covered with small fishes. There were no fishponds nearby, but there had been a great tempest of thunder and rain some time earlier. The fish, mostly young whitings, were exhibited before the curious in Maidstone, Dartford and London. Many people had seen the fishes scattered all over the field, and they had no other explanation than that they had rained down from the sky. The early fellows of the Royal Society of London were no strangers to anomalous precipitation: another issue of the *Philosophical Transactions* contains a report of a rain of a substance resembling wheat in Wiltshire. In yet another volume, the Bishop of Cloyne reported some prodigious showers of a greasy, foul-smelling matter in the counties of Limerick and Tipperary. The country people eagerly collected this substance, for use as an ointment for 'Scal'd or Sore Heads'; their body odour is unlikely to have benefited from this practice, since the grease was reported by the Bishop to have 'a strong ill Scent, something like the smell of Church-yards or Graves'.

There was another shower of fish near Paris in the 1780s. After a violent thunderstorm, which had thrown down both trees and buildings, the streets were full of small fish, about four to eight inches in length. The common opinion was that the fishes must have fallen during the thunderstorm; it is interesting to note that several fishponds nearby were found to be empty of both fishes and water. These early observations of large numbers of fishes found outside their natural element do not provide any conclusive proof that they had really rained down from the sky, however. This lack of proof made the fish-rains an obvious target for the rationalists who denied the existence of rains of live animals altogether. In 1771, little fish had been alleged to fall during a heavy thunderstorm in Cotbus, Germany. A savant named Raphael Eglini described this happening in a scholarly magazine, but when the fish were thoroughly examined, one of them proved to be of a species occurring nowhere near Cotbus. Eglini shamefacedly had to withdraw his article, and declared the entire incident incredible.

But as with the rains of amphibians, there are also cases in which people had actually observed the fishes fall down with rain. When, in 1809, a large troop of British soldiers was on the march, a short distance from Pondicherry in India, they encountered a heavy shower of rain. To the astonishment of all, a great number of small fish fell with the rain, some of them actually landing on the soldiers' hats. They were not flying fish; all were dead, and they descended with no other means than gravity. The commanding officer, General Smith, ordered that some of these fish were to be collected and cooked for his dinner. Another Indian fish rain occurred in 1830 and was described by the naturalist James Prinsep. He himself had not seen the fish fall, but he observed the Indians collecting fish in the fields the day in question. A fish was actually found in the brass funnel of his own pluviometer. Nine independent witnesses made out affidavits that they had seen fish – some of them rotten, others quite fresh – fall to the ground with the rain.

What was perhaps the most remarkable shower of fish of all times struck Aberdare in Wales on 9 February 1859. It was raining hard, with a rather stiff wind from the south-west. While the sawyer John Lewis was busy dragging timber to the saw, he was struck by several objects falling on his head and back, and even down his neck. He reached under his sweater and shirt, and pulled up several small fish! When looking up, he saw fish falling with the rain all around him. The whole ground was covered with fish, and when Lewis took off his hat, its brim was full of them. The other workmen helped gather up a whole bucketful of fish, which was emptied into a large pool of rainwater. Both the local and the national newspapers published articles about this 'extraordinary shower of fish'. But as could be expected, it was not long before some rationalists objected that a rain of fish was manifestly impossible, and contrary to the laws of nature. Fish were as unlikely to rain down from the sky in showers as they were to ride along Regent Street in a coach and four, dressed in tailcoats and top hats. The veracity of John Lewis was called into doubt by these sceptics, but the vicar of Aberdare, the Rev. John Griffiths, interceded on his behalf, pointing out that Lewis was a sober, reliable character, and that it was certainly beyond his capacity to make up a story like this one. The vicar had recorded Lewis's own testimony, and sent it, along with several specimens of the fish, to the zoologist Professor Richard Owen. These fish, apparently still living, were exhibited in an aquarium at the Zoological Gardens, Regent's Park. No report on the matter from Professor Owen himself has been kept for posterity. Another savant, Dr J.E. Gray, of the British Museum, instead entered the debate, but hardly did himself proud. He bluntly suggested that the whole thing was a fraud and imposture, and that the other workmen had poured a large basin of fish and water over John Lewis, as a practical joke. The Welsh sawyers were probably having a good laugh at the expense of the many gullible journalists and amateur scientists who had been taken in by their prank. This feeble attempt at debunking does not explain the several wheelbarrows full of fish that could be collected in the vicinity of the barnyard; nor that the fall occurred over a considerable area and was observed by several people. The editor of the *Zoologist*, Edward Newman, who seems to have been a sworn enemy to all kinds of anomalous precipitation, seconded Dr Gray's objections; he agreed that a rain of fish was manifestly impossible, and that a fraud was the most likely explanation. On the other hand, Dr Robert Drane, of Cardiff, and the Rev. W.S. Symonds, reported to the British Association for the Advancement of Science that they were convinced that a considerable number of fish had really descended with the rain. According to the contemporary newspaper correspondence, both the journalists and the British public took their side against the narrow-minded rationalists. In the 1862 volume of his magazine *All the Year Round*, Charles Dickens commented on the fish and frog rain debate, quoting several of the Indian reports as well as the recent Welsh one, and supporting the veracity of John Lewis against the onslaught of the British Museum officials.

Worms from Space

On 9 December 1923, some people taking a walk through the cold Scandinavian landscape in Halmstad, Sweden, suddenly observed small dark objects falling down with the snowflakes. They were much frightened to see that these objects were writhing, reddish worms, between one and four inches in length, falling down like confetti. The police was summoned by the startled observers, but when the constables finally came pounding along, the worms had ceased to fall. The local journalists wrote lengthy epistles about this unheard-of occurrence; the story spread to various news agencies, and the worms of Halmstad appeared on the 'funny pages' of many foreign newspapers. When some Swedish zoologists were consulted by the journalists, these worthies seem to have felt insulted to have been asked such an absurd question. Some believed that the witnesses had hallucinated, others that it was all a tasteless practical joke; all were unanimous that worms could not fall with the snow.

But just as the newspapers had published these dismissive comments from the sceptics, new showers of worms occurred on several locations in Sweden, spreading terror and confusion among superstitious people. In early 1924, both Uppsala and Stockholm were bombarded with worms from the sky. A lady walking in a park just outside Stockholm was struck by a violent shower of worms that were crawling about on her hat and fur coat. The zoologists could no longer deny that something strange was afoot, but they were at a loss to explain this eerie phenomenon. An entomologist suggested that the worms had crept up onto the newly fallen snow after their lairs had been flooded with water, to give the illusion that they had rained down. This completely disregarded, of course, the many observations of worms falling with the snow. While the men of science were faltering, the Scandinavian crackpots had a field-day. Some of them suggested that the worms fell from other planets, and demanded that the air force should be mobilised to stop this invasion from outer space. Other enthusiasts believed that the worms were no mere space invaders, but the super-intelligent ambassadors of a race of highly developed beings from another galaxy. The worms would not take kindly, they warned, to the brutal Swedes treading them underfoot instead of inviting them to the Royal Castle to meet the King and the Prime Minister.

One of the zoologists pondering these remarkable showers of worms was Dr Herved Berlin, Conservator of the Museum of Zoology at Lund University. After a year of diligent study, he published a booklet promising to provide the final solution of this mystery. He had found several earlier instances of rains of worms: one of them occurring in Hungary in 1672, another in Filipstad, Sweden, in 1749. The latter rain of worms was described before the Swedish Academy of Sciences, and some specimens of worms were sent to the entomologist Charles de Geer. It was not recorded if the academicians had had the foresight to mark the envelope 'Live animals! Handle with care!' but it nevertheless speaks highly of the eighteenth-century Swedish postal service that Charles de Geer remarked that the worms arrived 'alive and in excellent health'! His examination demonstrated that they were black with six brownish legs, much resembling the specimens described in Hungary seventy-seven years earlier. Herved Berlin procured specimens from several of the Swedish rains of worms, and studied the animals closely. Just like those examined by Charles de Geer 175 years earlier, they were compost worms, which normally spent the winter season adherent to leaves in composts and dung-heaps. In a series of clever experiments, Berlin demonstrated that when there is much rain, low atmospheric pressure and generally mild weather, these worms encapsulate quite shallowly in their composts and heaps of leaves. Even if the winter is particularly cold, they remain in this position. If there are some days of mild weather, followed by a snowstorm, these worms will sail up into the air using the compost leaves as sails. When they gain sufficient altitude, the freezing cold makes them all release their hold of the leaves, and they fall down as a shower. Berlin pointed out that all these three meteorological conditions must be fulfilled if a genuine shower of worms is to occur; this was really the case during the extreme Scandinavian winter of 1923–1924. This strange epidemic of rains of worms appears to be unique in modern times; nothing even remotely like it has ever been observed.

Even Odder Showers

In August 1708, the town of Norrköping, Sweden, experienced a thunderstorm 'with a great thundering and continuous lightning, the like of which has scarcely been observed in this country'. Just after a house had been struck by lightning, with a tremendous thunderclap, a large animal rather resembling a beaver fell from the sky and crash-landed on the high street, just by the pharmacy, with an audible thud. This extraordinary happening was investigated by Bishop Johan Bilberg, who did not doubt that the strange animal had really dropped down from the sky, since several sober and reliable witnesses had actually seen it fall. He was at a loss to explain where it had come from, and how a heavy, wingless beast such as this could have been airborne in the first place. From spiritual reasons, he scornfully rejected the idea of some of his parishioners that it was a flying troll, or even the Devil himself, who had been struck by lightning while hovering, on mischief bent, over the quiet Swedish municipality. The space beaver of Norrköping has lived on, not only in obscure books about Scandinavian mythology, but in the present-day tomes on 'the unexplained'. The strange animal dropping down from the sky has been considered an absolutely inexplicable occurrence, and yet another piece of evidence that God, UFOs or teleportation was at work shifting beavers about in the upper stratosphere.

From a contemporary newspaper report, written by a clergyman who was opposed to Bishop Bilberg's theories, it would seem that even this strange and unparalleled happening has a perfectly rational explanation, one that would delight even the most hardened debunker and show that truth is indeed stranger than fiction. It is recorded that, on the fateful evening, some unfastidious individual had kept a capacious tub full of seal's lard and blubber, apparently intended for human consumption, stored on the roof of a rather tall building. This tub also contained the body of a seal cub. When lightning struck the building, the tub of lard suffered a direct hit: it was completely shattered, and its contents were blown sky high. The space beaver was thus instead a flying seal, and the people responsible for its taxonomic classification would have been well advised to concentrate on theology, and leave the realm of zoology well alone.

The 'Beaver from Hell' is not the only large animal reported to have fallen down from the clouds. The earliest instance was reported by the old Avicenna, who claimed that a calf had once fallen from the sky, possibly through being carried off from a tall mountain by a strong gust of wind. Showers of lizards, snakes and salamanders occurred in various parts of the United States during the late nineteenth century, if various provincial newspapers are to be relied on. One of these reports was merely based on the finding of some snakes crawling in the main street of Memphis, Tennessee, after a heavy torrent of rain; no animals were actually seen to fall. Some of the other alleged falls of larger animals are even more poorly authenticated, while others, like a shower of venomous rattlesnakes striking a party of Irish immigrants in Arizona, seem very much like practical jokes. Even today, reports of larger animals falling from the sky can be encountered in the cheap tabloid newspapers, whose reporters care little about authenticity in their hunt for some really exciting news.

In September 1945, an old lady telephoned the weather bureau of St Louis, Missouri, to inquire whether the end of the world was near. The reason was that green beans were raining down from the sky just outside her house. The weather expert's reply to this strange query is unknown, but it may well have been to purchase a pair of new spectacles, or even to 'take more water with it'! Had he been better read in the annals of odd showers, he could have informed her that, at least according to the newspapers, strange objects from the vegetable kingdom were regularly falling down from the clouds onto the American countryside. In 1961, green peaches rained down in Louisiana, and the year after, peas fell in Blackstone, Virginia. Britain provided two even odder showers: in 1974, eggs fell in Wokingham, and in 1977, nuts rained down near Bristol.

The old German chronicler Conradus Lycosthenes, who did much to preserve records of Europe's strange downfalls to posterity, also described a shower of small crosses which was said to have fallen in Germany in 1503; his illustration of this miracle shows a religious man dashing about to collect them in his tunic. In later years, a strange array of artefacts have been claimed to fall from the sky. In 1923, fragments of broken porcelain fell during a thunderstorm near Portland, and in 1954, nails fell down in Raritan, New Jersey. In November 1965, a man in Louisville, Kentucky, heard a tremendous explosion coming from his rear garden: when he went out to investigate, the entire patio, as well as the surrounding gardens and garage roofs, were full of plastic bags of cakes. It was suspected that they had been dropped from an aeroplane, but the tabloid press reported that no identified flying objects had been in the area; the police and the meteorologists were completely flummoxed. Four years later, golf balls fell from the sky during a thunderstorm in Punta Gorda, Florida, and hundreds of them rolled about in the street. After a week of investigation, the local police department declared that unnatural freak accidents like this were outside their field of expertise: the identity of the heavenly golfer remained unknown.

Several old chronicles mention showers of silver or money, and it is curious to note that similar occurrences have been reported in the twentieth century. In 1940, silver coins worth several hundred kopeks fell during a storm in the Gorkij area of the former Soviet Union. In January 1976, when ten-mark notes descended from a clear sky over Limburg, Germany, two observant clergymen managed to gather up more than 2,000 marks of this money from heaven. Another shower of money, although coins of lower denominations only, puzzled the parishioners of St Elizabeth's Church, Reddish, in May 1981. Pennies were heard to tingle on the gravel of the churchyard, and a girl claimed to have seen a fifty-pence coin fall from nowhere in front of her. The children found many pounds worth of copper and silver coins, which led to a roaring trade in the local sweet shops. The Rector got wind of this, and suspected that the children had raided the church poor box, but he was convinced by their tall tale of pennies from heaven when he found over two pounds worth of coins in his own churchyard. The investigation could provide no explanation whatsoever, although the clergymen seem to have spent much time searching for magpies' nests, rather than considering the possibility of a cunning practical joker.

Manna and Letters of Condolence from Above

In the late nineteenth century, the progress in natural history had begun to catch up with the odd showers of olden times, and several phenomena that had seemed strange and inexplicable 200 years earlier received a rational explanation. For example, the Biblical rains of 'manna' may well be based on actual observation. In several instances, travellers in the desert parts of Egypt, Persia and Turkey had found large amounts of light, whitish, round objects, about the size of a hazelnut. They are quite edible and can be used in baking bread. Well into the nineteenth century, the local inhabitants of these parts commonly believed that this manna had fallen from heaven, but modern botanists have provided a rational explanation of this phenomenon. The substance known as manna consists of lichens of the genus *Lecanora*, which sometimes occur in great numbers. They may easily be blown away over the surface of the ground. They tend to accumulate in depressions and are easily drifted into masses during the run-off of rainwater. The hungry desert traveller finding them is likely to fall on his knees and praise the Lord, just like the Children of Israel.

Modern scientists have also been able to explain the rains of blood, which were considered as dreadful portents throughout antiquity and the middle ages. A shower of blood had fallen at the death of Julius Caesar, and blood rains foreboded the war against Carthage, the death of Hadrian II, and the marauding of Attila the Hun. Gregory of Tours tells of a rain of blood that fell over the city of Paris in 582, during which many people had their clothes stained with blood, and cast them off in horror. In 1648, a heavy shower of blood fell in Mecklenburg, and a voice from above called out 'Wehe! Wehe!' According to the nonconformist minister Samuel Clarke's strange *Mirror or Looking Glass both for Saints and for Sinners*, a black cloud was seen over the town of Poole in 1653; it was dissolved into a shower of blood that fell warm upon men's hands. Some green leaves with drops of blood upon them were sent to learned men in London. These red rains are caused by the air becoming charged with scirocco dust following sandstorms in the Sahara desert; this dust may, during certain meteorological conditions, colour the rain a bright red. Another eerie phenomenon of medieval times were the 'rains of sulphur and brimstone'; the explanation is that the yellow rain is charged with huge amounts of pollen from nearby pine woods.

One of the most remarkable downfalls in all times occurred on 31 January 1687, near the village of Dauden in Courland. Large amounts of a blackened, paper-like material fell during a storm. This Trauer-papier, or mourning-paper, was considered a dire portent that the end of the world was near. Some people imagined that there was writing on the paper, and racked their brains to find out what was written on these letters of condolence from the sky. After several years, without any cataclysm occurring, they believed themselves secure, and the black-edged paper was deposited in a museum. When, 150 years later, this mourning-paper was examined by the German scholar C.G. Ehrenberg, it was found to consist of dried algae, which had assumed a paper-like texture. This substance was light enough to be carried by the wind a considerable distance.

Do Little Fishes Rain from the Sky?

At the advent of the twentieth century, the majority of zoologists and weather experts were still unwilling to accept the possibility of rains of fish, amphibians and other animals. The early cases were dismissed as due to superstition; the later ones either as hoaxes or as misinterpretations of floodings or mass migrations of amphibians by imaginative laymen. Dr E.W. Gudger, associate and bibliographer in ichthyology at the American Museum of Natural History, worked for many years to produce a *Bibliography of Fishes*, covering all aspects of the natural history of these animals. He was puzzled to encounter many reports of rains of fishes in the older literature, and decided to publish a review on this subject, detailing not less than forty-eight cases, from AD 300 to 1901. It began with the words: 'Do fishes fall in rains from the sky? To this question both the layman and the scientist are well-nigh unanimous in giving a negative answer.' Dr Gudger was somewhat wary of the reaction of his professional brethren to his new undertaking, since at least one of them has expressed himself in strong language on being asked such a bizarre question. Gudger was probably relieved to note that his article, published in the *Natural History* of 1921, was favourably received; indeed, many people wrote to him to add further cases, or even to tell him about their own experience of fish rains. In two supplements to his original article, Gudger was able to describe twenty-three additional fish rains. It is rather strange that he never discussed rains of frogs and toads, or, indeed, any kind of anomalous precipitation other than showers of fishes; perhaps he had made it a rule, as an ichthyologist, never to venture outside his own field of expertise.

In 1946, Mr Bergen Evans, Professor of English at Northwestern University, ridiculed the old belief in rains of blood, milk, frogs and little fishes in a popular book entitled the *Natural History of Nonsense*, and also in several magazine articles. His book is an amusing overview of various modern myths and 'vulgar errors', but its author's lack of knowledge in medicine and zoology did not impede him from expressing decided opinions on matters within these fields – and his passion for debunking sometimes seems to have got the better of him. Bergen Evans had read only the first of Gudger's articles, but boldly declared himself to be unimpressed by its reasoning, and implied that this obscure boffin's imagination must have run away with him. Gudger answered him in *Science* magazine, pointing out that he had collected seventy-eight cases of rains of fish alone, some of them described by reliable naturalists. Other cases had been observed by several independent witnesses, often simple, uneducated people, who knew nothing about the fish rain debate. Bergen Evans was adamant, however. He ridiculed Gudger's claim that some cases were 'scientifically attested', declaring that the whole thing was manifestly impossible, and that rains of little fishes was nothing more than a silly old wives' tale. It was not until an expert zoologist personally witnessed fishes falling from a sky free from birds or other objects, and local air traffic controllers made out an affidavit that the air space was free of planes on the time in question, that he was prepared even to consider the question. None of Gudger's cases passed these stringent criteria, but in 1949, the scientist Dr A.D. Bajkov reported, in a letter to *Science*, a rain of fishes that he had personally witnessed, in Marksville, Louisiana. The people in town were very much excited by this strange phenomenon. The bank cashier and two merchants were struck by falling fish, and many other people saw them fall with the rain, along a corridor 1,000 feet long and 75 or 80 feet wide. Dr Bajkov noted that the day before, numerous small tornadoes or 'devil dusters' had been observed in the area.

A thorough review of the annals of anomalous precipitation would support Dr Gudger's viewpoint: between the years 687 and 2006, not less than 123 probable or verified showers of fish occurred, and in thirty-seven of them, the fish were clearly seen to fall through the air. During the same period of time, there are also records of sixty-one showers of frogs or toads; in thirty-nine of these, the animals were observed to descend from the clouds. These showers of fish and amphibians have been observed all over the world. Quite a few occurred in the United States, India, Ceylon and Malaysia. In Europe, there is a marked concentration of both fish and frog rains to the British Isles. France and Spain are also among the preferred targets, whereas much fewer instances have been reported from central Europe. Contrary to the predictions of Olaus

Magnus, there is also a scarcity of Scandinavian instances, the strange epidemic of worm showers of 1923 to 1924 excepted.

The intensity of these showers of fish or amphibians has varied greatly. Sometimes, only a few animals fall with the rain, but on other occasions, they resemble the plague of raining frogs striking the cities of Peonia and Dardania, or the tremendous shower of toads witnessed by M. Gayet in 1794. On 2 July 1901, frogs and toads fell over Minneapolis during a violent rainstorm: according to the newspaper reports, certain streets and sidewalks were completely filled with 'quackers', and neither people nor cart horses could wade through the mass of squirming bodies. After a rain of eels outside Coalburg, Alabama, many farmers brought carts to take away large loads of dead eels, which they used as a fertiliser in the fields. In 1969, a lady living in Buckinghamshire was on her way to a party, when it suddenly started to rain violently. The doors and windows of her house had been left open, and hundreds – or even thousands – of frogs poured in with the rain. Only with great difficulty could she clear the house of the invading amphibians. When she reached the party, many people doubted her tale of the frog shower, but she silenced them by picking up a couple of frogs that had got stuck in her baggy trousers.

The eccentric American journalist Charles Fort spent twenty-seven years at the New York Public Library and the British Library, scanning the files of many periodicals, newspapers and popular science magazines for articles and reports about various strange and macabre phenomena. He collected early UFO observations, reports of ball lightning and spontaneous human combustion, and appearances of ghosts, ghouls and poltergeists. Quite aptly, he called these phenomena 'damned', since they were sneered at or ignored by the scientists of his time. Instead of classifying his observations, Charles Fort presented them in veritable disarray. Being a 'phenomenalist', he argued that anything might be possible in nature, and that all attempts at interpretation were futile. An amazing number and variety of tales about anomalous precipitation are scattered throughout his books: rains of frogs, fish, fungi, stones, hatchets, masks and the 'ceremonial regalia' of savages. His own explanation of these occurrences was that what he called a 'Super-Sargasso sea' hovered over planet Earth, and that live animals and other substances regularly rained down from it.

For modern devotees of paranormal phenomena, Charles Fort has become a cult figure: both in Britain and in the United States, there are societies devoted to the continuation of his life's works. His theory about the Super-Sargasso sea has proved a trifle *risqué* even for the most audacious modern 'crypto-biologists': no aviators or astronauts have reported that their planes or rockets have encountered such an anomalous ocean. The modern Forteans have instead suggested that mysterious forces sometimes teleport animals from the face of the earth up amongst the clouds, and that they later fall down with the rain on some other location. The Forteans have not provided any explanation, however, why only small animals, like frogs and fish, are affected by this strange uplifting power: there are no reports of flying pigs and cows buzzing about; nor has any rhinoceros fallen through the roof of a suburban sitting-room.

In view of the compelling evidence from both historical and modern cases, it cannot be denied that fishes, frogs and toads sometimes fall down in showers with the rain. Although some cases can be explained as hoaxes, ill-researched or fraudulent newspaper stories, or misinterpretation of mass migrations of amphibians, the vast majority are beyond reproach. There is also a quite natural explanation of these odd showers, which, unlike the musings of the Forteans, does not only fit all the facts, but also keeps within the established laws of nature. A waterspout is a pillar of water drawn up by a powerful whirlwind; it can suck up vast amounts of water, mud and earth from the ground. Some waterspouts resemble a giant hourglass, with one end traversing the earth, and the other being in contact with a large cumulus cloud. It has several times been observed that waterspouts can transfer large quantities of sea or lake water up towards the cloud; the amphibians or little fishes in this water are also taken for a ride in the huge merry-go-round, whirling round in the waterspout with tremendous speed. In 1836, a report of whirlwinds accompanying a storm over Florence mentioned that among various larger objects spinning in the air, several large fish, apparently drawn out from the river Arno, could be discerned. Sometimes, the fishes and amphibians travel ten, or even twenty miles from their natural habitat before being precipitated with the rain; the hardy animals are often still alive when hitting the ground. In some occasions, the low temperature had frozen the fishes stiff, however, and they were shattered into fragments when hitting hard objects on the ground; a bizarre sight indeed! Sometimes, it has even been observed that an enormous hailstone has contained a frog or a little fish. In 1896, a large hailstone falling in Essen, Germany, contained a crucian carp, one and a half inches in length; two years earlier, a gopher turtle, six by eight inches in size, was stated to have fallen with the hail in Vicksburg, Mississippi, entirely encased in ice.

Already the famous French naturalist, Count de Castelnau, who had examined a fish rain occurring near Singapore in 1861, suggested to his incredulous colleagues that a whirlwind or tornado might have caused this phenomenon. Dr Gudger, the greatest modern authority on fish showers, also advocated the whirlwind theory. British zoologists and meteorologists, belonging to the Tornado and Storm Research Organisation, have even been able to reconstruct the path of the tornadoes, and the site where the fishes were drawn up into the cloud. What is strange, and hitherto unexplained, is how such an enormous amount of toads or fish can fall from the sky; in some instances, the whirlwind must have emptied an entire lake or bog of its fish or amphibian population. Nor has it been explained why the falling animals are seldom accompanied by mud, algae and other debris; furthermore, it has many times been remarked that the falling frogs are often of approximately the same size. It is possible that the animals are separated, by some obscure kind of 'air chromatography', making big toads fall before smaller specimens. Another interesting question is to what degree the fish rains may contribute to the movement of a particular species of fish between one lake and drainage system to another, and thus play a role in the biogeography of freshwater fishes.

Clouds of Frogs over London

In the old chronicles, the British Isles were stated to have been frequently bombarded by strange objects from above, and this has been continued well into our times. London itself has several times been targeted by these anomalous downfalls. The *Mirror* of 4 August 1838 contains an article with the promising heading 'A shower of Frogs in London!' The facts themselves are less impressive: a man strolling down Tower Street saw some dozens of young frogs hopping about on the foot and carriage pavements, and naively presumed that they must have been precipitated to the earth in a heavy shower of rain, which had fallen about a hour earlier. Another alleged shower of frogs struck the garden of the zoologist Edward Jesse. One morning in the early 1850s, this gentleman went for a walk in his walled Fulham garden. He was much surprised to find it full of little frogs, jumping merrily about. The day before, it had been wholly devoid of amphibians, and the soil was dry gravel, with no moist spot in which spawn could have been deposited. The garden was walled, like many others in this area, and he could see no apparent way for the animals to enter it, except through the house – and from the sky. This curious experience converted Edward Jesse from being a sceptic to keeping an open mind with regard to odd showers.

Another anomalous downfall struck London in 1984. While watching TV, Mr Ronald Langton, of East Ham, heard some heavy slapping sounds from the roof. The morning after, several flounders and smelts were found in the garden and on the roof. In nearby Canning Town, fish were found in at least two gardens. There had been a heavy thunderstorm in the night. The fish were taken to the Natural History Museum, where the ichthyologists declared them to be just what to expect in the Thames below Newham. A sceptic pointed out that there was a heronry at Barking, and that a flight of herons returning from the Thames might have been attacked by crows, forcing them to disgorge their catch over East Ham. But the amount of fish being found (at least forty or so) speaks against this theory. The most likely hypothesis is that a waterspout had lifted the fish from the Thames, or from the Essex coast, and transported them a couple of miles to East Ham.

Another shower of fish was reported in 2000 in Great Yarmouth, Norfolk. It was suggested that powerful updrafts during a thunderstorm had formed mini-tornadoes, which had sucked up a shoal of small sprats a mile or so off shore and carried them along in the storm clouds, before they fell in a heavy rainstorm half a mile inland. The most recent anomalous downpour was reported from Knighton, Shropshire, in August 2004. Several people saw the small fish fall, some of them still showing signs of life when they landed. Knighton is fifty miles from the nearest coastline, but the fish may well have been sucked up from some lake nearby. Just like in the Great Yarmouth case, there was a heavy thunderstorm that day.

It is difficult to gauge the reaction to a frog or fish rain striking the heart of London. A shower of 'quackers' pattering against the umbrellas of a crowd of travellers at Sloane Square or Fulham Broadway would naturally arise some curiosity, although it is unlikely that mass hysteria would break out. The Londoners would probably be catching the frogs in their bowler-hats and handbags, to bring them to the Natural History

Museum. Things were very much different when a small American town, situated in the thick of the 'Bible Belt', was struck by a brisk shower of fish in the mid-1920s. According to newspaper reports, people ran wildly along the streets, calling out 'It's raining fish!' The roof of the Baptist church was covered with fish: inside, the congregation was kneeling, confessing their sins before the Last Judgment. Some religious men ran into the haberdashery to buy expensive suits and tailcoats, to be well dressed before the Resurrection; others bought expensive coffins instead, lay down in them and slammed the lid shut. In midst of this pandemonium, some individuals, probably hard-necked rationalists, could be seen to gather the fishes from the sky into their corfs and frying-pans, planning, no doubt, to cook them for their dinner.

II

TOAD-IN-THE-HOLE

Let dotards with tenacious force
  Cling to this waning planet –
I'd rather soar to death's abode
On eagle's wings, than live like a toad
  Pent in a block of granite.

James Smith, *Chigwell Re-visited.*

On 8 May 1733, the master builder Mr Johan Gråberg went to the quarry of Nybro, situated near the village of Wamlingebo on the Swedish island of Gotland. In this quarry, he was supervising the cutting of a shipload of large stone boulders, which were to be used for the building of the new Royal Castle in Stockholm. The work proceeded in good order, and the master builder was thinking of his luncheon, when two of the quarrymen, Anders Halfwarder and Olof Sigräfwer, suddenly came running up from the excavation, both in a most excited state of mind. While cutting large blocks of sandstone more than ten feet below the level of the earth, Anders Halfwarder had been frightened out of his mind when he saw *a large frog* sitting in the middle of a large boulder that he had just cut in two with his hammer and wedge. Reluctantly, Gråberg followed the superstitious workmen down into the quarry, where he, too, was greatly startled by the sight of the frog sitting inside the boulder. Unfortunately, the part of the stone nearest to the frog was so porous that the violence of the blow had fragmented it, and the impression of the animal's body was destroyed. The frog was in a lethargic state and Gråberg could not provoke it to move, even when he lifted it out on a spade. Its colour was a greyish black, with some speckles on the back; under the belly, its colour was paler. When Gråberg touched its head with a stick, it closed its eyes. Its mouth was closed and covered with a yellow membrane. The master builder's examination of this mysterious stone-frog, which was regarded with superstitious awe by the workmen, was cut short by his impatience: for some reason, the brutal Swede wantonly beat it to death with his heavy shovel. The quarrymen put the flattened body of the supernatural animal on a polished slab of stone, and laid it in state in their cabin.

The Stone-Frog Before the Academy of Sciences

Later that afternoon, when Mr Gråberg was leaving the Burgsvik quarry, he was struck by belated qualms of conscience 'for being the Slayer of that extraordinary Animal, that might have lived for many hundreds of years within its stony Prison'. He returned to the quarry and recovered the frog's corpse, which he took with him to Stockholm. Six quarrymen and farmers, who had been present when the supernatural animal was freed from its prison within the stone, all signed a certificate of the truth of this extraordinary happening, and the Parson of Wamlingebo assured that all six were 'sturdy and reliable men'. Some days after the stone-frog had been discovered, the quarryman Anders Halfwarder fell badly ill, and Gråberg wrote that all the workmen believed that the frog, or rather the malignant mountain spirit inhabiting it, had poisoned him.

When Mr Gråberg came to Stockholm, he told several scholars about his remarkable experience. One of them, a provincial medical practitioner named Dr Johan Pihl, fancied himself as an authority on natural history. He speculated that frogspawn had entered the stone in some way and gradually developed into a fully grown frog during a period of many years. Dr Pihl's great ambition was to become a Fellow of the Swedish Academy of Sciences. He wrote a thirty-nine-page treatise about the strange stone-frog, which was submitted for the Academy's scrutiny.

Unfortunately for Dr Pihl, the referees were wholly unimpressed by his verbose speculation. At the Academy's meeting of 14 November 1741, it was decided that the Doctor's paper was to be put in the archives, where it is still kept today. Only the brief section containing Gråberg's account of the discovery of the frog was published in the Academy's *Transactions*. It was illustrated by an excellent engraving showing the upper and lower aspect of the frog's cadaver, and a transverse section of the quarry where it was found. It does not seem as if the frog was dissected, or even examined, by any naturalist of repute. Gråberg's naive statement that 'within its Skin, there did not seem to be any Innards, although the Frog, while she lived, had seemed reasonably thick' does not inspire confidence in his knowledge in amphibian anatomy. Indeed, from the existing account and illustration, the animal may just as well have been a toad.

Dr Pihl felt deeply hurt that his learned treatise had been refused in favour of the simple-minded builder's notes on the subject, and he made no further attempts to become a Fellow of this ungrateful Academy. He may have hoped that Carl Linnaeus would have been a referee of his paper, since this great biologist shared his belief in these tenacious underground amphibians. In one of his manuscripts in Swedish, *Beskrifning öfwer Stenriket*, written in 1747, Linnaeus stated his belief that frogs and toads could live for centuries enclosed in sandstone. This variety of stone was remarkably porous and was filled with water, from which the silent, immobilised stone-frog obtained its frugal nourishment. Carl Linnaeus also claimed that frogs had an almost supernatural capacity to survive without contact with fresh air. There was a rumour in Stockholm at the time that Linnaeus himself had examined Gråberg's stone-frog, but this cannot be substantiated from his published writings. In the 1760s, after Gråberg's death, his frog was kept in the natural history collection of Count Carl Gustaf Tessin at Åkerö Castle, where it was described by the lecturer in chemistry at the University of Uppsala, Mr Philip Tidström.

Toads and Frogs in Stone

Mr Gråberg's paper on the stone-frog was originally written in Swedish, but it was translated into German, Dutch, French and Latin. It aroused much interest in this phenomenon among European scholars and natural historians; many of them reviewed other, older cases of entombed frogs and toads from the literature, or made experiments to determine the longevity of toads enclosed in narrow stone containers. Using a modern expression, the entombed toad phenomenon became a priority field of research during the second part of the eighteenth century. This did not happen through the infusion of government grant money into laboratories and research institutes, but because the scholars of the Age of Improvement, who believed themselves capable of explaining all obscure phenomena in natural history, were unwilling to accept the presumed immortality of these elusive frogs and toads.

In the old chronicles of monsters and marvels, the eighteenth-century investigators found several ancient tales resembling that of the Swedish master builder. In William of Newbury's *Rerum Anglicarum*, it was told that, in 1186, a large stone was found that seemed comprised of two stones joined by some adhesive matter. When a bishop ordered it to be split, a living toad with a gold chain around its neck was sitting in its centre. Everyone understood that this could be nothing but sorcery and witchcraft, and the stone was buried intact without anyone being intrepid enough to divest the toad of its ornament. A more reliable observation was reported by the old chronicler Fulgosius: in his treatise *De Mirabilibus*, published in 1509, he briefly reported that once, at Autun, several people had seen a fat toad being found inside a stone.

The famous surgeon Ambroise Paré supplied details of another French entombed toad. In 1575, he had ordered some workmen at his vineyard near Meudon to break up a couple of large stones. In the middle of one of them was found a large living toad. Paré was greatly astounded, since the stone had no visible opening to the outside. He wondered how the animal had been born and how it had been able to grow and stay alive within the block of stone, but the quarryman, who was apparently a greater authority on entombed toads than the founder of French surgery, said that this was not the first time he had encountered toads and other animals in the centres of stones. Ambroise Paré concluded that the entombed toads must have been formed through spontaneous generation: some humid matter within the stone had putrefied to produce these animals.

Some other sixteenth-century writers believed that the entombed toads were of demonic origin; they were cousins of the basilisk and almost as poisonous as this monstrous being. A seventeenth-century German mining manual advised the workers to leave the mine at once if a subterranean toad was discovered: these supernatural animals were extremely poisonous, and their breath was enough to kill a man. The mineralogist Georg Agricola wrote that the German millers used to scrutinise the blocks of stone that were to be made into millstones, to avoid those that contained an entombed toad. When the millstones ground, the animal would get hot and spew forth its poison into the grain, thus becoming a mass murderer, to the detriment of the miller's future reputation. A most remarkable occurrence was reported by another German scholar, Dr P.J. Sachs, in his *Gammarologia Curiosa*. In 1664, a friend of his, Count Hermann of Gleischen and Hatzfeld, had visited the castle of Count Fürstenberg near Cologne. The latter nobleman had in his possession a round stone, which contained a living frog. When the stone was lifted up, the frog croaked loudly; this strange, hollow sound was likened to the chorus of frogs in the play of Aristophanes: *Koax brekekex*! When, finally, the stone was broken, the frog jumped out alive.

Professor Robert Plot, the first Keeper of the Ashmolean Museum in Oxford, was greatly interested in the subject of entombed toads. In his *Natural History of Staffordshire*, published in 1687, he could describe not less than three cases of a 'toad-in-the-hole', as the phenomenon became known in the British Isles. One of them had been described in a letter from Dr Pierce, a Bath physician, to Mr William Musgrave, the Secretary of the Philosophical Society of Oxford. A large limestone block had been put as a stepping-stone for passengers in the middle of a cartway over two rills. People had been puzzled by a loud croaking sound coming from this stone! At length, it was resolved that the stone was to be broken open: 'in a cavity near the middle a large Toad was found as Bigg as a man's fist, which hop't about as briskly, as if it had been bread in a larger room'. An even more astounding case came from Statfold, where the top-stone of the spire of the church tower had fallen down and broken: 'There appear'd a Living Toad in the Center of it, which (as most of the rest are said to doe) dyed quickly after it was exposed to the Air'.

The records of Chillingham Castle give details about another seventeenth-century English toad-in-the-hole. Legend has it that when a large block of stone was sawed into a huge chimney-piece, which was to be put in the spacious entrance-hall of this castle, a cavity containing a living toad was found. To celebrate this occurrence, a large heraldic device was painted, displaying a large toad on a shield, held up by two frogs, with the motto 'Est et a Jove Bufo'. A Latin inscription was made, allegedly by the learned Bishop of Durham, which would explain a reference to William Harvey's novel work on generation in the second part of the poem, and place the discovery of the toad in the 1660s or early 1670s. The poem contains a challenge to Aristotle (the Stagyrite), since the toad-in-the-hole was a greater marvel than the tides of the Strait of Euripus, which had puzzled Aristotle. It was translated into English by Lord Ravensworth:

> Ho, Stagyrite!
> If you wish something more wonderful than your Euripus,
> Come hither!
> Let the tides flow and ebb, and be he lunatic
> Who robs Trivia of her due honour.
> Lo, for you something novel, which Africa bears not,
> Nor Nile on his sandy shores.
> To wit, fire and pure flame,
> Yet without vital air.
> Out of the dark recess of the split rock,
> As much as you see, the hands
> Of the midwife stonecutter gave light
> To a living toad.

In 1858, a writer in the *Archaeologia Aeliana* could well remember having seen this chimney-piece with the toad's cavity; another antiquary, writing in 1884, was able to inspect both chimney-piece, painting and inscription. According to the present-day custodians of Chillingham Castle, they are still there.

One of the most influential mid-eighteenth-century writers on the entombed toad problem was the Frenchman Claude Nicolas Le Cat, whose thesis on this subject was laid before the Academy of Sciences at Rouen in 1762. After a small toad had been found in a rock near Écretteville outside Rouen, some local dignitaries instructed M. Le Cat, who was a noted surgeon and naturalist, to investigate. Like many contemporary scholars, he disregarded the spontaneous generation hypothesis. Nor did he believe in another notion, coming from some conservative French academics, namely that toads created by God at the beginning of time had accidentally been encased in stone. Le Cat believed that there was a general law of nature that a sober, frugal and inactive manner of living could prolong the individual's life to a remarkable degree. Even a man could live to be several hundred years old if he was imprisoned in a narrow cell and denied access to alcoholic beverages, tobacco and unwholesome, rich food. He estimated that the toad-in-the-hole was about 3,000 years old. He presumed that it had entered the stone after its spawn had trickled down a crevice in the rock, but without theorising further how this could have been accomplished.

The majority of seventeenth- and eighteenth-century reports of a toad-in-the-hole were of English origin. Other reports hailed from the European continent, mainly France and Germany, and a few were from more exotic locations; one of Le Cat's cases was discovered at Guadeloupe. An American toad-in-the-hole was described by the plantation owner Mr Samuel Peters of Hebron, in the Colony of Connecticut. In 1770, this gentleman had become increasingly annoyed with a large stone boulder that had been situated in the high road opposite his house for more than 150 years; by the wear and tear of the road, it had gradually grown quite high, becoming a nuisance to carriages. Mr Peters decided to do something about this. He ordered his slaves to dig a wide ditch around the stone, and a miner to perforate it with an auger. The hole was charged with gunpowder, which was fired off after the spectators had retired to a safe distance. After the tremendous explosion, chips of stone flew about, but two large fragments of the rock still lay inside the ditch. One of them had a small orifice, a circumstance that puzzled Mr Peters. When the men had widened this orifice, they were astounded to see a cavity as large as a goose egg, in which lay a frog that almost completely filled it. The animal was bleeding from one leg, but otherwise seemed unaffected by being so rudely awakened from its stupor. Mr Peters exhibited the strange stone-frog before the curious for many weeks.

The toad-in-the-hole also entered the realm of literature. A certain Mr G. Dodsley, writing a book of fables in imitation of Aesop in 1761, included a story titled 'The Toad and the Ephemeron'. A toad-in-the-hole, freed by some workmen, sat swelling and bloating, and bragged that it was 'a specimen of the antediluvian race of animals. I was begotten before the flood. And who is there among the present upstart race of mortals that shall dare to contend with me in nobility of birth, or dignity of character?' An ephemeron that was flying by replied that the vain boaster was 'as insensible as the block in which thou wast bred'. Itself, it had enjoyed the warmth of the sun and the light of the day: 'My whole life, 'tis true, is but of twelve hours; but even one hour of it is to be preferred to a thousand years of mere existence, which have been spent, like thine, in sloth, ignorance and stupidity'. John Wesley made a similar analogy in a sermon preached in Rotherham in July 1790, comparing the empty, valueless lives of men living without God with the trance-like state of the entombed toad. Edward Bulwer Lytton, the celebrated writer of sensation novels, made quite another use of the entombed toad metaphor in one of his short stories, 'A Manuscript found in a Madhouse', which was published in 1847. In this highly strung Gothic tale, a hideously deformed boy laments his lonely, wretched childhood: 'I was like the reptile whose prison is the stone's heart – immured in the eternal penthouse of a solitude to which breath of friendship never came – girded with a wall of barrenness and flint, and doomed to vegetate and fatten on my own suffocating and poisoned meditations'.

Bizarre Experiments

In September 1770, a live toad was found inside a stone wall at the castle of Le Raincy in France. This once more stirred the interest in the subterranean amphibians, and there was much speculation about this subject. M. Jean Guéttard, a Fellow of the French Academy of Sciences, made a long speech describing the toad-in-the-hole as one of the most puzzling enigmas in natural history, and urged his fellow academicians to spare no labour to solve this mystery, which had baffled the naturalists for more than 200 years. His colleague M. Louis Hérissant was inspired to perform an ambitious series of experiments to test the capacity of toads to withstand hunger, thirst and suffocation. Three fully grown toads were put in boxes, which were sealed with plaster in the presence of several academicians. When they were opened eighteen months later, two of the toads were seen to be alive. The boxes were sealed and put away a second time, but M. Hérissant was not destined to see the result of his experiment: he died in October 1773 and the toads survived him. In his eulogy on M. Hérissant, read before the Academy in 1777, Jean Guéttard mentioned that this gentleman, apparently a scientist to the last, had left him the boxes of toads in his will, with instructions to open them some time after his death. This was done, just as prescribed, but the toads were all dead and desiccated.

From the mid-eighteenth century onwards, many English clergymen and amateur natural historians were eager to put the viability of toads to the test. Usually, they put a toad in a flowerpot, sealed it with plaster or mortar, and buried it in their gardens. After waiting for a period of time, the pot was unearthed and the toad freed. Usually, in these experiments, the animal turned out to be alive and in good health. In one of his unpublished manuscripts, the naturalist Gilbert White described an experiment made by an Oxford undergraduate who buried a toad in a garden pot for thirteen months; when dug up, the animal was alive and well, and 'considerably grown'. Even the zoologist Edward Jesse's toad, which had been closed up in a flowerpot for twenty years, jumped out with vigour when the pot was opened. These experiments were often widely publicised in the local newspapers, and it was concluded that toads could live forever if left alone in a small cavity without anything to eat or drink.

Dr William Buckland, the Professor of Geology at Oxford, and later Dean of Westminster, became interested in the entombed toad phenomenon when his friend Luke Howard suggested that the existence of the toad-in-the-hole might provide evidence for or against the gradualist and catastrophic theories of the origin of the Earth. Buckland asked several scientists of his acquaintance how long they believed a toad could survive imprisoned inside a rock, but since their estimates ranged from a few days to 4,000 years, he rightly decided that they knew as little of this subject as he did himself. Buckland did not rely on the primitive experiments with toads in flowerpots, which were often carelessly done. Sometimes, the pots were imperfectly sealed, and in other instances, they had corroded, enabling moisture and insects to enter the toad's enclosure. In November 1825, William Buckland himself planned a rigorous set of experiments to determine the reality of the toad-in-the-hole phenomenon once and for all.

In a block of coarse oolitic limestone, twelve circular cells were prepared, each about one foot deep and five inches in diameter. Six large toads and six smaller ones were put in these holes. The cells were all sealed with circular plates of glass, which were fitted into a groove in the stone and sealed by a luting of soft clay. Twelve smaller holes were prepared in a block of siliceous compact sandstone, provided with toads and sealed with glass plates in the same manner. After a double cover of glass and clay had been placed over each block of stone, the blocks were buried in Professor Buckland's garden under three feet of earth. One year later, in December 1826, the blocks of stone were dug up and examined. All the toads in the sandstone block were dead and decayed. All the small toads in the limestone block were also dead. To his amazement, Buckland found that the larger toads in the porous limestone block were still alive, and two of them had even gained weight. The block of stone was resealed and the mute prisoners buried alive for a second time. Buckland examined them several times during the second year, to see if they hibernated, but this was not the case; they were all awake, sitting in their cells, but their emaciation increased each time the stone was unearthed, until finally, they were all dead.

The results of William Buckland's experiment made him doubt the reality of the toad-in-the-hole phenomenon. It was now proven that these animals could not survive in the compact sandstone, which did not admit air to their cells. Even in the porous limestone, the best-nourished toads starved to death within two years. The majority of Buckland's contemporaries agreed with his conclusions, particularly as the French zoologists Duméril and Edwards had performed a series of similar experiments, with results much resembling those of Buckland. The major part of the zoological establishment had thus permanently lost faith in the toad-in-the-hole phenomenon; even today, zoologists quote William Buckland's experiments as the strongest argument against the existence of these subterranean amphibians. It is interesting to note that the stones used in William Buckland's experiments were made by masons employed to work on the old residence attached to the canonry. The house that he occupied at the time has since been assigned to the Archdeacon of Oxford, and according to the *Life and Correspondence of William Buckland*, by Elizabeth Gordon, the Archdeacon Palmer, who resided there in 1894, placed the stones in his garden in memory of the toad experiments. According to one of the later archdeacons, they have since been removed.

The immediate reflection, when surveying these bizarre experiments, is that it is a barbaric practice to immure living animals in this manner. Such qualms did not occur to the nineteenth-century vivisectors, who freely used both toads and higher animals in their cruel experiments, but ethical concerns of course prevent these investigations from being repeated today. The most competently carried out, and clearly described, of these experimental immurements of toads were those performed by William Buckland. But in spite of his careful preparations, these experiments have certain important flaws, and there is good reason to doubt whether they really disprove the toad-in-the-hole legend. Since Buckland had been collecting toads for some time, at least some of his specimens may just have come out of hibernation, and thus not have been strong. He also disregarded the fact that the toad's metabolism and disposition to hibernate is temperature dependent; no record was kept of the climatic conditions during the experimental period. It may also have been unwise of him to dig up the slab of stone at regular intervals, thus disturbing the toad's attempts at reaching a hibernating state, and exposing them to the light. Buckland's theory that insects had gained entry through a crack in the glass pane does not seem particularly likely. If the toad that had gained in weight had devoured such a considerable amount of insects, its cell would have been likely to contain excrements with the shell parts of these insects, but this was not noticed, even by an observer as astute as William Buckland. An alternative explanation of the animal's gain in weight may be that it was dehydrated when put in its cell, and later absorbed moisture through the skin.

The Blois Toad-in-the-Hole

In June 1851, some French workmen were digging a deep well near the city of Blois. They found a large flintstone, which was split in two by a hard blow with a pickaxe. In the middle of the stone sat a large toad! It appeared greatly astonished again to see the light of day. The toad-in-the-hole jumped out and started to crawl away, but it was captured by the workmen, who carried it in triumph to the Society of Sciences in Blois. Both the toad and the stone were put in a damp cellar, and embedded in moss. The French journalists had a field-day speculating how many thousand years this toad had existed within its stone. The whole thing was termed 'mysterious' and 'absolutely inexplicable', and it seemed as if the Britons' morbid interest in the toad-in-the-hole had spread, like some strange contagion, across the English Channel. The hammer that shattered the stony encasing of the toad-in-the-hole would also shatter the fundaments of science.

The French Academy of Sciences was a more sceptical body, and they were dismayed to 'see this ancient vulgar error once again raise its ugly head', as expressed by one of its more eloquent Fellows. In view of the strong popular interest in the Blois toad, they appointed a committee of experts to look into the case. It was chaired by the veteran herpetologist Professor André Duméril, who had taken part in the debate about the French rains of frogs and toads seventeen years earlier. Although he was a convinced sceptic and much inclined to disbelieve the toad-in-the-hole phenomenon altogether, he could not help being impressed by the way the toad's body exactly fitted the cavity in the flintstone. The members of the committee also noted that the toad's jaw had the mark of an irregularity in its hole, indicating that it had been growing within its lair for a prolonged period of time. After their investigation was concluded, Professor Duméril and his colleagues had to declare that they could find no evidence whatsoever of a fraud, and that the toad had apparently been situated within the flintstone, without any communication with the outside world. They confessed themselves completely baffled by this strange occurrence.

When Professor Duméril's paper was published in the Academy's *Comptes Rendus*, several other academicians were aghast at this revival of an old fallacy, which had now been given support by one of their own number. They objected that Duméril and his colleagues had been overly credulous, and that they had naively given the sanction of the Academy to a ridiculous old error. Professor François Magendie, the great neurobiologist, suspected that the whole thing was an imposture, instigated, perhaps, by the workmen who had pretended to find the toad. He suggested that the toad should have been killed and dissected as soon as it was taken out of the stone; if incompletely digested insects were found within its intestinal canal, it was of course highly unlikely that it had spent many years inside the flintstone without food. But Magendie's advice was not acted upon. At the next session of the Academy, both Duméril and Magendie were thanked for their contributions to zoology, but the Academy did not make any kind of official statement with regard to the Blois toad, probably because of the persistent rumours that it was a clever hoax.

Scandal at the Exhibition

In the mid-nineteenth century, the British nation's unhealthy fascination for the toad-in-the-hole reached the height of a veritable mass hysteria.

Every year, several novel cases were reported, both in the scientific periodicals and in the daily newspapers. The editor of *Zoologist* magazine, Dr Edward Newman, was deluged with letters and case reports, which he did not appreciate at all, since he was a firm opponent of the toad-in-the-hole phenomenon. Ironically, he wrote in one of his leaders that a considerable proportion of the toads of Britain were likely to spend all their lives within flower-pots, due to his countrymen's abnormal interest in experimentation on toad longevity. In 1859, Charles Dickens read one of the articles in the *Zoologist*, which he later reviewed in his own journal *All the Year Round*. Dickens compared the toad-in-the-hole with the equally controversial phenomenon of toad showers: 'not content with puzzling me with their subterraneous doings, these provoking reptiles are said to come down from the skies in showers'. The British public, whose knowledge of natural history was otherwise unremarkable, knew at least two things about toads: they could fall from the clouds in showers, and they could live thousands of years embedded in solid stone.

In the autumn of 1862, just when Charles Dickens's article had been published, the Great Exhibition was opened in London. One section had geological specimens from English and Welsh mines, one of which was a large block of coal from the mine of Cwmtillery, which, when cloven in two, was found to contain a living frog. The newspaper writers all gathered round the frog's exhibition case, and the Londoners rejected the curiosities of three continents in favour of the Welsh frog-in-the-coal. In a sermon, a clergyman urged all Englishmen to watch this frog with reverence: it was one of the creatures first created by God, and had 'breathed the same air as Noah and sported in the limpid streams in which Adam bathed his sturdy limbs'.

Dr Frank Buckland, the son of William Buckland and Assistant Surgeon to the Second Life Guards, shared his father's interest in the toad-in-the-hole problem. He was dismayed to see the renewed popular interest in this question, and to debunk the newspaper reports about this 'antediluvian' frog, he obtained permission to examine it closely. It seemed to be a young frog rather than a fully grown specimen. The alleged century-long stay in the block of coal had not diminished its vivacity, and it jumped merrily about. Frank Buckland was seconded by his friend Professor Richard Owen, who suggested that frogspawn could have fallen into the pit and developed in some pool of water there. After having developed, the frog could have crawled into some dark crevice or fissure in the coal, to come tumbling out when the block of coal containing this fissure was broken by the workmen. It is a testimony to the British nation's great interest in the toad-in-the-hole controversy that the contributions of Buckland and Owen on this subject were not published in some obscure naturalist journal, but as letters to the editor of *The Times*. In *Punch* magazine, the frog was honoured with a jocular poem:

> Oh, who is this toad in a hole,
>   With face so expressively dark,
> Who spends all his life in a coal,
>   And only comes out for a lark?
>
> From Grub Street to Bridgewater Place
>   This *Opéra comique*'s all the go;
> Where Buckland does alto and bass,
>   And Brown, Jones and Scroggins *Buffo*.

Several other rationalists wrote to *The Times*, to ridicule the ignorant populace for its persistent belief in the toad-in-the-hole and other dubious phenomena, and to demand the instant expulsion of the frog and the block of coal from the Exhibition. Some irate sceptics even suggested that the exhibitor of the frog should be charged with fraud and imposture; the commissioners of the Exhibition were accused of being credulous fools. Meanwhile, members of the public defended the frog's honour in no uncertain terms, and more new cases of toad-in-the-hole were reported than ever before. Many of these were second- or even third-hand accounts, and seem rather unconvincing; one newspaper article came from a man who had found a live toad inside his marble mantelpiece, when it has tipped from its position and broken in two. Richard Owen was sent many specimens of toad-in-the-hole by mail or special delivery, but the busy academic turned them over to his wife Caroline for examination; she managed to expose at least one of them as a fraud, since the toad was much larger than the cavity in a block of coal it was said to have inhabited. Another living toad, which was found embedded in mortar when a wall was pulled down inside the church of North Wingfield, was sent by the vicar to Frank Buckland's home address. Buckland presumed that 'the ecclesiastical toad' had been protected by divine powers during its perilous journey; having merely been put inside a paper parcel by the unworldly cleric. The animal, which was presumed to be several thousand years old, would have perished ignominiously if some careless railway porter had put a heavy box on top of it! Otherwise, Frank Buckland declared himself to be wholly unimpressed by this new specimen: it did not seem to be more than a year old, and jumped merrily about in its bowl.

Although the debate about the frog-in-the-coal was a victory for Frank Buckland and Richard Owen, they failed in their objective to get the frog expelled from the exhibition. Nor did the British public seem to be wholly convinced by their arguments, although Mr Punch mocked the Welsh frog-in-the-coal with the verses

Then what awe must each bosom overspread
   As we gaze on that petrified bark;
On the bust of this quaint figure-head
   That has yachted with Noah in the ark:

When we think that these somnolent eyes
   With morning primæval awoke, –
That this solo (though sweet for its size)
   Preluded Labyrinthidon's croak!

The Antediluvian Toads

Some commentators have marvelled at the extreme interest for entombed toads in mid-nineteenth-century Britain: this obscure topic seems to have been given more attention in the newspaper press than any other biological problem. At least part of an explanation may be that the toad-in-the-hole played a part in the debate about Darwinism. Certain conservative clergymen enrolled the entombed toads among their ranks to fight Charles Darwin's blasphemous theories. They considered the toad-in-the-hole as one of the firmest arguments that a universal deluge had really happened. According to their version of geology, the rocks had later been formed from sedimented matter left by the deluge; certain toads, which had survived the Flood, had thus been encased in stone and lived there for thousands of years.

It was thus no coincidence that many of the British toads-in-the-hole were described by clergymen. In April 1865, the debate was refuelled after some workmen claimed to have found a live toad in a large block of magnesian limestone, at a depth of twenty-five feet from the surface of the earth. The cavity was no larger than its body, and presented the appearance of being a cast around it. The toad's eyes shone with unusual brilliancy, and its mouth was found to be completely closed. The claws of the hind feet were unusually long. The Rev. Robert Taylor, Rector of St Hilda's Church, Hartlepool, adopted the toad and gave it a home in the Hartlepool Museum. The Rector reported to the press that the toad was still living several days later, and seemed to be in excellent health, in spite of its inability to take nourishment; although its mouth remained closed, it occasionally uttered a 'barking' noise through the nostrils. He claimed that the toad was 36 million years old, and that it had been sitting in its hole since the stone was first formed. Both the toad and the bold geologist parson became national celebrities. A party from the Manchester Geological Society visited Hartlepool to see the toad and inspect its hole in the block of stone. But when one of the geologists put his hand inside the hole, he could feel marks of a chisel! He accused the collier who claimed to have found the toad of having perpetrated this fraud. The man first persisted that he was telling the truth, but when the geologist threatened to bring the stone and toad to the Natural History Museum in London for a closer examination, he refused and ignominiously withdrew. After this exposure, the Rector took back his daring statements about the antediluvian toad, but this did not prevent him from being much laughed at during one of the Manchester Geological Society's monthly meetings, where this revival of an old vulgar error was greeted with amused incredulity.

The Victorians' fascination with the toad-in-the-hole slowly faded away during the 1870s and 1880s. The final outbreak of the hysteria occurred in 1901, when a certain Mr W.J. Clarke, who was sitting in front of the fire in his Rugby home, suddenly gave a start when a large coal fell out from the fireplace. When he struck it with a poker, it burst in two and a live toad fell out from its midst. In the fanciful newspaper accounts, this toad was stated to lack both a mouth and a rectum. Like some of its predecessors, the Rugby toad-in-the-coal became quite a celebrity: it was even the subject of stereoscopic photographs available at the time.

During the remainder of the twentieth century, not much has been written about the once-famous toad-in-the-hole, in Britain or elsewhere, and the phenomenon has gradually become almost totally forgotten. Not even zoologists specialising in herpetology (amphibian biology) are aware of this obscure piece of toad lore, although some ethnologists have used the toad-in-the-hole to exemplify the ridiculous nineteenth-century popular fallacies in natural history. This is not the end of the insults directed toward the wretched subterranean toads by modern rationalists. When the once famous expression 'toad-in-the-hole' is looked up in the *Oxford Modern Dictionary*, the reader is informed that it can denote either a game or a dinner recipe. Both these attributes were derived from the legend of entombed toads, however. The objective of the game toad-in-the-hole, which dates from the seventeenth century, is to throw discs of lead into holes in a wooden structure; the piece of lead represented the toad and the wood the stone surrounding its lair. Games of toad-in-the-hole were played at some old-fashioned Sussex public houses as late as the 1930s.

It is even more remarkable that toads-in-the-hole actually can be eaten. In the late eighteenth century, when the entombed toad phenomenon first gained notoriety, a dish made by seasoning a beefsteak and then baking it in batter became fashionable. The beefsteak symbolised the toad and the batter the surrounding stone. It survived for many years, but due to austerity the beefsteak was replaced by a brace of sausages. In 1934, T.S. Eliot wrote about 'restaurants where you could get sausage and mashed or toad-in-the-'ole for twopence'; one wonders if he knew the true origin of the word! Whereas a home-made toad-in-the-hole made of beefsteak and batter is a pleasant meal for any person who is not on a diet, the awful supermarket version of this food, with foul-smelling grease and a disgusting brace of sausages instead of a beefsteak, can be recommended only to one's worst enemy.

Old Rip

On 28 January 1928, two thousand people had gathered round the derelict old courthouse of the little town of Eastland, situated near Fort Worth, Texas. One might have presumed that it was an election, a cattle auction or a distribution of free beer, but it was an unprecedented incident in these parts that has roused most of the local population. When the old courthouse had been built thirty-one years earlier, a young local named Will Wood, who was known as a practical joker, suggested that they were to put some things into the great hollow cornerstone of the building. The master builder put in a Bible and some newspapers and photographs, but Wood himself put a horned toad (*Phrynosoma cornutum*) into the stone before it was closed. The reason for this was that he wanted to test the local legend that this lizard-like reptile, which occurs in Mexico and the southern states of the United States, could survive for more than 100 years without food, water, or air. There was much talk about Will Wood's experiment, and speculation was rife whether the horned toad was still alive. Several bets were wagered, and it was often suggested that the stone should be taken out of its fundament, but Wood always refused. When the courthouse was to be pulled down, the moment of truth had arrived. Judge E.S. Pritchard was entrusted to remove the cornerstone, assisted by the three parsons of the community. Excitement grew when the stone was removed; the Judge took out the Bible and the newspapers, and the Methodist pastor pulled out the blackened, lifeless body of the horned toad, holding it by one of its hind legs. Suddenly, the animal's other hind leg started twitching, and it violently gasped for breath. The pastor dropped the horned toad, which fell into the sand. There was a great uproar among the onlookers, and shouts of 'The critter's alive!' The horned toad was carried in triumph to the town hall, where it was named 'Old Rip' after Rip van Winkle, the fictional character who had slept for twenty years; Old Rip had slept for thirty-one!

The local newspapers all published Old Rip's picture on their front pages, and the Texas horned toad soon became a media celebrity. Reporters and tourists from all over the US visited Eastland to see its foremost attraction. Old Rip was exhibited in the window of a grocery store, and slept there in his bowl during the night. One morning, Will Wood and his cronies were amazed to see that the famous reptile had vanished. There were soon rumours that a local crook named C.F. Sheppard had kidnapped Old Rip to take him on tour. The toadnapper got as far as El Paso before being apprehended and returned to Eastland, where the Judge placed the reptile in Will Wood's custody. A Dallas showman named Dick Penney sued Will Wood for more than 6,000 dollars, claiming to have a ten-week contract for exhibition of

Old Rip, but without success. Instead, Will Wood himself became Old Rip's manager, and exhibited the horned toad in various venues all over the United States. The horned toad was particularly successful in New York, and history has it that President Calvin Coolidge broke several other engagements to receive Old Rip in a personal audience in the White House. When Old Rip returned to Eastland after his grand tour, he was the model for many posters and postcards. A scholar from the Texas Christian University, Dr W.G. Hewatt, examined Old Rip: and concluded that it was a perfectly normal specimen, whose horns about the head region were considerably worn, indicating that it was quite old. In January 1929, Old Rip was found dead in his bowl. No autopsy was performed, since Will Wood wanted to keep the body intact, but the cause of death was presumed to be pneumonia.

Old Rip was embalmed and laid out in state in a little blue coffin lined with purple velvet and white satin, which was put in a marble sarcophagus in the lobby of the Eastland County Courthouse. One morning in October 1930, it was seen that the glass top of the marble tomb had been removed, and Old Rip's coffin was empty! The toad-nappers were hunted down, however, and the corpse of Eastland's most distinguished resident returned to its resting-place. He remained in peace until 1961, when he was kidnapped by some college students, who later shamefacedly returned the limp body in a paper bag, after having read the bloodcurdling threats against themselves in the local newspapers. The year after, Old Rip entered politics. When one of the candidates for governor of Texas, Mr John Connally, made a stop in Eastland during an electioneering tour, the local Democrats decided to hand over their most valued possession in a ceremony. During previous stops on his tour, Mr Connally had been given golden keys and giant pumpkins by the local authorities; in Eastland, the little blue casket containing Old Rip's limp body was handed over to the startled politician, who believed it to be a joke in rather bad taste. He picked up the embalmed body and swung it about by the leg, to the consternation of the old Eastlanders, who knew its age and fragility. Mr Connally forgot to return the lizard's corpse when he left Eastland, and the President of the Eastland Chamber of Commerce had to drive to Cisco at breakneck speed to recover it. Rather shamefacedly, Mr Connally returned Old Rip's body, which lacked one hind leg, perhaps due to further rough treatment by the candidate's entourage.

In 1971, the toad-nappers struck for the fourth time. The tomb was empty and this time there was no demand for ransom. But after more than a year had passed, an anonymous tip led to the fairground. Old Rip was rescued and triumphantly returned to his tomb, which was belatedly equipped with a solid lock. Since 1972, Old Rip's body has been allowed to repose undisturbed in its marble tomb, admired by the Eastlanders and by thousands of tourists, many of whom had come merely to see the supernatural horned toad. Many zoologists have been disposed to doubt the tale of Old Rip, since horned toads rarely live for any prolonged period of time. It has also been hinted that the cunning Will Wood may well have substituted another horned toad for the corpse of the original one, just before the cornerstone was opened.

The Toad-in-the-Hole on Trial

If the toad-in-the-hole would be summoned before judge and jury, charged with fraud, imposture, and breaking the laws of nature, its barrister would not lack arguments to support the claim that his client was a reality. He could put a file containing more than 210 cases of frogs and toads found inside stones, lumps of coal, or within the trunks of large trees. There have been reports of entombed toads from all over the world: from Europe, the United States, Canada, Africa, New Zealand and the West Indies. The earliest of them are from the late fifteenth century; the latest occurred in Australia, in 1982. Many times, the frogs or toads were seen by several independent witnesses. Sometimes these people were entirely ignorant that similar prodigies had ever been described, like Mr Peters of Connecticut and the Swedish master builder. After a close study of twenty of the best attested cases of entombed toads, the immediate conclusion is that the legend of the toad-in-the-hole surely cannot have been based on imagination alone. Certain remarkable details about the subterranean toads and frogs often recur: the mouth was covered by a viscous membrane; the eyes shone brightly (perhaps owing to a maximal dilatation of the pupil, to adjust to a life in constant darkness?); and the colour of the toad's skin was darker than usual. The latter phenomenon was also observed in some of the nineteenth-century experiments with entombed toads; this would support the notion that, at least in these cases, the toads had lived within their stony enclosure for a considerable period of time. Some early chroniclers of the toad-in-the-hole claimed that the toads usually died when liberated from their prison; this happened in a number of instances, it is true, perhaps because the animal did not cope with the adaptation from its hibernating torpor to an active life. These cases are a minority, however, and quite a few of the alleged entombed toads were stated to have been in excellent health and vigour immediately upon being released, something which in itself arises suspicion.

The prosecutor in the trial of the toad-in-the-hole would be likely to claim that the existence of living amphibians within solid stones is contrary to scientific opinion and common sense alike. Such a phenomenon is both pointless and irrational, and no reasonable explanation can be found as to why these toads had preferred a living death to the active existence of the rest of their tribe. The few twentieth-century biologists at all acknowledging this obscure phenomenon have merely sneered at this ridiculous old vulgar error in natural history, and likened it to the popular fallacies that hedgehogs were milking the cows in the fields, or that living snakes could live for years as parasites in the human stomach. The herpetologist Professor G.K. Noble was one of the last briefly to mention the toad-in-the-hole in his authoritative textbook *Biology of the Amphibia*, published in 1931, but only to bluntly declare that 'the story that a toad can live for centuries entombed in stones or in old wells is sheer fable'. The toad-in-the-hole is not mentioned in any present-day herpetological textbook of repute. After being forgotten, or ignored, by the zoologists, the toad-in-the-hole has been adopted by the modern pseudo-scientists and devotees of paranormal phenomena, and put on par with UFOs, crop circles, spontaneous human combustion, and the horrors of the Bermuda Triangle. The most ridiculous hypotheses have been employed by these enthusiasts to explain the entombed toad phenomenon: some authors still advocate the theory of a universal deluge, and others claim that the unsuspecting amphibians have been teleported into the rocks by mysterious powers.

It may be asked why only frogs and toads should be teleported in this way, but it is true that there were some nineteenth-century instances of snakes and lizards found enclosed in cavities underground. Furthermore, Dr Oliver Fiske MD, of Worcester, Massachusetts can be credited for describing (in the Memoirs of the American Academy of Arts and Sciences of 1803) the only known case of a 'mouse-in-the-hole'. A farmer digging in a meadow found a hard lump of some solid substance, the size of a goose egg, which he broke with a spade; inside, he was astonished to see a little mouse, which 'left a vacancy of the same dimensions as its size'. After being warmed up in front of the fire, the little mouse 'was restored to a perfect, living state, and ran off with activity'; it was speculated that it had been immured for a century. An even more ludicrous tale can be found in the *Physica Curiosa* of Gaspar Schottus: in England, two dogs 'of fierce countenance' had been found enclosed in a block of stone from a quarry! They were as big as greyhounds, but with no hair, and gave off an infernal smell. One died, but the other was taken to the Bishop of Winchester, who is recorded to have played with this malodorous, subterranean canine for several days.

If the temporal distribution of the 218 cases of toad-in-the-hole is studied closer, it is seen that these observations of entombed toads became increasingly frequent from the early seventeenth century onwards. M. Guéttard, writing in the 1780s, was quite right to consider this phenomenon one of the great unsolved biological riddles of his time. The remarkable series of entombed toad observations culminated in the mid-nineteenth century, but there has been a steady trickle of new cases well into the twentieth century. In our own time, much fewer entombed toads have been discovered, and the rationalists have of course used this as an argument that they belong to the realm of mythology rather than that of zoology. The friends of the toad-in-the-hole retort that the use of modern mining technology has been disastrous to the subterranean amphibians: instead of being carefully freed from its hole by the quarryman, the entombed toad is ground into mincemeat by the powerful mining drills. Another factor likely to decrease the number of entombed toad cases is that the people finding them are afraid of being ridiculed when reporting such an odd and 'impossible' occurrence. It is interesting to note that when an Australian zoologist made a broadcast about entombed toads in 1983, treating the subject quite seriously, several people contacted him to describe their own experiences of toads and frogs in stone.

The geographical distribution of the toad-in-the-hole phenomenon is also of interest. Not less than 150 of the 218 cases known to me are from the United Kingdom; 105 of them were described in the nineteenth century, many during the 1850s and 1860s when the interest in this phenomenon was at its peak. Although the toad-in-the-hole lore was well known all over the civilised world at the time, one marvels at the strong British interest in this obscure phenomenon. The religious debate about Darwinism contra the Deluge, into which the entombed toads were recruited by certain conservative clergymen, may have played its part, but it cannot explain all aspects of the great popular interest in this phenomenon. It may be that the toad, pent up in a block of granite, which was one day freed through a mighty blow from the midwife stone-cutter's hammer, had a strange symbolic significance for the repressed Victorians. For some individuals, it seems to have become a veritable *idée fixe* that the toad-in-the-hole really existed. They even went as far as to forge preparations with dead or living toads encased in blocks of stone or coal. The Rev. Taylor's toad is likely to have been a hoax, as well as at least one of those sent to Professor Owen; there were also surreptitious rumours that the famous frog-in-the-coal at the Exhibition had been a forgery, prepared to advertise the mine where it was said to have been found. During the heyday of entombed toad lore, the zoologists Edward Newman and John Plant travelled to several mines and quarries and spoke to the workmen, buying them rounds of ale and porter in the pubs. They promised that the miner who showed them an undoubted toad-in-the-hole would be richly rewarded. The miners and quarrymen eagerly drank their ale, bragging that, since entombed toads were frequently occurring in the rocks they were working, they would soon be claiming their reward. After several years, no toad-in-the-hole was forthcoming, although Plant had visited the mines and quarries several times. The workmen often said that one of their colleagues, who had recently moved to another mine, had once discovered a toad-in-the-hole, but Plant remained incredulous.

A Gloucester naturalist, who promised a guinea to the quarryman who could show him a toad-in-the-hole, received a specimen soon after. But the antediluvian toad died the same evening! When dissected, it proved to have several half-digested insects in its stomach, a diet that it could not very well have attained while pent up in a block of granite for thousands of years. In the 1860s, the Victorians' unwholesome interest in self-immured amphibians had risen to such a peak that there was a market for mass production of faked toads-in-the-hole. In his workshop in Leeds, an individual called Toad Jack baked toads in an oven to make them black, before putting them into bisected pieces of rock or lumps of coal, in which a hole corresponding to the animal's body had been carefully cut out. These forged specimens were readily purchased by avid curiosity-seekers. Not a few of them were bought by publicans, who exhibited them in their pubs, knowing that a toad-in-the-hole attracted more visitors than a comedian or pub musician, and caused the ale-barrels to be emptied quicker than either of these attractions.

Many of the British nineteenth-century cases of a toad-in-the-hole were reported in the newspapers, without receiving notice in any scholarly journal. Some of these seem reasonably trustworthy, but by no means all. Some of the newspaper accounts about 'A Wonderful Toad' or 'Remarkable Fact in Natural History' have almost exactly the same wording. It does not seem overly fanciful to suspect that certain unscrupulous hack journalists copied interesting articles from old newspapers and sold them on to their editors as fresh news; this practice is known to have been widespread in the mid-nineteenth century, and may not be totally extinct today. Articles about entombed toads were particularly attractive, due to the great topical interest of this phenomenon. Some other newspaper stories about toads-in-the-hole being discovered are likely to have been hoaxes, perpetrated by clever pranksters who wanted to make fun of the gullible, sensation-seeking journalists. The result of the most audacious of these practical jokes was published in the *Illustrated London News* of 1856. When a railway tunnel was being blasted through a mountain between Saint-Didier and Nancy, the workmen were horrified to see a monstrous creature flutter out from a hole in a large boulder, which had just been cloven in two by an explosion. The creature was the size of a goose, with an abominably ugly head and a long beak armed with rows of sharp teeth. It uttered a hoarse cry and then fell down dead. A prominent French naturalist had, it was stated, identified as a long-extinct saurian flying lizard, a *Pterodactylus anas*, a species which had flourished during the Jurassic era. The clue to this hoax is that *anas* is the Latin word for duck: the erudite prankster must have had a jolly time when he saw the current issue of the *Illustrated London News*, exulting at having served the ignorant Victorian newspaper men such a juicy *canard*!

Richard Owen and Frank Buckland were probably right when they claimed that many of the nineteenth-century toads-in-the-hole had not spent any prolonged period of time inside the stone. At the height of the toad-in-the-hole debate, it was sometimes enough that a toad or frog leapt forth when a block of stone was split for the entombed toad hysteria to have another outbreak. Frank Buckland suggested that many of the other cases might well have a perfectly natural explanation: an adventurous young toad might crawl through some rocky crevice to reach a natural hollow within a block of stone. It could hibernate in here with ease, living off the insects that ventured into the same crevice, as well as its own deposit of fat. In the early spring, the toad faced an unpleasant surprise: either it had grown in size and become too large to get out, or the hole had been plugged by gravel or calcific deposits. In either case, the toad was a prisoner within its block of stone, which was likely to become its coffin, if it was not freed by a quarryman to become a national hero in a flurry of newspaper publicity.

In zoological gardens, it has been noted that toads may live to be thirty-five years old if allowed to lead a sedentary life with ample provisions of food. The Victorian naturalist Thomas Pennant kept a toad as a family pet for thirty-six years. Each evening, this venerable toad emerged from its lair underneath the steps of his house, politely waiting to be picked up and put on the dining table, where it was given a meal. The question of how long a toad can live in a hibernating state, enclosed within a stony cell, is still unsolved and likely to remain so. Some of the older experiments speak in favour of the tenacious amphibians being able to live for many years in a hibernating state without access to food. If some demented scientist attempted to reproduce William Buckland's experiment today, he would run into considerable difficulties with both the university board and the ethics committee.

During the heyday of the toad-in-the-hole, many of the specimens were presented to various museums, but the vast majority of these relics of the credulous Victorian era seem to have been discarded by the latter-day museum curators. For example, it is recorded that in 1821, Lord and Lady Duncan donated a toad-in-the-hole to the Edinburgh University Museum, which is now part of the Royal Scottish Museums; the toad is no longer within its collections. Nor has a lump of rock, containing a live frog found at a depth of many feet below ground, which was exhibited at the museum of the Midlands Institute in Birmingham in the mid-nineteenth century, been kept for posterity. The world's only toad-in-the-hole today resides at the Booth Museum of Natural History in Brighton. It was donated by a certain Mr Charles Dawson, a solicitor and amateur naturalist, in 1901. The preparation consists of an oval, hollow flintstone nodule, containing a desiccated toad. Dawson said that he had been given it by some workmen, who had noticed that the stone seemed lighter than could be expected, and broken it with a spade to see what was inside. The flintstone, which is probably 75 to 100 million years old, is likely to have been formed around one of the primitive sponges extant during this period. These sponges were formed like a bag with a narrow, spoutlike stem. At a later period, water must have entered the stone, and the sponge was dissolved. There was a connection between the hole inside the stone nodule and the outside world, by way of the narrow channel once occupied by the sponge's stem; this can still be seen in the Brighton preparation. Dawson suggested that a young toad had crawled in through this aperture when very young. In some way, it was able to procure food in there; perhaps some insects and larvae chose the same way in. Finally, the toad had grown in size, as to be unable to get through the narrow passage through which it had entered; after some time, it starved to death within its stony prison. If the workmen had split the stone before the animal had died, it would have joined the ranks of the living toads-in-the-hole. Since the Brighton stone nodule is not the only one formed around a sponge, Dawson suggested that his explanation could be extended to cover quite a few of the other entombed toads, and even provide a tentative explanation of the phenomenon.

There is, however, one serious objection to this theory. The name of Charles Dawson has been blackened by his involvement in the most notorious scientific forgery of all time: the Piltdown scandal, in which a faked anthropoid skull was claimed to belong to Darwin's 'missing link' between human and ape. Although there are some other suspects, Charles Dawson has roundly been accused of having forged the skull and other Piltdown 'fossils' with his own hands. In his 2003 book *Piltdown Man*, archaeologist Miles Russell has presented the most comprehensive analysis to date of Dawson's weird activities, demonstrating that over a period of more than twenty years, Dawson was guilty of wholesale scientific fraud and plagiarism. His pretended 'discoveries' were often of a spectacular nature, just like the toad-in-the-hole. Nor can the toad itself be taken at its face value. Comparison with the original 1901 photographs demonstrates that it has shrunk in size since then, indicating that it was quite recently dead and dried up when submitted to the museum. This would agree with the hypothesis that Dawson had found the right flint and dried the toad to concoct one of his hoaxes. Another suspicious circumstance is that it succumbed neither to mould nor to fungal attack, but to mummification. As for Dawson's explanation of the entombed toad phenomenon, it must be pointed out that it is far from natural for a young toad to spend much time on the dry chalk. And if the flint nodule had by some strange coincidence ended up in the vicinity of a stream, why had the toad not just rotted once it died?

The toad-in-the-hole is an anomaly in the true sense of the word. The phenomenon is not only irrational but completely inexplicable, and there is no reasonable explanation to this remarkable series of observations of toads and frogs discovered inside blocks of stone. The counter-arguments proposed here are hardly enough to completely exorcise the unblessed, prematurely buried toads, which have led their own slumbering, accursed half-life outside the boundaries of biology for several centuries. It is a fitting final tribute to the entombed toads to quote from Dante Gabriel Rossetti's poem *Jenny*, written in 1870:

> Like a toad within a stone
> Seated while time crumbles on;
> Which sits there since the earth was cursed
> For man's transgression at the first;
> Which, living through all centuries,
> Not once has seen the sun arise;
> Whose life, to its cold circle charmed,
> The earth's whole summers have not warmed;
> Which always – whitherso the stone
> Be flung – sits there, deaf, blind, alone…

SOURCES

The Cat Orchestra

The main sources about Bisset's cats are the *Eccentric Mirror* 1(3) [1813], 26–31; *Chambers' Edinburgh Journal* 9 [1848], 22–25; and T. Frost, *The Old Showmen and the Old English Fairs* (London 1874), 176–79. Cappelli's cats were described in the *Literary Gazette* of 21 February 1829, 132, and in *The Times* of 2 March 1829, 1a and 25 May 1829, 1b. See also H. Morley, *Memoirs of Bartholomew Fair* (London 1859), 487; R.D. Altick, *The Shows of London* (Cambridge, Mass. 1978), 307; and R. Jay, *Extraordinary Exhibitions* (New York 2005), 88–9. On other feline performers, see *La Nature* 1902: 223–24; A. Lehmann, *Tiere als Artisten* (Wittenberg 1956), 104–6; and the *New York Times* of 17 September 2005.

The Dancing Horse

The best two essays on Mr Banks and his horse are those by J.O. Halliwell-Phillipps, *Memoranda on Love's Labour's Lost* (London 1879), 21–57, 70–73, and A. Freeman, *Elizabethan Eccentrics* (New York 1989), 123–39. Other worthwhile articles are those by C.E. Browne in *Notes and Queries* 5th Ser. 6 [1876], 387; S.H. Atkins in *Notes and Queries* 167 [1934], 39–44; R.A. Fraser in *Shakespeare Quarterly* 5 [1954], 98–99; and W. Schrickx in *Notes and Queries* 227 [1982], 137–38. The pamphlet *Maroccus Extaticus* was reprinted by the Percy Society (Vol. 9(37), London 1844) and discussed further in the Collectanea Anglo-Poetica, *Historical & Literary Remains* 52 [1860], 152–56. Modern performing and 'clever' horses and other animals have been discussed by E.A. Dawes, *The Great Illusionists* (Secaucus, N.J. 1979), 26–34; H. Cazier-Charpentier in *Le Cirque dans l'Univers* 122 [1981], 9–11; M. Dif, *Histoire Illustrée de la Prestidigitation* (Paris 1986), 97–104; P.R. Levy, *Les Animaux du Cirque* (Paris 1991), 13–24; and D.K. Sandland, *Feral Children and Clever Animals* (Oxford 1993).

Lament of the Learned Pig

The two most important sources on learned pigs are the article by G.E. Bentley Jr. in *Colby Library Quarterly* 18 [1982], 87–104, and R. Jay, *Learned Pigs and Fireproof Women* (London 1986), 8–27. There are many prints, handbills and newspaper cuttings about learned pigs in Lysons's *Collectanea*, in Miss Banks's Collection of Broadsides, and in the Menageries section of the Fillinham Collection of Cuttings from Newspapers, all three of which are kept at the British Library. In addition, there is much primary material in *The Times*, particularly 5 April 1785, 2d; 2 May 1785, 2b; 28 July 1785, 3b; 20 February 1817, 1a; 13 May 1817, 1a; 22 November 1825, 3d; 29 July 1844, 7d; and 12 April 1845, 6d. *The Symbolic Pig*, by F.C. Sillar & R.M. Meyler (Edinburgh 1961), 59–67, and the articles in the *New Penny Magazine* 2 [1899], 768, and by H. Stepstone in *Royal Magazine* 8 [1902], 442–44, provide further information about pigs in show business. A background in eighteenth-century popular zoology and the anthropomorphising of animals is given by K. Thomas, *Man and the Natural World* (New York 1983); H. Ritvo in *Harvard Library Bulletin* 33 [1985], 239–79; and O.D. Oerlemans in *Mosaic* 46 [1994], 174–90. The books by Pinchbeck and Haney, quoted in the text, provide information about nineteenth-century animal training, a subject later discussed by M. Gardner in *Scientific American* 240(5) [1979], 20–24; P.T. Mountjoy & A.G. Lewandowski in *Psychological Record* 34 [1984], 25–38; C.J. Nicol in *Animal Science* 62 [1996], 375–91; S. Held *et al* in *Behaviour* 138 [2001], 1337–54; and J. Nickell in *Skeptical Inquirer*, November 2002.

Munito, the Wonderful Dog

Short accounts of Munito have been given by P.-M. Henry, *Poodlestan* (New York 1965), 14–17; P. Bräuning, *Circus und autverwandte Künste* (Königstein 1990), 361; S. Oettermann, *Ankündigungs-Zettel von Kunst-Reitern* (Wiesbaden 1993), No. 536; R. Jay, *Jay's Journal of Anomalies* (New York 2001), 4–8, 165; and S. Hirn in *Hufvudstadsbladet* 27 March 1970 and *Den Gastronomiska Hästen* (Helsinki 2002), 38–39, 218. There is primary material about the Wonderful Dog in Lysons's *Collectanea* and in the Fillinham Collection of Cuttings from Newspapers, as well as in *The Times* of 25 May 1817, 1a and 15 March 1819, 1e. Six French sources are Anon., *On en parlera longtemps… dans une des séances du célèbre Munito* (Paris 1817); Anon., *Notice historique sur la vie et les talens du savant chien Munito* (Paris 1820); A.-A. de Berruyer, *Epître à M. le Marquis de La Londe, par Munito, Chien Savant* (Versailles 1827); Anon., *Levons-nous en masse! Proclamation de Bianco et Fido, écrite sous leur dictée, par un élève de Munito* (Paris 1830); J.-F. Bertachon, *Notice sur les Chiens Munito* (Nantes 1836); and E. de Tarade, *Education du Chien* (Paris 1866). Charles Dickens described Munito in his *All the Year Round* (17 [1867], 105–6). On other learned dogs, see Rev. C. Williams, *Dogs and Their Ways* (London 1868), 356–76; E. Jesse, *Anecdotes of Dogs* (London 1884); and A. Lehmann, *Tiere als Artisten* (Wittenberg 1956), 168–79.

Obituary of an Elephant

Some excellent books on the natural and cultural history of elephants are R. Carrington, *Elephants* (London 1958); F.C. Sillar & R.M. Meyler, *Elephants Ancient and Modern* (Ontario 1968); S. Oettermann, *Die Schaulust am Elefanten* (Frankfurt am Main 1982); S.K. Eltringham (ed.), *Elephants* (Poole 1991); A. Haufellner *et al* (eds), *Elefanten in Zoo und Circus* (London 1993); and E. Scigliano, *Love, War, and Circuses* (New York 2002). Additional information is in the articles by N. Kourist in *Zoologische Beiträge* 18 [1971], 141–48; R. Delort in *L'Histoire* 20 [1980], 32–40; and S. Sivasundaram in *Historical Journal* 48 [2005], 27–63. The most important sources on Chunee and the Exeter Change menagerie are the collections of press-cuttings, pamphlets and drawings in the Enthoven Collection, Theatre Museum, London, and the Archives of Westminster City Libraries, London. Much additional material, including several scarce pamphlets and prints, are in the British Library (Bartholomew Fair, Sadlers Wells and Lysons collections). Four important contemporary sources are E. Cross, *Companion to the Royal Menagerie, Exeter Change* (London, 1820); J. Taylor, *The Life, Death and Dissection of the Largest Elephant ever known in this Country* (London 1826); P. Egan, *Anecdotes of the Turf, the Chase, the Ring, and the Stage* (London 1827), 281–93; and W. Hone, *Every-Day Book* (London 1834), Vol. 2, 321–45. *The Times*, *The Morning Chronicle* and *The Mirror* newspapers for 1826 contain many articles about Chunee's tragic death and the elephant-mania that ensued. Important information about Chunee's skeleton is contained in the manuscript Diaries of William Clift (entries for 1 March 1826, 26 May–10 June 1831 and 1 November 1831), kept in the Archives of the Royal College of Surgeons of England, and in the descriptive catalogue of the osteological series in the Museum of the Royal College of Surgeons. Charles Dickens wrote about Chunee in *All the Year Round* (13 [1865], 256–57); two later articles were in *Once a Week* (Nov 1863, 586–88) and *Picture Magazine* (April 1894, 205–6). Some modern descriptions of the Exeter Change and its animals are those by R.D. Altick, *The Shows of London* (London 1978), 302–16; C.H. Keeling, *Where the Lion Trod* (London 1984), 2–25; H. Ritvo, *The Animal Estate* (London 1990), 205–42; and D. Hahn, *The Tower Menagerie* (London 2003), 199–209.

Jumbo, King of Elephants

The only full-length biography of the King of Elephants is W.P. Jolly, *Jumbo* (London 1976). In its preface, it is remarked that the biographer of an elephant has the great advantage not to be overburdened with the personal papers of the deceased; nor is there any worry of offending the family! Other valuable sources are A.H. Saxon, *P.T. Barnum, the Legend and the Man* (New York 1989), 291–302, and J. Edwards, *London Zoo from Old Photographs 1852–1914* (London 1996), 66–96. Five important articles about Jumbo are those by J. Bannerman in *Maclean's Magazine* 68(23) [1955], 28–29, 43–50, 84; J.L. Haley in *American Heritage* 24(5) [1973], 62–68, 82–85; T. James in *Smithsonian* 13(2) [1982], 134–52; D.J. Preston in *Natural History* 92(3) [1983], 80–83; and S.L. Shoshani *et al* in *Elephant* 2 [1986], 86–122. While R.L. Carpenter in *Tuftonian* 1941, 6–11, J.R. Russell in *University of Rochester Library Bulletin* 3 [1947], 12–20, and G.G. Goodwin in *Natural History* 61(1) [1952], 16–21, 45–46 have described the preparation of Jumbo's skeleton and hide, B.C. Landauer in *New York Historical Society Quarterly Bulletin* 18 [1934], 43–52 has studied the advertisement campaigns inspired by the famous elephant.

Animals on Trial

Several books have been written on this subject: the earliest, and best, of them is E.P Evans, *The Criminal Prosecution and Capital Punishment of Animals* (London 1906). Other works include H.A. Berkenhoff, *Tierstrafe, Tierbannung und rechtsrituelle Tiertötung im Mittelalter* (Strasbourg 1937); M. Rousseau, *Les Procès d'Animaux* (Paris 1964); and J. Vartier, *Les Procès d'Animaux du Moyen Age à nos jours* (Paris 1970). Three important articles are those by K. Seifart in *Zeitschrift für deutsche Kulturgeschichte* 1856, 424–32; K. von Amira in *Mitteilungen des Instituts für Oestereichische Geschichtsforschung* 12 [1891], 529–601; and W.W. Hyde in *University of Pennsylvania Law Review* 64 [1916], 696–730. Later papers include those by J.J. Finkelstein in *Transactions of the American Philosophical Society* 71(2) [1981]; J. Heritier in *Histoire* 84 [1985], 72–76; L. Price in *Police Review*, 8 August 1986; E. Cohen in *Past and Present* 110 [1986], 6–37, and *Crossroads of Justice* (London 1998), 110–33; P. Mason in *Social Science Information* 27 [1988], 265–73; M. Pastoureau in *Histoire* 172 [1993], 16–23; P.S. Berman in *New York University Law Review* 69 [1994], 288–326, and *Hastings Law Journal* 52 [2000], 123–80; and P. Dinzelbacher in *Journal of Interdisciplinary History* 32 [2002], 405–21.

The Riddle of the Basilisk

Many of the older sources are mentioned in the text. More recent articles on basilisks include those by H. Phillips Jr. in *Penn Monthly* 14 [1882], 33–42; A. Garboe in *Teologisk Tidsskrift* 3R. 8 [1917], 17–30; G. Polivka in *Zeitschrift des Vereins für Volkskunde* 28 [1918], 41–56; J. Avalon in *Aescupale* 25 [1935], 244–56; R.McN. Alexander in *Greece & Rome* 2s. 10 [1963], 170–81; L.A. Breiner in *Isis* 70 [1979], 30–47; E.V. Walter in *Comparative Civilization Review* 10 [1983], 51–72; and R.N. Doetsch in *Pacific Discovery* 36 [1983], 25–30. The books *Die Zauberkraft des Auges und das Berufen* by S. Seligmann (Hamburg 1922), 183–95, 522–25, and *Animal Lore in English Literature* by P.A. Robin (London 1932), 84–95, 181–88, provide additional information. Faked basilisks have been described by A. Forti in *Atti del R. Istituto Veneto di Scienze, Lettere et Arti* 88(2) [1928], 225–38; E.W. Gudger in *Scientific Monthly* 38 [1934], 511–23; and F. Grondona in *Physis* 11 [1969], 249–66. Four excellent Danish sources are the article by H.F. Feilberg in *Naturen og Mennesket* 12 [1894], 164–96), and the books *Fabeldyr og andre Fabelvæsener* by J. Anker & S. Dahl (Copenhagen 1938), 192–97; *Thomas Bartholin*, Vol. 1, by A. Garboe (Copenhagen 1950), 110–12, 196–97; and *Fabeldyr og Sagnfolk* by B. Holbek & I. Piø (Copenhagen 1967), 341–53. Masculinised hens laying eggs have been discussed by L.J. Cole in *Journal of Heredity* 18 [1927], 97–106; T.R. Forbes in *Yale Journal of Biology and Medicine* 19 [1947], 955–70; and U. Mittwoch in *Perspectives in Biology and Medicine* 24 [1981], 595–606. Strange eggs with 'young basilisks' inside them have been described by C. Davaine in *Comptes Rendus des Séances et Mémoires de la Société de Biologie* 3. Sér, T. 2 [1860], 183–266; M. Henry in *Bulletin de l'Académie Vétérinaire de France* 1 [1928], 157–58); G.O. Hall in *Poultry Science* 24 [1945], 496–98; W.M. Read *et al* in *Poultry Science* 52 [1973], 2316–24; and B. Skinner in *Fortean Times* 46 [1986], 46–49.

The Vegetable Lamb and the Barnacle Geese

E. von Lippmann, *Urzeugung und Lebenskraft* (Berlin 1933), gives a broad overview of the older history of spontaneous generation. J. Rostand, *La Genèse de la Vie* (Paris 1943), and L. Thorndike, *History of Magic and Experimental Sciences* (New York 1941), provide further information. Later articles include those by S. Lindroth in *Lychnos* 1939, 159–92; W. Capelle in *Rheinisches Museum für Philologie* NF 98 [1955], 150–180; D.M. Balme in *Phronesis* 7 [1962], 91–104; E.I. Mendelssohn in *Actes XIIe Congrès d'Histoire des Sciences* 1 [1971], 201–29; D. Passmann in *British Journal for Eighteenth-Century Studies* 11 [1988], 1–17; and R. Kruk in *Journal of Semitic Studies* 35 [1990], 265–82.

The Boramez articles of Sir Hans Sloane and Dr Breyn were published in *Philosophical Transactions of the Royal Society of London* 20 [1695], 461–62, and 33 [1725], 353–60. Henry Lee, *The Vegetable Lamb of Tartary* (London 1887), is a standard work. Later articles include those by G. Schlegel in *Actes du 8:e Congrès des Orientalistes* 4 [1889], 17–32; B. Laufer in *Journal of American Folk-lore* 28 [1915], 103–28; A.W. Exell in *Natural History Magazine* 3 [1932], 194–200; A.F. Tryon in *Missouri Botanical Garden Bulletin* 43 [1955], 25–28; I. Malaxecheverria in *Romance Philology* 35 [1981], 266–68; and J.H. Appleby in *Notes and Records of the Royal Society of London* 51 [1997], 23–34. Sir Richard Lea's account is in the archives of the Royal Society of London (CC.P. XV(I).14).

The most important source on the barnacle geese is E. Heron-Allen, *Barnacles in Nature and Myth* (Oxford 1928). M. Guéttard's article was published in his *Mémoires sur différentes parties des Sciences et Arts* (Paris 1783), Vol. 4, 238–303. Later works worth consulting are Sir Ray Lankester, *Diversions of a Naturalist* (London 1915), 108–41; E.A. Armstrong, *The Folklore of Birds* (Cambridge 1959), 225–37; and the articles by F. Moll in *Archiv für die Geschichte der Mathematik, der Naturwissenschaften und der Technik* NF 11 [1928–9], 123–49; J. Seide in *Centaurus* 7 [1961], 207–12; and F. Egmond & P. Mason in *Journal of the History of Collections* 7 [1995], 25–43.

The later debate about spontaneous generation is described by J. Farley, *The Spontaneous Generation Controversy from Descartes to Oparin* (Baltimore 1977), and H. Harris, *Things come to Life* (Oxford 2002). The articles by P. Smit in *Nieuwe Nederlandse Bijdragen tot de Geschiedenis der Geneeskunde en der Naturwetenschappen* No 8 [1982], 169–85, and E.G. Ruestow in *Journal of the History of Biology* 17 [1984], 225–48, describe Leeuwenhoek's campaign against spontaneous generation. The eighteenth-century debate is further discussed by S.A. Roe in *Isis* 74 [1983], 159–84, and M. Carozzi in *Gesnerus* 42 [1985], 265–88. The modern debate on spontaneous generation and the origin of life has been described by K. Dose in *Interdisciplinary Science Reviews* 13 [1988], 348–56; L.E. Orgel in *Scientific American* 271(4) [1994], 53–61; and J. Strick in *Journal of the History of Biology* 33 [2000], 371–84. The books by C. de Duve, *Vital Dust* (New York, 1995), P. Davies, *The Origin of Life* (London 2003) and R.M. Hazen, *Gen-e-sis* (New York 2005) contain a broad overview of the origins of life on earth.

Odd Showers

Many older sources are given reference to in the text. Carl Linnaeus's paper about the lemmings was published in *Kungliga Vetenskapsakademins Handlingar* 1 [1740], 320–5. The French nineteenth-century debate about showers of frogs is reviewed by A.-M.-C. Duméril & G. Bibron in their *Erpétologie Générale* (Paris 1841), Vol. 8, 223–33. A valuable older review of all kinds of odd showers is that by W.L. McAtee in *Monthly Weather Review* 45 [1917], 217–24. Dr E.W. Gudger collected numerous fish showers in three articles, in *Natural History* 21 [1921], 607–19, *Annals and Magazine of Natural History* 10. Ser. 3 [1929], 1–26, and *Scientific Monthly* 29 [1929], 523–27. Two later reviews are those by R.E. Martin in *Popular Science Monthly*, July 1932, 24–25, 108, and M.W. Martin in *Science Digest* 67 [1970], 32–36. Herved Berlin wrote on rains of worms in an obscure pamphlet: *Maskregnsproblemet och dess Vetenskapliga Lösning* (Lund 1925). Charles Fort's *Complete Books* have been reissued by Dover Publications (New York 1974). The Fortean books by S. Welfare & J. Fairley, *Arthur C. Clarke's Mysterious World* (London 1980), and J. Michell & R.J.M. Rickard, *Phenomena* (London 1977) and *Living Wonders* (London 1982), contain reviews of all kinds of odd showers. Some modern scientists have written about these odd showers, like G.P. Whitley in *Australian Natural History* 17 [1972], 154–59; M.W. Rowe in *Journal of Meteorology UK* 7 [1982], 177; and D. Elsom in *New Scientist* 118(1615) [1988], 38–40. A valuable review is that by W.R. Corliss, *Tornados, Dark Days, Anomalous Precipitation, and Related Weather Phenomena* (Glen Arm 1983), 39–80.

Toad-in-the-Hole

The tale of Mr Gråberg and his stone-frog was originally published in *Kungliga Vetenskapsakademins Handlingar* 2 [1741], 248–55. Dr Pihl's discussion is kept in the Archives of the Swedish Academy of Sciences (sekr. arkiv 1), and A.Ph. Tidström's paper is kept in Archives of the University Library of Uppsala (D 1457, f. 161). The Swedish stone-frog is further discussed by E.W. Dahlgren, *Svenska Vetenskapsakademins Protokoll* (Stockholm 1918), Vol. 1, 340–57, and C. Sahlin, *Med Hammare och Fackla* (1938, 128–36). Five important early articles are those by C.N. Le Cat in Alléon-Dulac's *Mélanges d'Histoire Naturelle* 3 [1764], 95–105; J.S. Guéttard in *Mémoires sur Differentes Parties des Sciences et Arts* 4 [1783], 615–36, 683–84; W. Buckland in *Zoological Magazine* 5 [1831], 314–20; M. Vallot in *Bibliothèque Universale des Sciences* 56 [1834], 251–66; and A.-M.-C. Duméril in *Comptes Rendus des Séances de l'Academie des Sciences* 33 [1851], 105–16. Gilbert White's manuscript account is in the British Library Department of Manuscripts (Add. MSS 31847). The Chillingham toad was described by Lord Ravensworth and by J. Raine in *Archaelogia Aeliana* NS 3 [1858], 1–8 and 277–87 respectively. The Blois toad was described by A. de Rochas in *La Nature* No. 606 [1885], 85–87. Two valuable later reviews are those by P.H. Gosse, *Romance of Natural History* 2nd Ser. (London 1861), 147–90, and Sir Ray Lankester, *Diversions of a Naturalist* (London 1915), 376–82. Charles Dawson described the Brighton toad in the *Annual Report of the Brighton and Hove Natural History and Philosophical Society* 1901, 1–7; it was later discussed by G. Vines in *New Scientist*, 9 August 2003. Old Rip is the subject of an admiring biography, *The Story of Old Rip*, by H.V. O'Brien (Eastland 1965). The Fortean interest in the toad-in-the-hole is discussed in J. Michell and R.J.M. Rickard, *Living Wonders* (London 1982), 98–102. Two excellent accounts of the toad-in-the-hole, with extensive lists of references, are those by Bob Skinner, *Toad in the Hole* (Fortean Times Occ. Paper 2, London 1986) and W.R. Corliss, *Anomalies in Geology* (Glen Arm 1989), 60–71.

LIST

OF

Illustrations

All illustrations are author's collection unless otherwise stated.

LIST OF ILLUSTRATIONS

TEMPUS – REVEALING HISTORY

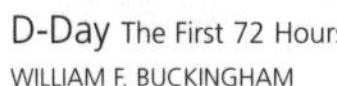

D-Day The First 72 Hours
WILLIAM F. BUCKINGHAM
'A compelling narrative' ***The Observer***
A ***BBC History Magazine*** Book of the Year 2004
£9.99 0 7524 2842 X

The London Monster
Terror on the Streets in 1790
JAN BONDESON
'Gripping' ***The Guardian***
'Excellent... monster-mania brought a reign of terror to the ill-lit streets of the capital'
The Independent
£9.99 0 7524 3327 X

London
A Historical Companion
KENNETH PANTON
'A readable and reliable work of reference that deserves a place on every Londoner's bookshelf'
Stephen Inwood
£20 0 7524 3434 9

M: MI5's First Spymaster
ANDREW COOK
'Serious spook history' ***Andrew Roberts***
'Groundbreaking' ***The Sunday Telegraph***
'Brilliantly researched' ***Dame Stella Rimington***
£20 0 7524 2896 9

Agincourt A New History
ANNE CURRY
'A highly distinguished and convincing account'
Christopher Hibbert
'A *tour de force*' ***Alison Weir***
'*The* book on the battle' ***Richard Holmes***
A ***BBC History Magazine*** Book of the Year 2005
£25 0 7524 2828 4

Battle of the Atlantic
MARC MILNER
'The most comprehensive short survey of the U-boat battles' ***Sir John Keegan***
'Some events are fortunate in their historian, none more so than the Battle of the Atlantic. Marc Milner is *the* historian of the Atlantic campaign... a compelling narrative' ***Andrew Lambert***
£12.99 0 7524 3332 6

The English Resistance
The Underground War Against the Normans
PETER REX
'An invaluable rehabilitation of an ignored resistance movement' ***The Sunday Times***
'Peter Rex's scholarship is remarkable'
The Sunday Express
£12.99 0 7524 3733 X

Elizabeth Wydeville: The Slandered Queen
ARLENE OKERLUND
'A penetrating, thorough and wholly convincing vindication of this unlucky queen'
Sarah Gristwood
'A gripping tale of lust, loss and tragedy'
Alison Weir
A ***BBC History Magazine*** Book of the Year 2005
£18.99 0 7524 3384 9

If you are interested in purchasing other books published by Tempus, or in case you have difficulty finding any Tempus books in your local bookshop, you can also place orders directly through our website

www.tempus-publishing.com

TEMPUS – REVEALING HISTORY

Quacks Fakers and Charlatans in Medicine
ROY PORTER

'A delightful book' ***The Daily Telegraph***
'Hugely entertaining' ***BBC History Magazine***

£12.99   0 7524 2590 0

The Tudors
RICHARD REX

'Up-to-date, readable and reliable. The best introduction to England's most important dynasty' ***David Starkey***

'Vivid, entertaining... quite simply the best short introduction' ***Eamon Duffy***

'Told with enviable narrative skill... a delight for any reader' ***THES***

£9.99   0 7524 3333 4

The Kings & Queens of England
MARK ORMROD

'Of the numerous books on the kings and queens of England, this is the best'
Alison Weir

£9.99   0 7524 2598 6

The Covent Garden Ladies
Pimp General Jack & the Extraordinary Story of Harris's List
HALLIE RUBENHOLD

'Sex toys, porn... forget Ann Summers, Miss Love was at it 250 years ago' ***The Times***
'Compelling' ***The Independent on Sunday***
'Marvellous' ***Leonie Frieda***
'Filthy' ***The Guardian***

£9.99   0 7524 3739 9

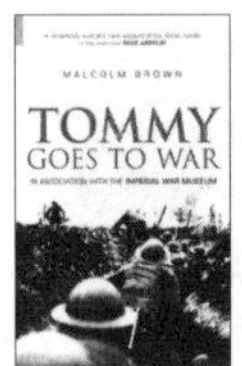

Okinawa 1945
GEORGE FEIFER

'A great book... Feifer's account of the three sides and their experiences far surpasses most books about war'
Stephen Ambrose

£17.99   0 7524 3324 5

Tommy Goes To War
MALCOLM BROWN

'A remarkably vivid and frank account of the British soldier in the trenches'
Max Arthur

'The fury, fear, mud, blood, boredom and bravery that made up life on the Western Front are vividly presented and illustrated'
The Sunday Telegraph

£12.99   0 7524 2980 4

Ace of Spies The True Story of Sidney Reilly
ANDREW COOK

'The most definitive biography of the spying ace yet written... both a compelling narrative and a myth-shattering *tour de force*'
Simon Sebag Montefiore

'The absolute last word on the subject' ***Nigel West***

'Makes poor 007 look like a bit of a wuss'
The Mail on Sunday

£12.99   0 7524 2959 0

Sex Crimes
From Renaissance to Enlightenment
W.M. NAPHY

'Wonderfully scandalous'
Diarmaid MacCulloch

£10.99   0 7524 2977 9